The Agricultural Regions of the United States

The Agricultural Regions of the United States

LADD HAYSTEAD & GILBERT C. FITE

University of Oklahoma Press : Norman

Ladd Haystead

The Squires Can Take It (New York, 1948)
The Business of Farming (with Herrell DeGraff) (Norman, 1948)
If the Prospect Pleases (Norman, 1945)
Meet the Farmers (New York, 1944)
Preacher's Kid (New York, 1942)
Farm for Fortune and Vice Versa (New York, 1942)

Gilbert C. Fite

George N. Peek and the Fight for Farm Parity (Norman, 1954)
Mount Rushmore (Norman, 1952)
Peter Norbeck: Prairie Statesman (Columbia, Mo., 1948)

Library of Congress Catalog Card Number: 55–9620

 Composed and printed at Norman, Oklahoma, U.S.A., by the University of Oklahoma Press. First Edition.

To the parents of both of us,
who saw and heard the land, took the land,
and dwelt in it: before God

Acknowledgments

MANY INDIVIDUALS and agencies have given the authors valuable assistance in preparing this book. The United States Department of Agriculture, as well as the various state departments of agriculture, have generously met our every request for statistical data on recent agricultural developments in various areas. We owe special thanks to the Standard Oil Company of New Jersey and the Standard Oil Company of California for many of the choicest photographs reproduced on the following pages. The United States Department of Commerce, Bureau of the Census, generously supplied us with the crop and livestock maps, and data for the regional soil maps were taken from "General Pattern of Great Soil Groups" provided by the United States Department of Agriculture. We are grateful to the following individuals who have in one way or another given assistance: John M. Johnson of Miller, South Dakota; Garel Grunder of St. John, Kansas; Harold Edwards of Tekoa, Washington; Rich Royce and George V. Ferry of Bakersfield, California; James H. Shideler and Arthur Shultis, the College of Agriculture, University of California, Davis; Dale O. Hull, Iowa State College, Ames; H. C. Schwalen, University of Arizona, Tucson; and John W. Morris, University of Oklahoma, Norman. We are also indebted to Miss Opal Carr, reference librarian, University of Oklahoma, for her usual efficiency in helping to dig out facts and figures. Finally, a most sincere bow is made to Herrell DeGraff of Cornell who originated the idea of this book.

The present work is not quite what he envisioned, but it would not have been attempted without his fundamental research and drive.

March 24, 1955

Ladd Haystead
Gilbert C. Fite

Wherein We Aim

THIS BOOK is designed to be severely functional. It aspires to be a tool for students, county agricultural agents, teachers of vocational agriculture, businessmen, and all others interested in why the greatest industrial nation in the world should also have the largest farm output and be one of the most varied in agricultural production. But against these utilitarian goals, it is hoped that some of the drama, the beauty, and the quiet emotional liaison between the husbandman and his environment show through.

To the layman, farmers often seem an inarticulate lot. The rich earthiness and fulsome orchestration of the Biblical writers appear to be nonexistent today. Instead of the songs of the shepherd, we hear parity, surplus, and the groanings of petulant orators who pour out vast and tinny sympathy for that "misunderstood" and put-upon fellow to whom is relegated the stewardship of our basic wealth.

These misconceptions do little to enforce our cohesion as a people. True, farming is a business. In recent years it has become as commercial as running a grocery store. Its operators are businessmen whose risks are higher than those in most other vocations. Its chance for riches is not great. Its supposed security has almost disappeared as self-sufficiency has given way to dependence on the equipment man, chemist, petroleum producer, and banker. Yet, though three-quarters of a million people leave the farms every year, there is a greater lack of farms than of would-be farmers.

This discrepancy is explicable in only one way. Certain people —and they are by no means all of rural origin—can find their fulfilment in life only by marriage to the soil and the domestic animals it supports. Perhaps they are more reticent than a psalmist, but they are nonetheless as quietly, even as passionately, in love with the land.

They are the folks who, even as this is written, are buckling their belts a little tighter, grimly prepared, if necessary, to sweat somehow through the fourth year of drought. They are the ones driven from the soil by a barren cupboard and forageless fields to factories where they are working and saving for another try when they get a new grubstake. They are the ones whom turnpike, shopping center, or airfield have turned off the acres to roam the land looking for another home and living, right back in the furrows. They are the reason why demand for farm lands is so steady that falling farm-commodity prices and rising costs of operation have not been adequately reflected in the asking price of farm property. The continued pressure of population upon land resources is little short of amazing.

Herein we have concerned ourselves with the economic and geographic factors that make our agriculture what it is. But if we merely stop there, with no word of caution, an insufficient picture may ensue. For no matter how commercial the enterprise, in farming, as in sports or religion, there is an emotional factor that must always be kept in sight, albeit dimly in the background. In this favored nation where men still report to a God, no man farms because he has to. He farms because he wants to. And this is one of the most vital things in our agricultural economy.

Certainly farmers want better prices, cheaper costs, and a more equable opportunity in the market place. They want new cars, better homes, and parity of living with urban people. But if you travel from Key West to Vancouver, from Presque Isle to San Diego, as these writers have done and continue to do, you don't find the seething resentment, the self-pity, and the revolt too many publicists would have us believe is the constant attitude of the farm population.

Given anything short of atomic destruction, farmers will still farm. When the arable land runs short, they will reclaim more desert, drain more swamp, plant a little higher on the hill (one hopes with the necessary protective practices), and urge weather, soil and bugs to co-operate and bring another crop to fruit.

The farm home becomes more like the city home every day. The family habits of the farm are getting indistinguishable from those of the urban. Every luxury from TV sets to wrist watches is enjoyed in the farm home. Farm literacy is on a constant rise, with the highest quotient in the farm state of Iowa. There is no such thing as a "farm dialect." But there is a hidden factor that ties a farmer to his job—something which is not so common in urban life—that is, his endless and faithful love affair with the soil.

Consequently, while here we explore the dollars and cents of food, feeds, fats, fibres, and oils, be it not overlooked that behind the profits and losses there is a spiritual affinity that neither tractor nor test tube has supplanted.

Contents

Illustrations

Maps and Charts

The Agricultural Regions of the United States

CHAPTER 1

The Nonexistent "Typical" American Farm

WHEN a national magazine prints a story on our agriculture, the "Letters" editor sighs in resignation. He knows he will be bombarded from all sides with burning missives stating in no uncertain terms that the writer of the story is ignorant, a city fellow who never has seen a farm, and that the magazine's reputation for accuracy is forever blemished. Curiously enough, usually both the writer and the letter senders are right. This paradox arises from the unheralded fact that almost everybody has a picture of a type of farming in mind that he thinks represents most American farming, when actually the concept he has may represent only a tiny segment of the entire farm picture.

This fallacy of reasoning from the specific to the general in farming probably explains why we have so much inept agricultural legislation. It accounts for such enormous historical errors as the original Homestead Act of 1862, largely enacted by men from the humid East who thought 160 acres of any land anywhere in this favored nation would be quite adequate to support a family. It explains why otherwise intelligent copy writers in advertising agencies get so far off base in their appeals and statements. It is why sales managers, even of farm equipment companies, waste many a good dollar trying to persuade a mythical "typical" farmer to buy their wares.

There are two reasons for this misconception of what is, and what is not, the American farm. One is geographical, the other historical.

For example, a highly literate magazine editor, product of a California fruit ranch, makes errors in judging the American scene because he cannot comprehend the importance of livestock to our farm economy. Another very competent workman gets off the track because he sees agriculture from the vantage point of a boyhood spent among the rocks of a New England farm. The *raison d'être* of the practices and goals of an Iowa corn-hog operation does not make sense to him for he is thinking from a completely different background, one not only dissimilar in topography and climate, but, what is more, thirty years out of date.

Farm patterns not only have changed incredibly in the last generation, but are in a continuous process of change right now. Nothing is so constant in modern American agriculture as change.

TABLE 1.—*Number of farms, average acre per farm, value of farms, and value of land and buildings per acre in the United States, 1850–1950.*

	Number of farms	*Average acreage per farm*	*Value of farms (total dollars)*	*Average value of land and buildings per acre*
1950	5,382,162	215.3	$75,260,606,000	$64.96
1940	6,096,799	174.0	33,641,738,726	31.71
1930	6,288,648	156.9	47,879,838,358	48.52
1920	6,448,343	148.2	66,316,002,602	69.38
1910	6,361,502	138.1	34,801,125,697	39.60
1900	5,737,372	146.2	16,614,647,491	19.81
1890	4,564,641	136.5	13,279,252,649	21.31
1880	4,008,907	133.7	10,197,096,776	19.02
1870	2,659,985	153.3	7,444,054,462	18.26
1860	2,044,077	199.2	6,645,045,007	16.32
1850	1,449,073	202.6	3,271,575,426	11.14

Source: *United States Census of Agriculture, 1950,* II, 48.

The crop shifts of today no doubt will make this book obsolete in a relatively short time if it is not revised. What you learn today will be just background ten years from now. As an example, in the mid-thirties it was quite correct to speak of the Cotton South. But the geographical center of cotton has been moving steadily westward. California ranked third in cotton production in 1953. A decade from now, it may be correct to speak of the Dairy-and-Beef-Cattle South, meaning the area east of the Mississippi and south of Mason and Dixon's line. But if you say Cotton South and do not use the term historically, the hearer may quite properly think you mean an area running from the Mississippi Delta to the Pecos River in New Mexico.

It is useful to remember that New York State, still a major agricultural producer despite its vast industrial and commercial plants, was once a leader in wheat, potatoes, sheep, grapes, and flax—not forgetting mulberry bushes and the domestic silkworm industry. Today Kansas is the undisputed leader in wheat. Maine, Idaho, and California are favored producers of potatoes. But here is another change. New York State ranked first in production of Irish potatoes until the early nineteen twenties, when it was passed by Maine. Today New York rates fourth in potato production, and this crop is most intensively cultivated on Long Island.

Sheep long ago took up their major residence in the Mountain States and, very importantly, in Texas. Fresh grapes, raisins, and wine are the boast of California. The production of flax for oil is centered in western Minnesota and eastern North Dakota, for fibre in Texas and Oregon. Silk and hemp, other onetime New York products, have gone back to the Orient. Now it is a good question if either can ever enjoy its prewar eminence in its native habitat. Rayon and nylon threaten the silk industry with extinction, just as coal-tar dyes ruined the indigo industry. Ramie, now cultivated in Florida, may be, if not the death knell, at least a stiff competitor to hemp.

These continuous crop changes not only tend to create widely held erroneous impressions among nonstudents of agriculture, they also have significant effects on foreign trade. For instance, we raise paprika in Louisiana now, when once we imported it from

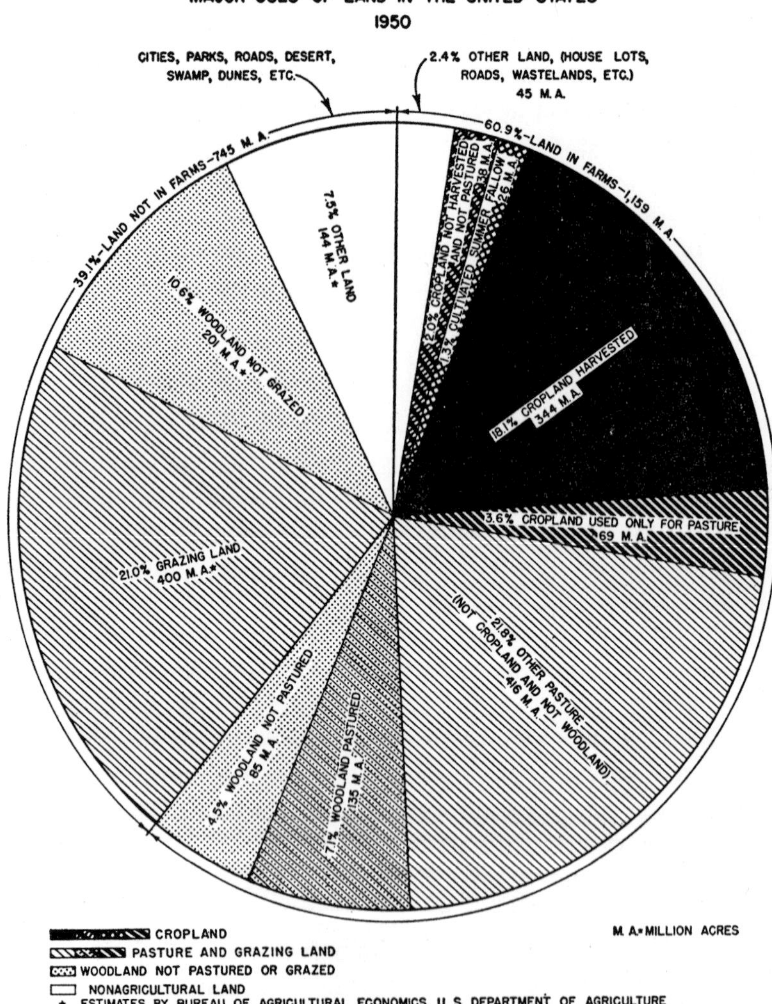

Central Europe. A cork industry is getting under way that may put a crimp in Spain's exports. Before World War II, our seeds came largely from the Low Countries and the Danube Valley. Now Arizona and the area around Shenandoah, Iowa, are prominently in seed production and show every intention of fighting for the

American market, or a large piece of it. Guar, an Asiatic crop useful to the adhesive industry, is increasing its southwestern acreage.

The basic point is that nobody can make a fair judgment on anything concerned with American agriculture unless he has a clear picture in mind of the scope, variegation, and transitions of this highly mutable industry. Nor can he maintain that fair attitude unless he keeps up with the cause, the nature, and the effects of never ending changes. American farming seems to be in a constant state of revolution. Witness the effect of hybrid corn in the nineteen thirties and the revolution currently being effected by nitrogen applications.

What is the picture of United States agriculture in the sixth decade of this century? First, it is not dominated by diversified or self-sufficient farms, no matter how many words have been written and spoken on these topics. It does not settle, as it once did, into major areas where a particular kind of farming is the overwhelming plan. It is not divided, as is so much of Europe, into many little farms, growing a dab of everything, and a few large specialty regions, such as the wine country of Bordeaux or the dairy lands of the Low Countries. Actually, there is nothing like our agriculture any place else in the world, or in all world history.

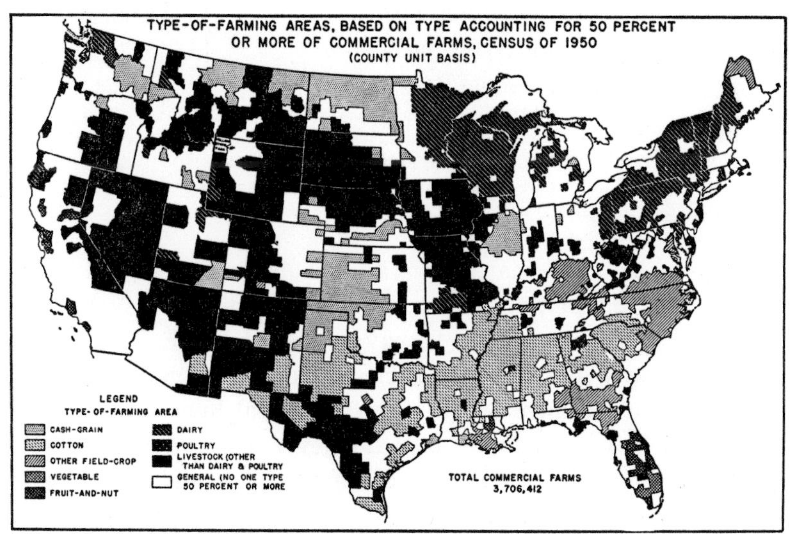

It is a unique complex of scores of commercial crops, plus the greatest livestock economy on the globe. It is a 365-days-a-year job in some sections, a mere 40-days job in others. In the high valleys of the New Mexico Rockies, it is husbandry on a Biblical scale, scarcely changed by all the centuries. In some places, notably California and Kansas, it is mechanized to almost the industrial level. It can be a part-time subsidiary job on one farm, a part-time major job on the next, and a full-time job on a neighboring place. That full-time job can provide a good living on one farm and a bare subsistence on another, although both may be comparable in acreage.

TABLE 2.—*Value of farm property, land and buildings, and machinery and equipment in the United States, January 1, 1910–50.**

Year	*Land and buildings*	*Machinery and equipment*†
1910	$34,810,000,000	$1,395,000,000
1915	39,597,000,000	1,762,000,000
1920	66,316,000,000	3,891,000,000
1925	49,468,000,000	2,933,000,000
1930	47,880,000,000	3,428,000,000
1935	32,859,000,000	2,211,000,000
1940	33,642,000,000	3,118,000,000
1945	54,606,000,000	6,288,000,000
1950	75,255,000,000	13,018,000,000

Source: *Agricultural Statistics, 1952,* p. 625.

* This table shows clearly the increasing investment in machinery and equipment in relation to the value of land and buildings on United States farms. The value of land and buildings a little more than doubled between 1910 and 1950, but the value of machinery and equipment increased nearly ten times.

† Includes automobiles, tractors, trucks, other machinery, etc.

It may be a large farm from an income standpoint at twenty-five acres or a minor operation at twenty-five hundred, depending upon soil type and climate. It may support a family comfortably with as little as ten acres of truck near a metropolitan center. It may be a big business operation with several hundred cows in a factory in Brooklyn, cows that have never seen grass growing. It can be less than a fenced acre of barren, rock-and-sand hillside near El Paso and be of greater value as a dairy operation than a quarter section of rich Webster silt loam. It can be a tree farm in Washington growing only posts, piling, pulp, and saw timber. Or it may be silver foxes in the Lake States, mushrooms in abandoned Pennsylvania mineshafts, blueberries on an otherwise nonagricultural New England hillside, a tung orchard along the Gulf Coast, a cornfield that will yield ten bushels to the acre in the Appalachians, another cornfield that never gets ripe in Maine, or still another that grows nothing but broomcorn in Oklahoma, or a three-hundred-bushel-per-acre operation that a national magazine is promoting.

In short, our agriculture is of seemingly endless variety, with new crops constantly being bred at home or imported. The cost of the operation may run from a few hundred dollars capitalization to literally many millions, the size from a hydroponic tub to the nearly one million acres of the King Ranch. The outstanding fact about it is that *there is no typical American farm.* And no matter what you may say as a generality about our farms, someone can probably bring up an exception to your rule and prove it.

Lest this seem as frightening a prospect of indigestible rules as French irregular verbs, let us hasten to answer the question that foreigners sometimes ask when they get their first breath-taking view of the myriad facets of our national "farm." Is not there one product that is typically American, if not typical of all American farms, something like sheep in Australia, tea in Ceylon, or rubber in Malaya?

Yes, there is. It is not all American agriculture. It does not make the biggest single cash contribution. But it does enter into our agricultural picture more prominently than any other one crop when its collateral effect is considered. It is corn.

From Europe we have imported grapes and wheat. Asia and Africa gave us the sorghums, those new-old crops that sprang to prominence during the war. Asia gave us soybeans. Alfalfa came from North Africa. The list of contributions from other countries to the Americas could go on almost indefinitely. But when all is said and done, three items that the Americas gave world agriculture would just about balance all the rest. Those three, of course, are potatoes, tobacco, and corn.

If Central Europe did not have potatoes, its whole crop economy would be sadly different from what it is, despite its current unhappy state. The same could be said for Eire. South Africa would be in a bad way if its standard native dish, mealies (corn), were not available. And almost all of mankind seems to be grateful for tobacco. That indigenous bird, the turkey, might be added, but it is doubtful if the comedian of the barnyard, with its all-time low in mentality, has added greatly to anyone's economy except our own, and that of very recent happening, even though the gobbler greeted the Pilgrim Fathers. Yet while corn as a crop has not taken a dominant place in any other country's agro-economy, the effect of its prominence in America is felt world-wide.

TABLE. 3.—*Acreage and production of specified crops in the United States, 1899–1949.*

	Corn for grain	*Wheat*	*Cotton*	*Tobacco*
1949				
Acres	75,132,672	71,161,061	26,599,263	1,532,298
Production	2,778,190,131 bu.	1,006,559,285 bu.	15,419,458 bales	1,769,769,030 lbs.
1939				
Acres	77,431,592	50,526,015	22,811,004	1,853,230
Production	2,311,399,925 bu.	708,851,598 bu.	11,481,300 bales	1,699,727,914 lbs.
1929				
Acres	83,161,523	61,999,908	43,227,488	1,888,365
Production	2,130,751,782 bu.	800,648,955 bu.	14,574,405 bales	1,456,510,003 lbs.
1919				
Acres	87,771,600	73,099,421	33,740,106	1,861,480
Production	2,345,832,507 bu.	945,403,215 bu.	11,376,130 bales	1,371,504,261 lbs.
1909				
Acres	98,382,665	44,262,592	32,043,838	1,294,911
Production	2,552,189,630 bu.	683,379,259 bu.	10,649,268 bales	1,055,764,806 lbs.
1899				
Acres	94,913,673	52,588,574	24,275,101	1,101,460
Production	2,666,324,370 bu.	658,534,252 bu.	9,534,707 bales	868,112,865 lbs.

Source: *United States Census of Agriculture, 1950,* II, 539 ff.

Corn has something over six hundred uses, ranging all the way from bourbon whiskey to the sizing that makes the paper in magazines slick, shiny, and capable of fine reproductions of pictures. Important as the numerous industrial uses are, they do not have the effect on world supplies of food that corn does as the prime livestock feed. Livestock and livestock products have steadily climbed up in the ratings of contributions to farm income until in 1950 they were supreme, making approximately 57 per cent of the total cash receipts from farm marketings. Livestock and livestock products brought $15,975,585,000, while crops totaled only $12,352,224,-000. The most important cash crop, but a long way down the scale, was cotton, which made up about 8.6 per cent of the cash income. Wheat followed with 6.1 per cent.

It is true that our far-flung grasslands are the basis of our predominantly livestock economy. But it is also probable that we would have made much less agricultural progress had it not been that corn will grow in most parts of the country, and superbly well from the 98th meridian to the Appalachians, north of the Ohio. It grows, after a fashion, south of this line, but in no such abundance as it does to the north. However, even here new strains of hybrids, plus anhydrous ammonia (NH_3), suggest that the Southern States may one day do a much better job of fodder and silage production.

Besides its own direct contribution, corn has suggested ways in which other crops, more suitable to certain soil types and climates outside the Corn Belt, might be good substitutes for the prime feedstuff. Thus, the search for a corn substitute has tremendously increased the grain sorghum area from Texas to the Canadian border in lands that are too dry for corn culture, that is, the Great Plains region. The West Texas Chamber of Commerce has been active in promoting the use of sorghum grains as a substitute for corn, both in the feeding of livestock and for industrial uses. Sweet potatoes are being developed and promoted in the South as a corn substitute. Florida, where natural concentrates are nonexistent, is experimenting with many things, from citrus pulp to peanut products, as corn substitutes.

The reason is, of course, that greater gains and higher quality are achieved when corn or one of its substitutes is added to the natural grass diet of ruminants. For the animals (poultry, swine) that originally depended on nuts, seeds, and aboriginal grains and used grass only in a minor way, corn has practically effected a revolution. This is most noticeable, perhaps, in comparing the southern razorback hog with the sleek, corn-fed Corn Belt porker. Or compare the original chicken from the jungles of India, laying around fifty eggs a year, with the three-hundred-egg birds which are now the American poultryman's goal. To be sure, breeding has a lot to do with these changes, but breeding without feeding could scarcely have made the strides it has.

Where corn came from, nobody knows—yet. That last qualifier is added because, at this writing, serious students are ranging all the way from the Andes up through Guatemala trying to find some clue to the origin of this crop, which seemingly has no wild ancestors and, as far as is known, is about the most dependent-on-man crop in the world. That is, it does not seem likely that corn, as we know it, could have gotten as far as the primitive Indian corn of Squanto without a lot of help from some unknown ancient farmers.

Corn is a grass. How it developed the cob, no one knows. It does not seem likely that it started existence that way. Wind would hardly scatter the seed. Even in modern cultivated fields, volunteer corn does not make much of a showing. By all logic, it seems that man must have done some rudimentary selection and given a great deal of care to this crop which seems helpless to propagate itself.

It is not too difficult to imagine how this supposed native of the Andes got north to the valleys of New Mexico and Arizona. There are reasonably good theories concerning how it might have been traded from the Southwest across the Plains, finally winding up in New England. The mystery is how it evolved from its parent, whatever plant that was, to its shape and characteristics when the white men first learned about it from the Indians.

Historians have long speculated on what would have happened to our early history without corn. When the Pilgrims landed, they did not have enough food for that first terrible winter. As it was, not half of them came through. But corn, either supplied by or taken from the Indians, proved to be a lifesaver. The earliest settlers as well as later generations of pioneer farmers, found corn ideal for both man and beast. It is abundantly clear that corn is both historically and economically our key crop.

When this is all admitted, and even when consideration is

given to the miracle hybridization effected in corn (and other crops), it is not at all sure that corn will continue indefinitely to occupy its present position. Who knows what will come out of the search for substitutes? After all, corn is a soil-depleting crop. It is expensive to grow. Perhaps we have used more corn for livestock feeding than we should. And we must remember that the heavy corn users are natural ruminants whose digestive systems are peculiarly designed to handle grasses. Some agriculturists (called Grasslanders) think that many other grasses besides corn can have their protein built up, through genetics, to a point that they will compete with corn economically, if not nutritionally. Thus, already, it appears that beef cattle fed to prime or choice may be much less in evidence in the future than in the past. Could it be that those greatest of all corn consumers, the hogs, could be switched backward, economically, to subsist again on nuts, or some variant of the acorns they originally utilized? Before that thought is brushed away as so much vaporing, consider that vast areas of this land are suitable for tree culture. Again, note that while we do not consume all the fruits we should, it would not take very many plantings to glut the foreseeable market. But suppose someone were to develop a nut tree that would be at home, say, on the barren New England hills which once supported huge forests. Suppose those nuts not only appealed to hogs but provided the feed values they now get from corn. It is possible, although admittedly not probable in the near future, that the states closest to the big metropolitan centers might again become prominent swine producers. At least it is a thought to ponder, for now we know there are few limits that agricultural thought may not jump over. And don't forget peanuts are a traditional hog feed in the South.

Just as the discovery that corn would do better in the Mississippi Basin than in New England once made a mighty change in our farming pattern, so does the shifting of great masses of our population. For a generation or so, Pacific Coast farmers had a very slim time of it from the cash angle because they were so far away from the major consuming centers. Then World War II sent millions of people to the Coast industries. Suddenly there appeared to be an almost unlimited market right at the back door of Coast

TABLE 4.—*Number of specified livestock in the United States, 1900–1950.**

Year	*Number of horses and colts*	*Number of cattle and calves*	*Number of hogs and pigs*	*Number of sheep and lambs*
1950	5,401,646	76,762,461	55,721,977	31,386,801
1940	10,086,971	60,674,736	34,037,253	52,107,000
1930	13,510,839	63,895,826	56,287,920	56,975,084
1920	19,767,161	66,639,556	59,346,409	35,033,516
1910	19,833,113	61,803,866	58,185,676	52,447,861
1900	18,267,020	67,719,410	62,868,041	61,503,713

Source: *United States Census of Agriculture, 1950,* II, 385 ff.

* All data were taken from the 1950 census except the number of sheep and lambs in 1940. That figure was taken from *Agricultural Statistics, 1952,* p. 420. The census date was April 1 for 1950, 1940, and 1930; It was January 1, 1920; April 15, 1910; and June 1, 1900.

farmers. It was popularly supposed that when the war was over, the new migrants would move back to where they came from, chiefly the Southeast. But they did not. Now it appears that the Pacific Coast States may achieve a stability they have not previously known. A few years ago, history was made when the first load of Nebraska hogs was sent to Los Angeles from Omaha, thus reversing for the first time the traditional west-to-east movement of agricultural products. As the new Coast economy is not self-sufficient in livestock products, this reversal may well become permanent.

But what about the places the modern emigrants left behind? A story from North Carolina provides a good clue. A southern journalist told the present writers of a one-time cotton farm that seemed fairly typical to him. After a fashion, it had supported ten families before the war. The ten families, even including the landowner, were at best a slight step above Tobacco Road. Their diet had been inadequate, their housing abominable. Each family had its ten-acres-of-cotton-and-a-mule. They made from one-half to three-quarters of a bale to the acre. When cotton sold at five cents, they very nearly starved and probably did not do as well as a displaced person in a concentration camp. Even when cotton sold at twelve cents, the income of a whole family did not amount to more than a few hundred dollars annually.

After the tenants moved westward to high industrial wages, the owner and his family were forced to mechanize and change the crop plan. Only half the acreage went into cotton. The rest was put to other crops that lent themselves to mechanization and carried a low labor requirement. When one of the writers called in the late forties, he found a modern home, decent barns, a new automobile, and an owner with a whole new vision of life and farming. Admittedly, high wartime prices had helped. But other things were even more notable.

Half of the land, receiving the full fertilizer placement that had previously been put on *all* the land, was being more intensively worked under rotation and conservation practices and was producing more cotton of better quality than full planting had orignally done. On top of that, the new livestock projects were leveling out the peaks and valleys of income and providing an all-year employment program, at the same time producing precious manure for the fields. All in all, the owner's family and one family of hired hands were doing much better than they would have had any possibility of doing under the old way, and will continue to do so even if prices fall disastrously. The self-displaced persons were known to be better off in their new home and new work. It seemed that everyone had gained by the shift, not forgetting the Pacific Coast farmers. Here is an example of what economists mean when they talk about getting surplus labor out of agriculture and adding capital expenditures to increase farm income.

This incident suggests that the geography of farming, no less than any other kind of geography, cannot be fully grasped without some consideration of the farmers themselves.

Who are the American farmers and what do they mean to each other and to the economy as a whole?

That thought of mutually beneficial relationship is injected because so often *one farmer is another farmer's best customer*. The northeastern farmer buys his concentrates from the middle western farmer. The western rancher buys his cottonseed cake from a southern farmer, and more recently from an Arkansawyer or Okla-

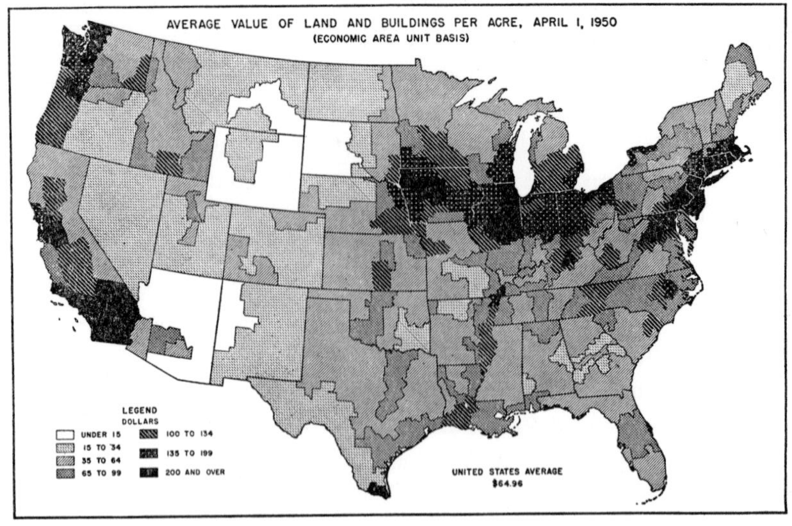

homan who is raising cotton not only for lint but also for its seed. Oklahoma, which is short on hard feedstuffs but has a relatively mild climate, is raising feeder pigs to be sold to Corn Belt feeders. Arizona farmers are selling seeds to other farmers all over the country. California poult breeders ship their product to the turkey-raising Mountain States. Western New York farmers buy feeder lambs from all over the West, and so on.

Let us look at farmers as businessmen, buyers, traders, and sellers. Immediately, as we found when considering farming types, it is obvious that there is no such thing as a "typical" farmer. The above consideration of patterns would prove that statement in part. But matters of farm size, soil type, climate, and relationship to primary markets contribute even more. Consequently, let us try to find representative groups. One of the best ways to get at this is through income breakdown.

The upper 13.1 per cent of the commercial farms in the United States, or 484,382, produced 50.8 per cent of the total value of farm products sold in the United States in 1949. These farmers may well be considered the aristocrats of American agriculture. This is particularly true of those in Economic Class I. The 103,231 farmers in this class produced 26 per cent of the total value of farm products sold in 1949. Sectionally, the West has the highest percentage of farmers in this group. For instance, 8 per cent of the commercial farmers in the Mountain States are in Class I, and 11.2 per cent in the Pacific Coast States fall in this category. It may sound incredible to those who are still unaware of the revolutions in agriculture, but 21.6 per cent of Arizona's commercial farms, numbering only 1,458, sold farm products averaging $110,685 per farm in 1949. This 21 per cent of the commercial farmers sold 79 per cent of the total farm products in that state.

At the other extreme, there are 1,618,517 commercial farmers in the United States, 43.7 per cent of the total, who got only 9.6 per cent of the total value of farm products sold. These farmers grossed less than $2,500 each. As far as farming goes, they are not earning enough to justify even a few months of farm employment. There are some, particularly in such poor farming areas as the lower Appalachians, who actually have total annual incomes which approach the starvation level (717,201 farms sold only between $250 and $1,199 apiece in farm products). However, there are a great many in this group who are not quite as bad off as it may at first appear. The value of farm products sold is only part of their total income. In other words, they have more than one source of

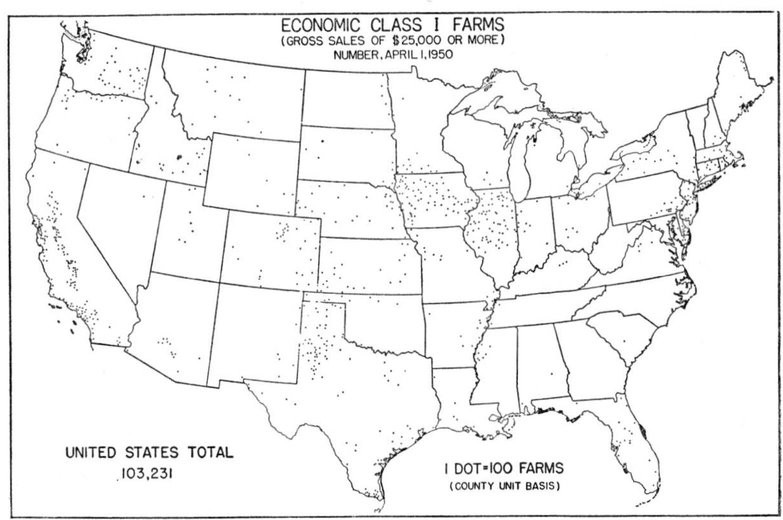

TABLE 5.—*Proportion of the total value of farm products sold by various classes of farms in 1949.**

	Gross value of products sold per farm	*Number of farms*	*Per cent of commercial farms*	*Value of farm products sold*	*Average value of farm products sold per farm reporting*	*Per cent of total value of farm products sold*
Total commercial farms		3,706,412		$21,713,216,602	$ 5,858	97.5
Class I	$25,000 and over	103,231	2.8	5,786,964,265	56,058	26.0
Class II	10,000 to $24,999	381,151	10.3	5,517,034,144	14,475	24.8
Class III	5,000 to 9,999	721,211	19.5	5,060,528,547	7,017	22.7
Class IV	2,500 to 4,999	882,302	23.8	3,198,160,839	3,625	14.4
Class V	1,200 to 2,499	901,316	24.3	1,634,395,317	1,813	7.3
Class VI	250 to 1,199†	717,201	19.4	516,133,490	720	2.3
			Per cent of total farms			
Other farms		1,672,838	31.1	566,345,997	432	2.5
Part-time	$250 to $1,199‡	639,230	11.9	391,193,954	612	1.8
Residential	Under $250	1,029,392	19.1	84,714,797	127	0.4
Abnormal		4,216	0.1	90,437,246	30,206	0.4
Total—all farms		5,379,250		$22,279,562,599	4,440	100.0

Source: *United States Census of Agriculture, 1950,* II, 1132 ff.

* All figures are estimates based upon sampling.
† With the operator not working off the farm more than 100 days a year and with farm sales greater than off-farm family income.
‡ With operator working off the farm 100 days or more a year, or other family income exceeding that of farm sales.

revenue. Yet these operators in Economic Class VI work less than one hundred days a year off the farm, and their nonfarm income is less than the value of all products sold. Thus, in Alabama, for example, 48 per cent of the commercial farms are in Class VI, and the average value of farm products sold in 1949 was $686. Assuming that the operator earned another $500 from nonfarm sources, his total income would still be substandard. And it must be remembered that, in the case of tenants, part of the value of farm products sold went to the landowner.

Somewhere between the extremes of farm income are 43 per cent of the commercial farmers, 1,603,513, who in 1949 sold farm products valued at $8,258,689,386. The average value of farm products sold by this group was from $2,500 to $9,999. Considering only commercial farmers, and they are really the only ones of importance as far as total products is concerned, 32.6 per cent of them got 73.5 per cent of the income from all farm products sold in 1949.

Further discussion of these variations in income is expanded later in the book. For our purpose here, we are concerned with the geographic distribution of the income groups. Where are the richest and where the poorest? Naturally, there can be rich cotton

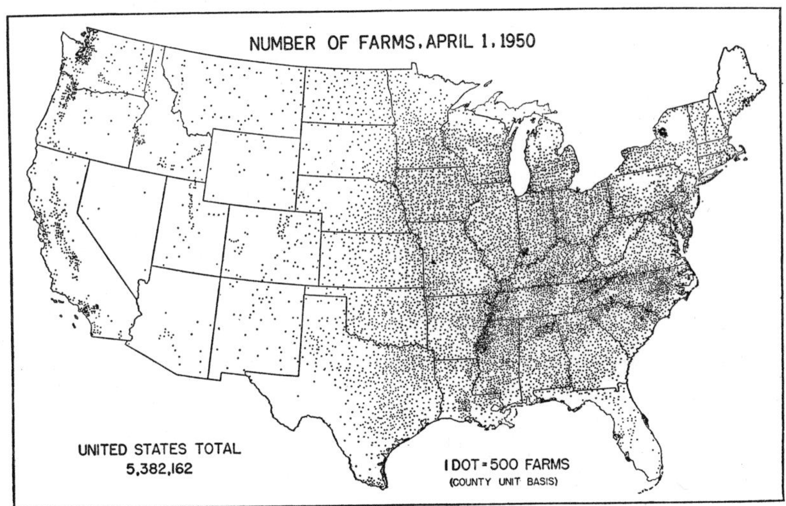

planters and poor sharecroppers side by side. There can be a New Englander on the verge of poverty trying to make a living from crops while his neighbor is nationally known and well-to-do from his breeding of excellent laying hens or meat birds. But there are areas that, because of soil type, climate, and the size of farm operation, are largely well-off or doing poorly.

Of the former, we find prosperous farmers among the truck gardeners contiguous to a congested market. That would include Boston, New York, Philadelphia, Baltimore, Washington, Cleveland, Chicago, Los Angeles, San Francisco, and Portland. How about just saying "any city 100,000 and over"? The answer is that there are some market gardeners doing well around any city of the size described, but for the cities named there is in each case a rather special and large group which play this game. It is a highly dangerous business. The difference between feast and famine may be a price drop of only a few days' duration. But, on occasion, those who stay with this business strike unusual riches. Note that these market gardeners as a rule grow strictly for the fresh market and not for the canning market. Those who sell to canners have little hope of "making a killing," but take their guaranteed price (contracts are usually made at planting time) and get more stability and less risk and less hope of big money.

In the concentrated poultry regions of the East, a high degree of prosperity is not unusual, but here again the element of risk is large. Thus, the farmers of Delmarva (the area where Delaware, Maryland, and Virginia come together) may enjoy a fine year when the metropolises are eating heavily of broilers, fryers, and roasters, and find the next year scarcely bringing in enough for feed bills. The New Jersey egg-producing areas carry the same risk. But note that around Chicago, for instance, such areas highly concentrated to industry are not so common. There the bulk of the poultry products come from the farm flocks of the surrounding states.

In the southeastern Pennsylvania region, with Lancaster County as its capital, prosperity is the usual thing. This is due to a limestone underlay of its soils, nearness to good markets, high diversification with a good cash specialty (tobacco), and the excel-

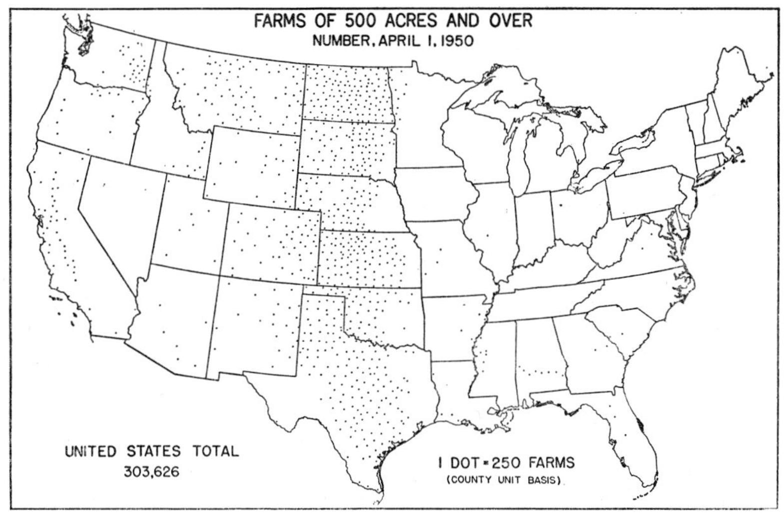

lent farming methods plus the character of the dominant strain of people, the Amish.

Skipping westward, the next nearly-always-prosperous region is in central Illinois, with McLean County as the heart. Here adequate farm size, a naturally rich soil, close markets, and smart farming have made most farmers from comfortable to well-off. The same thing could be said of the area directly north of Des Moines, where the fabulous Webster silt loam, one of the richest soils in the world, has given that area particular material blessings.

The state of Kansas can be rich as Croesus and poor as Job in alternate years. If the moisture supply is good, if smut, rust, or grasshoppers do not ruin the crop, and if the price is adequate, Kansas literally rolls in wheat dollars, as it has since the beginning of World War II. But if moisture is poor, or does not come at all, and if the wind blows, Kansas does not make money no matter what the price is. Worse, the drought may go on for several years, or if it does not, the world price of wheat may be so low the Kansan does not see how he can afford to take his crop to market.

On the irrigated projects of the Western States, a crop is about as sure a thing as it can be in farming anywhere. Here the great worry is price, for crops grown by irrigation carry a high cost. For the most part, however, Yakima (Washington) fruitgrowers, Colorado sugar-beet lamb feeders, people in the Pecos and Mesilla valleys (New Mexico), Utahans on irrigated lands, Salt River Valley (Arizona) dwellers, and most Californians who farm under irrigation usually manage to stay fairly solvent. In some years they make enormous sums of money. Fresno and Los Angeles counties should be put in the same category as Lancaster, Pennsylvania, and McLean County, Illinois, as places where there will be money, even in hard times. Add in the Delta country of Mississippi, the Río Grande Valley of Texas, and the Everglades of Florida, and you have the parts of the United States which usually do not go completely broke and where farm prosperity can be very high, no matter how legislators may mourn the plight of the soilman.

There are other occasionally rich spots, sometimes called, among the knowing, "shoot the moon" territories. Typical of these are parts of Montana and the Dakotas. Like Kansas, they need moisture, low pest infestation, and high market price to be in the money. Unlike Kansas, however, they can have complete crop failure for years on end. It used to be a common saying in the Dakotas, "Give me just one good year in seven and I'll make out." However, this area has seen more bad times than good, and although as this is written a sizable number of farmers in that region can afford Cadillacs, history shows that this area cannot compare with Kansas for good years.

In the same category are the citrus lands of California and Florida. Frost, pests, disease, and malnutrition have adverse effects on the crop quality and quantity, but price and a chronic condition of oversupply make the hazard even worse. Nevertheless, on occasion, such as wartime, profits in this industry and in these areas have been fantastic. Yet probably as many or more growers have gone broke as have made a competence.

If the above are in the favored class, where are the chronically poor? This is an easier, though sadder, job. New England crop farmers by and large have had a struggle just to get along almost from colonial times. The southern Appalachians, mentioned several times before, seem to be a permanent poorhouse. Topography (most of the farms are on hillsides too steep and too thin of soil for farming), obsolete methods, lack of capital, and possibly lack of a diet adequate to supply the requisite energy and thought, all conspire to make this region sad indeed. Throughout the South, where cotton and tobacco have depleted the soil, rural poverty is rampant. In 1949, Virginia, the Carolinas, Alabama, Mississippi, Georgia, Kentucky, and Tennessee had a farm population of 7,851,549, or about one-third of the total for the United States. But farmers in that region received only 12.8 per cent of the value of farm products sold.

At one time, Oklahoma was labeled as the poorhouse of the nation's farmers. The great migration of the *Grapes of Wrath,* the coming of conservation, and some changes in farming practices have partially changed that picture. But even with these changes for the better, Oklahoma produced a slightly smaller percentage of the total farm income in 1949 than in 1939.

Farther southwest, Texas has areas of almost continuous poverty, just as she has areas where prosperity runs from "now-and-then" to "usual." However, in 1949 she hit the No. 1 spot in the nation, topping Iowa and California, with cash receipts from marketing (plus government payments) amounting to $2,071,822,000. In New Mexico and Arizona, particularly among the Spanish-Americans and Indians, poverty is the rule. On the other hand, some of the large irrigated farms produce huge quantities of farm products. With 91 per cent of Arizona's farms reporting, the average value of farm products sold in 1949 was $21,476. The Mountain States have poor areas, but nowhere are they quite as bad off as real "have-nots." The same is true of the Coast States; nowhere are there large areas of chronic poverty. This does not mean farm laborers. Any downward swing of prices and production may see the Okies and Arkies back on that tragic, restless trek of the thirties. The rapid spread of mechanization on the Coast bodes no good for seasonal and unskilled workers in the fields.

This spotty picture of rich and poor brings up a topic which must be omnipresent throughout this book, for it is probably America's No. 1 agricultural problem. That is conservation.

Before World War II, we stood arraigned as the most wasteful people in all history. Nowhere else, except in the fabled Garden of Eden, had a people taken such a rich, virgin territory and in a short three centuries ruined large parts of it for all time and semi-destroyed other parts, while busily trying to do away with the rest. We were not husbandmen in the best sense of the word. We were miners.

We cut our forests as if they would grow back in a season. We wasted more than we cut. Like the miner, we threw away anything that was not high grade. We treated our soil even more cavalierly. We did not have the excuse that we could grow topsoil again. We

TABLE 6.—*Types of farms in the United States in 1950.**

Type	*Number of farms*	*Per cent distribution*
All farms	5,379,250	100.0
Commercial farms	3,706,412	68.9
Cash-grain	430,389	8.0
Cotton	609,307	11.3
Other field crops†	409,421	7.6
Vegetable	46,415	0.9
Fruit and nut	82,178	1.5
Dairy‡	602,093	11.2
Poultry	175,876	3.3
Livestock other than dairy and poultry§	806,080	15.0
General—primarily crop	84,569	1.6
General—primarily livestock	134,666	2.5
General—primarily crop and livestock	275,050	5.1
Miscellaneous¶	50,368	0.9
Other farms°	1,672,838	31.1

Source: *United States Census of Agriculture, 1950,* II, 1218–19.

* The 1950 census classified a farm by type if the value of a particular product or group of products represented 50 per cent or more of total farm sales.

† Peanuts, Irish potatoes, tobacco, sugar beets, etc.

‡ Classified as a dairy farm if dairy products accounted for 30 per cent of the total value of products sold; if sales of dairy products and cattle and calves represented 50 per cent of total sales; if milk cows represented 50 per cent or more of all cows.

§ Cattle, sheep, hogs, goats, wool, etc.

¶ Farms whose sales of horticultural products, horses, fur animals, etc., accounted for 50 per cent or more of the value of farm products sold.

° Part-time and residential farms.

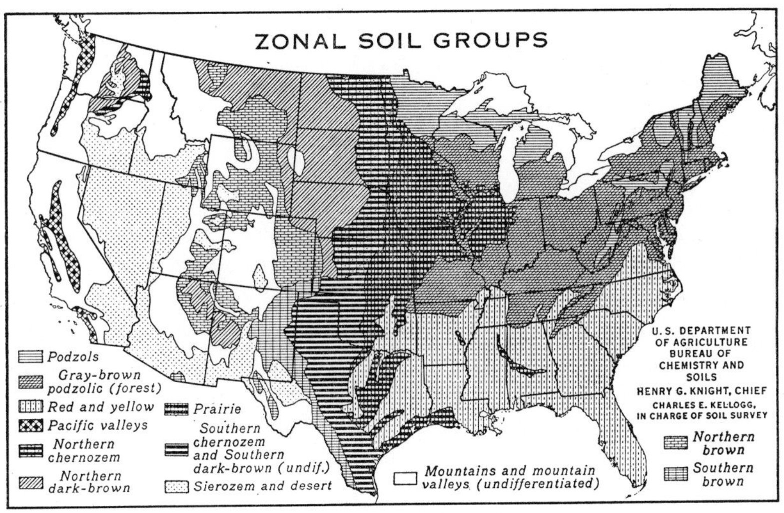

even boasted of what good farmers we were by bragging about the number of farms a man could wear out in a lifetime. But we were coming awake to the fact that soon we would have another Palestine or China on our hands. Some slight progress had been made in stopping this utterly immoral wastage of our children's heritage. In 1954, only 37 per cent of the conservation program was considered adequate by the Soil Conservation Service (SCS). But more is on the way.

During World War II, conservation projects and practices were not abandoned, but they were neglected, often with full knowledge of what was going on and what the eventual cost would be. However, with the world coming unstuck, it was not a time to think about a far Tomorrow. Today was bad enough. Heroic measures were necessary. The soil had to give as it had never given before, because "Food Must Win the War." The soil did give—almost 40 per cent more total production than ever before in our history.

V-J Day meant not only victory, but, to the farmer, the opportunity to stop the decline in fertility, to begin building back up. Hardly had the idea come to mind when we were reminded that "Food Must Win the Peace." The starvation in other lands could

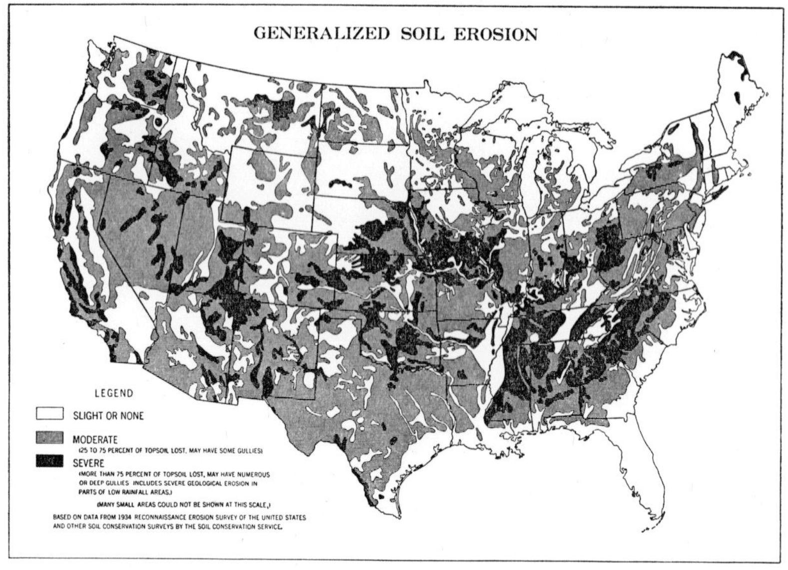

be allayed only by American farm production. The farmer eagerly complied and put off his rebuilding program. Then came the Marshall Plan and, most recently, the "set aside" plan. Now conservationists are wondering just how much further we can go before, for the first time in all history, there will not be enough domestic production to take care of our own people. Added to the downward slide in fertility is the upward swing in population. There are two million new American mouths to feed every year.

Somewhere along the road there must be surcease, or the famed American standard of living will become but a historical era. From the farmers' standpoint, the outlook is even more precarious. Look backward at the well-to-do farming areas and the chronically poor. In most cases the former are on good soils, the latter on poor soils. While soils are only one factor in farm prosperity, they are a vitally important one.

This brings us to one final item which may seem out of place in this book, but because it points up our own situation and throws some light on the future, let us for the minute consider Soviet agriculture, the little we know about it. We know that food plays an important part in winning wars. Many persons now living have twice seen this demonstrated. We know that the wastage of food during wars is fantastically enormous. Millions could be fed from what is wasted in transportation, spoilage, and serving during wartime. A country contemplating war must first assure itself of tremendous reserves to take care not only of the contingencies of nature, but also of wastage. Heaven only knows how much warehoused goods an atomic explosion would ruin. Even worse, what would area-spraying of fields with 2,4–D (which was invented for that purpose) or radioactive clouds do? These are things a warmaker must evaluate and plan for.

How is the U.S.S.R. situated in this regard compared to us? First, she has a much larger land area, but she also has a larger population. Next, on the whole her soils are supposed to be better than ours when the item of our erosion is considered. But it now seems evident that her far-famed mechanization in its prime did not get as far as we have gone. And it shows no signs of catching up.

Most important, however, is the matter of climate. Great areas, larger than Texas, offer little hope of ever growing crops. For the large part of the year, they are frozen solid. For the balance, they are marshes, tundra, and fens, suitable for waterfowl but not for

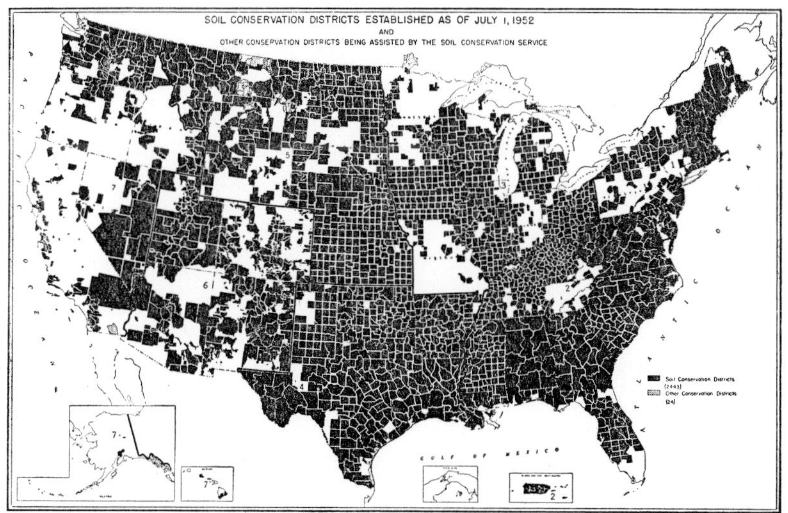

crops. Even the famed Ukraine region, where agronomists say some of the world's best soil is located, reportedly as much as thirty feet of rich black topsoil, does not have the kind of climate that insures a reasonable expectation of a succession of good crops.

In short, piecing together what is known, what little leaks out from behind the Iron Curtain, and considering some fairly accurate projections by our own scientists, it seems that Russia would have a much more difficult time prosecuting a war from a food standpoint than we would. Of course, if she had the opportunity to pirate other countries' foodstuffs as Hitler did, the picture might be different. But as it is, Russia is surrounded by starvation on all borders except the western. And Western Europe is dependent on imports.

While this may be slightly optimistic in these times of gloom, it is even more powerfully a reason for all-out conservation here at home. We dare not become a have-not nation agriculturally. That would even the odds. But as long as we can present to the world the best diet, sufficiency for everyone, plus some stockpiling, we have a strong argument for the men of the Kremlin.

CHAPTER 2

New England: Land of Abandonment

(Connecticut, Rhode Island, Massachusetts, Vermont, New Hampshire, and Maine—Six States Which Ought to be One)

IN AN agricultural sense it is customary to speak of New England as "rock-ribbed," thin-soiled, hilly, unfriendly, hard-scrabbly, and other uncomplimentary terms. Yet, when one travels over the area with an eye to farming rather than history, culture, or industry, even a native of the region must admit that the unenthusiastic terms, for the most part, approach the truth. There may have been a grain of realism in the old saying that if the white man had come to California first and had some knowledge of dry-land farming, New England would never have been populated—not, at least, by farmers.

A popular misconception is that New England has been "farmed out" by a series of soil miners. Actually, there was not much soil to start with. Prehistoric glaciers had scraped, slashed, picked up subsoil, mixed it with rocks, and made off with the topsoil except in a few favored places where a pause was made and a little farming land dropped by the wayside. One authority has estimated that at least 35 per cent of New England's soil is "predominantly stony."

While the general impression of this area is in truth "stony," it is not by any means all that way. For instance, in the northeast-

GENERAL PATTERN OF GREAT SOIL GROUPS

New England

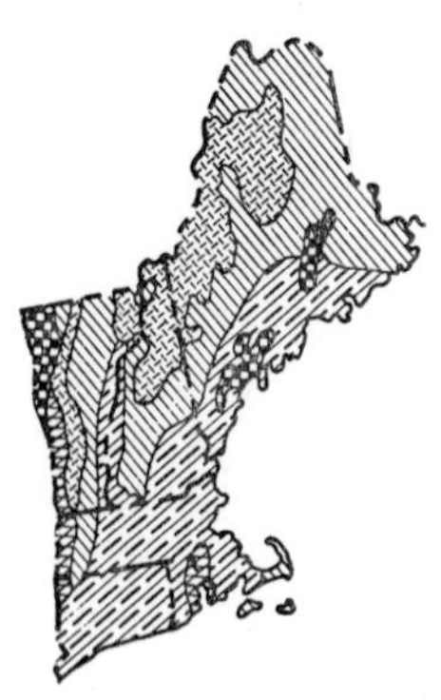

PODZOL SOILS

Light-colored leached soils of cool, humid forested regions.

BROWN PODZOLIC SOILS

Brown leached soils of cool-temperate, humid forested regions.

GRAY-BROWN PODZOLIC SOILS

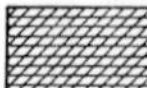

Grayish-brown leached soils of temperate, humid forested regions.

WIESENBÖDEN (1), GROUND WATER PODZOL (2), AND HALF-BOG SOILS (3)

(1) Dark-brown to black soils developed with poor drainage under grasses in humid and subhumid regions.

(2) Gray sandy soils with brown cemented sandy subsoils developed under forests from nearly level imperfectly drained sand in humid regions.

(3) Poorly drained, shallow, dark peaty or mucky soils underlain by gray mineral soil, in humid regions, under swamp-forests.

BOG SOILS

Poorly drained dark peat or muck soils underlain by peat, mostly in humid regions, under swamp or marsh types of vegetation.

LITHOSOLS AND SHALLOW SOILS

(HUMID)

Shallow soils consisting largely of an imperfectly weathered mass of rock fragments, largely but not exclusively on steep slopes.

MAINE
VT.
N.H.
MASS.
CT.
R.I.

ern portion of Maine is famed Aroostook County, which is blessed with fertile sandy loams. In southern Maine is the finest canning corn to be found; it always brings a premium on the market. The Connecticut Valley boasts a rich tobacco production. There are the cranberry bogs and a newly enlivened dairy industry based on planted pastures and heavy fertilization. And there is a new machine that picks up stones mechanically. But there is, also, the heavy hand of tradition.

Certainly, this area was not farmed under modern soil-conserving practices. And it is a region of fairly high precipitation, averaging around forty inches of rainfall each year. But on the whole, the damage from erosion does not compare with that in the South, or in such an area of modest rainfall as Oklahoma. No doubt New England's rivers have carried many tons of soil down to the sea. But grass grows naturally and abundantly in this area. If a field is left alone for a mere matter of months, grass cover appears, tying down what little soil there is. And long ago the New Englander became a livestockman, using hay and pasture primarily. That helped retain the area's soil. But New England soils were, from the beginning, not naturally fertile. Even within a decade of the beginning of farming in the seventeenth century, New England's soil needed to be replenished with plant nutrients.

Probably the greatest waste of resources was not of the poor, thin soil, but of the magnificent forests which were found by the early settlers. The colonists needed space for their rocky little fields. The Old World needed masts and ship materials. The villagers, shopkeepers, and cottage industrialists needed homes and work buildings. And as far as anybody could see in the early days, there was so much forest it could never be used up. There may have been some idea, too, that the forests seemed to swallow up the red man, while the open countryside gave him little more protection than it did the wild game.

At any rate, the forests were cut, burned, and a large part of them wasted, thus paralleling the course of British forests (but for another reason) in the sixteenth and seventeenth centuries. Much land that was, and is, only suitable for tree culture went under the plow. But it was a hard way to make a living, so hard that many

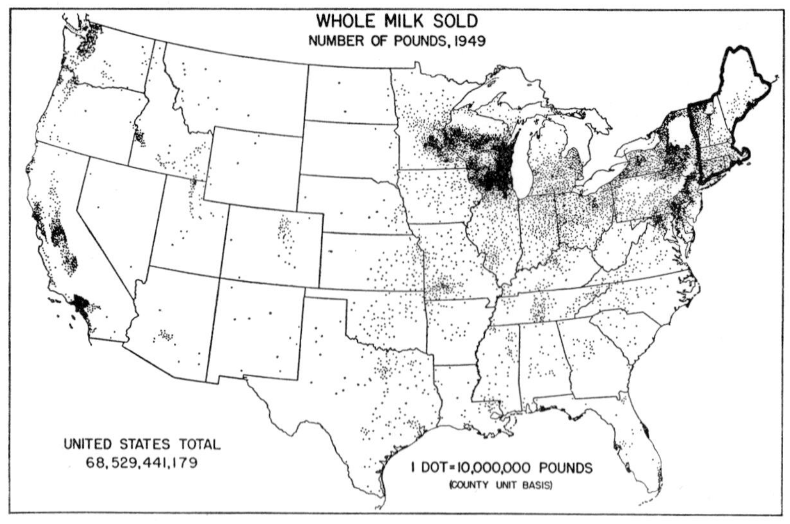

settlers left and moved elsewhere. Most anything was to be preferred to such a heartbreaking fight for a living. The first emigrants who left New England set a pattern which was to be continued for hundreds of years. And when they abandoned their farms, the grass came back, then the sumac, and finally the trees, as Heaven had ordained.

When the Ohio Valley was opened up and word came of land that was deep and rich, with a climate more equable, a steady stream of emigrants started out of the parent states. New England's many rivers suggested water power. Water power made it possible to expand the cottage industries into factory industries. Again life on the farm was so hard it is little wonder that industry did not lack for recruits. When the parents had grown old and gray, there were fewer children left who wanted to take over the old home place. More land was permitted to go back to grass and forest.

The frontier pushed ever westward, and in the van of frontiersmen were former New Englanders, forever seeking land that promised something more than bare existence for year-around hard work. This accounts for the Lexingtons, Concords, Salems, and Portlands of other areas, not to mention the Hub stores which are a feature of the business life of so many towns far removed from Boston.

In 1850 New England had 18,367,458 acres of farm land and 1,943,448 rural people. By 1900 the number of acres in farms had slightly increased to 20,548,499, although the rural population had dropped to 1,757,016. In 1950 the number of acres in farms had declined to 12,546,518 and the farm and rural-farm population had fallen to only 843,502. Of these people, only 440,402 were actually living on farms. The number of farms in New England declined from 167,622 in 1850 to 103,191 a century later. And the whole picture is befogged statistically because of the large and increasing number of part-time and residential farmers—many of them really suburbanites who should not be classed as farmers at all. Thus, by 1950 Massachusetts had 8,922 part-time and residential farms out of a total of 22,205, or 40.2 per cent. In Connecticut over 41 per cent of all farms in the state in 1950 were actually part-time, or country-home farms.

TABLE 7.—*Number of farms in the New England States, 1850–1950.*

	1950	1940	1930	1920	1910	1900	1880	1850
Maine	30,358	38,980	39,006	48,227	60,016	59,299	64,309	46,760
N. H.	13,391	16,554	14,906	20,523	27,053	29,324	32,181	29,229
Vt.	19,043	23,582	24,898	29,075	32,709	33,104	35,522	29,763
Mass.	22,220	31,897	25,598	32,001	36,917	37,715	38,406	34,069
R. I.	2,598	3,014	3,322	4,083	5,292	5,498	6,216	5,385
Conn.	15,615	21,163	17,195	22,655	26,815	26,948	30,598	22,445

Source: *United States Census of Agriculture, 1950,* II, 48–49.

One of the startling things in New England is the amount of farm abandonment. Between 1920 and 1950 the amount of land in farms dropped from 16,990,642 acres to 12,546,518 acres. Thousands of farms have been abandoned. Personal testimony that points this up comes from a New Hampshire man who left his farm, ten miles from town, and did not return for twenty years, or until the early nineteen forties. When he went away, the road from his home to town was lined with going farms. When he returned, it was lined solidly with trees. Not one farm was left. As previously shown, the people actually living on farms in New England dropped to about 440,000 by 1950. There was a 29 per cent drop in farm population between 1940 and 1950, the highest in any section of the country except the Oklahoma, Texas, Arkansas, and Louisiana area.

A modern item that causes much native bitterness is the steady stream of city men why buy farms, but who have no desire to farm their property. At first, they hire someone to cut the hay on the fields and they sell it locally. Next, as the yield declines, they share it with anyone who will harvest it. Then they give it away when the tonnage becomes light and the weed infestation heavy. Finally, they just give up and the weeds and the sumac take over. All the city man wants is country living, maybe a little fishing and shooting, and he is satisfied. He holds the idle lands around him for "protection," which usually means he wants no one not to his liking for a near neighbor.

Another touchy subject is the steady infiltration of people of foreign birth and parentage. To Poles, Portuguese, Italians, Balts, and French-Canadians, even New England acres look better than whatever kind of life they have come from. They are hardy, industrious, often very good farmers, and they do not expect to have immediately a scale of living equal to those ancient families Marquand writes about. They are content to work their large families

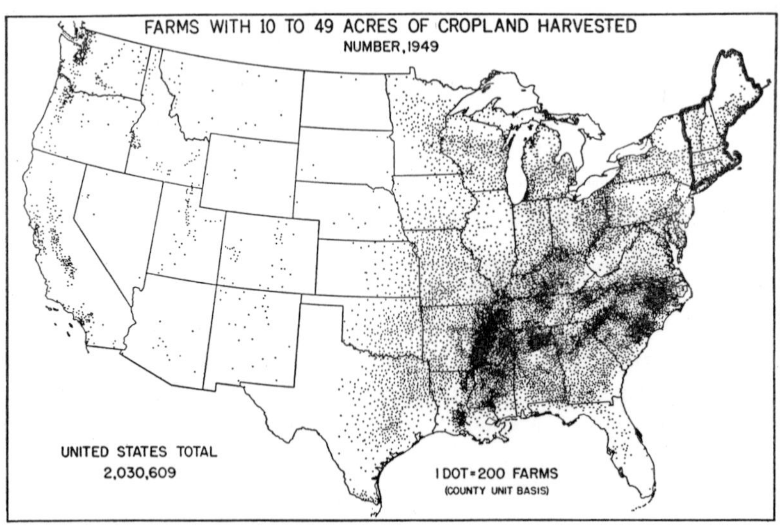

from dawn to dusk, waste nothing, coax the reluctant soil, and then, if necessary, market their products direct to retailer or even consumer. In a small way, they are revivifying some of the New England agriculture. But bitterness arises, for when they prosper they tend to move to the little good farming land left in such places as the narrow river valleys where a modicum of good soil can be found. In the tobacco-raising section of the Connecticut River, however, corporations control some of the good land for tobacco culture, which requires a very high capital investment in land, tools, cloth, poles, curing sheds, and labor.

Traditionally, New England farms have been small. They still are. There have not been any marked or sensational changes in the size of farms in New England as there have been in many other sections of the United States. Farms in New Hampshire, Rhode Island, Connecticut, and Massachusetts were actually smaller on the average in 1950 than in 1930, which is contrary to the national trend. In Vermont and Maine, acreages per farm have been increasing, and they have reached proportions similar to farm sizes in New York and Wisconsin.

TABLE 8.—*The average acreage of New England farms, 1850–1950.*

	1950	1940	1930	1920	1910	1900	1880	1850
N. England	121.5	98.9	114.3	108.5	104.4	107.1	103.7	109.6
Maine	137.7	108.3	119.0	112.5	104.9	106.2	101.9	97.4
N. H.	128.0	109.3	131.5	126.9	120.1	123.1	115.6	116.1
Vt.	185.2	155.5	156.5	145.7	142.6	142.7	137.5	138.6
Mass.	74.7	60.8	78.3	77.9	77.9	83.4	87.5	98.5
R. I.	73.5	73.6	84.1	81.2	83.8	82.9	82.8	102.9
Conn.	81.5	71.5	87.4	83.8	81.5	85.8	80.2	106.2

Source: *United States Census of Agriculture, 1950,* II, 799.

The average size of farms as revealed by the census does not show how small most of New England's farm operations really are by way of acreages. In Maine, for example, where the average size of farms was 137 acres in 1950, the same as Wisconsin, 22 per cent of the farms harvested only from 1 to 9 acres. In Massachusetts over 42 per cent of the farms harvested less than 10 acres of cropland. If Vermont is excepted, the rest of New England had 56.7 per cent of its farms harvesting less than 20 acres in 1950.

While most of New England's farms are small on the basis of acreage, a different picture emerges when the value of products sold is considered. The census of 1950 showed that New England had 59,169 commercial farms, of which 3,521 sold products valued at more than $25,000 in 1949. Maine actually had more farms with an annual value of products of over $25,000 than did Michigan (Maine, 964; Michigan, 949). Besides this, nearly 11,000, or 18.6 per cent, of the farms in New England had a value of products sold of between $10,000 and $24,999. A few areas of production lend themselves to large-scale operations, even though the acreage may not be large: potatoes in Aroostock County, Maine; tobacco in southern Connecticut; dairy farms, principally in southern New England; and a few fruit, truck, and specialty farms.

Many of the small-acreage operations in New England are highly capitalized. The average value of land and buildings per acre for all of New England farms in the ten- to twenty-nine–acre class was $524 in 1950. Part of this figure, of course, is represented in overvaluation of buildings, and part of it is due to residential use. Land values are especially high in the three southern New England states.

TABLE 9.—*Dollar value of land and buildings per acre in New England, 1850–1950.*

	1950	1940	1930	1920	1910	1900	1880	1850
Maine	$ 54.17	$ 29.38	$ 41.87	$ 37.62	$ 25.35	$ 15.32	$ 15.62	$ 12.04
N. H.	72.85	34.38	39.47	34.56	26.44	19.43	20.38	16.29
Vt.	55.68	30.30	37.46	37.56	24.14	17.58	22.40	15.36
Mass.	189.54	109.40	130.26	99.25	67.51	50.21	43.52	32.50
R. I.	232.02	118.67	123.52	79.58	63.01	50.76	50.27	30.82
Conn.	247.77	135.41	151.38	100.20	63.28	42.14	49.34	30.51

Source: *United States Census of Agriculture, 1950,* II, 48–49.

The value of products sold from New England farms was $531,-705,998 in 1949. This was just about the same as that for the single state of Pennsylvania, $545,926,998. But this was less than one-third of the value of farm products sold in Iowa. Between 1939 and

1949 New England's share of the total value of farm products sold in the United States dropped from 3.1 per cent to 2.4 per cent.

The leading agricultural activity in New England is dairying. Between 1936 and 1940 dairy products alone accounted for 34.1 per cent of gross farm income. The sale of cattle and calves, chiefly from dairy herds, added another 4.1 per cent. The census of 1950 revealed that dairy products still play the same dominant role in farm income. Although the number of milk cows has steadily declined, production has increased. In 1939, 2,987,847,174 pounds of whole milk were sold from New England farms, but ten years later this had increased by nearly 500,000,000 pounds, or to 3,419,438,570. Over 98 per cent of the total value of dairy products sold in New England in 1949 represented whole milk, most of which went into day-to-day consumption.

TABLE 10.—*Number of milk cows in the New England States, 1900–50**.

	1950	1940	1930	1920	1910	1900
Maine	101,861	132,160	124,952	175,425	126,762	173,592
N. H.	56,685	72,399	68,792	95,997	81,561	115,036
Vt.	247,107	281,883	254,520	290,122	222,838	270,194
Mass.	113,342	136,249	119,158	147,331	145,714	184,562
R. I.	16,440	19,543	19,171	21,431	20,068	23,660
Conn.	98,894	114,336	94,028	112,622	102,478	126,434

Source: *United States Census of Agriculture, 1950,* II, 403–405.

* The census date for 1950, 1940, and 1930 was April 1; for 1920, January 1; for 1910, April 15; and for 1900, June 1.

Vermont is the leading dairy state in this section. Of the $86,988,103 worth of farm products sold in 1949, $62,357,973 was represented by dairy products. The value of dairy products produced in Vermont nearly tripled between 1939 and 1949. In the rest of New England the value of dairy products only about doubled in the same decade. The 1950 census reported a total of 27,780 dairy farms in New England with an average of nineteen cows per farm. Farms which have a few dairy cows in addition to their dominant enterprise also play a part in making New England an important dairy section.

Omitting farms with only one or two cows, the most common size dairy herd in Maine and New Hampshire is five to nine cows. In Vermont, on the other hand, the largest group of farms have twenty to twenty-nine cows. Over 12 per cent of the farms in Vermont reporting milk cows in 1950 had herds of from thirty to forty-nine, and 3.4 per cent reported over fifty. In little Rhode Island, 4.1 per cent of the farms with cows had fifty head or more. The larger herds are found in Vermont and the three southern New England states, while Maine and New Hampshire's dairying is organized around smaller herds per farm. New England, however, has a high percentage of very large dairy farms. In Connecticut 38.2 per cent of the dairy farms had a value of products exceeding $10,000 in 1949.

The place of dairying in the rural economy of New England is emphasized when land use is considered. In 1949 a little more than 75 per cent of the cropland harvested was in hay. For Vermont and New Hampshire the proportion of hay land was even higher, 88 and 86 per cent respectively. No section of the country has such a high percentage of its cropland in hay. Even the premier dairy state of Wisconsin harvests hay from only 37 per cent of its cropland.

In northern New England, dairymen rely heavily upon grass for feed, and the production per cow is somewhat less than in the three southern states, where cows are fed various concentrates the year around. Maine, Vermont, and New Hampshire cows averaged 5,620, 5,840, and 5,600 pounds of milk per cow in 1950. In Massachusetts, Rhode Island, and Connecticut the output per cow was 6,400, 6,900, and 6,500 pounds respectively.

Improved grasslanding in connection with dairying offers hope for many New England dairymen, particularly in the north. All of this area, except where trees have taken over, will grow grass naturally, but the native grass is not very strong in total digestible nutrients. If the soil will grow grass at all, it can just as well support a highly palatable and nutritious plant as it can a poverty grass. Liming, fertilizing, clipping, spreading manure, use of new and often mixed seed strains does the trick. The result of this practice quickly appears in the milk bucket in higher butterfat and liquid weight.

What this can mean, even in hilly, rocky Vermont, is shown in the records of the Elbert S. Brigham farm at St. Albans. The Brigham farm has been experimenting with improved grasslanding for over thirty years. New and improved forage crops, such as Ladino clover, red and alsike clover, and sometimes brome grass and timothy, have been planted. These pastures have annually been given as much as 500 pounds of fertilizer per acre (mostly nitrogen, phosphorus, and potash). When the pasture appears to be declining in output, Brigham turns the soil and plants a rotation of corn and oats, also heavily fertilized. Then the land is sowed to pasture again. In 1920 the Brigham farm (300 acres tillable and 335 in woodland and permanent pasture) had a milking herd of 33 cows which annually produced 5,499 pounds of milk per cow; in 1930 there was an average of 49 cows producing 6,590 pounds per cow; by 1940 the increased herd of 99 cows averaged a milk output of 8,715 pounds; and between 1941 and 1944 the herd of 103 cows produced an average of 10,020 pounds of milk each. By Brigham's efforts in growing better and more nutritious forage crops, 46 cows in his herd had, by 1945, "won the American Jersey Cattle Club 'Ton of Gold' award by producing 2,000 pounds of butterfat in four consecutive herd test years." The main deterrent to expanding the dairy industry even further is the limited demand for fresh milk.

The poultry industry is second in importance in the over-all agriculture of New England, and it has made great strides in recent years. Poultrymen in this area make little effort to raise feed because, for the most part, they can import it from the Middle West for less than they can grow it, no matter how hard they work. Their contiguity to one of the biggest markets in the United States gives them an edge over those who can grow feed. On top of that, they have specialized.

Poultry production is mainly fresh egg production. The breeding of chicks for layers, meat birds, and a combination of the two, however, has grown into big business. In 1929 the total income from poultry, including eggs, was $48,910,948, but by 1949 this had increased to $128,054,762. This figure is especially impressive when it is kept in mind that the value of all farm products sold in

New England in 1949 was only $531,705,998. Even allowing for the difference in prices between the two periods, observation of the area in question shows that there has been remarkable growth. Where once a farmer broke his heart and winded his horses trying to crop a hundred acres, one now sees long, low, poultry buildings, maybe ten acres of native grass range, and neat homes with a shiny automobile in front. The farm sign tells that the owner is selling registered New Hampshire Reds, White Rocks, or a cross which may go under any quaint sort of name the poultryman or his advertising agent can imagine.

TABLE 11.—*Value of all farm products sold, and the value of specified products sold, in the New England States, 1939–49.*

		Value of all farm products sold	*Value of dairy products*	*Value of poultry and poultry products*
Maine	1949	$125,514,901	$22,070,916	$26,181,638
	1939	42,107,811	9,192,067	5,699,948
N. H.	1949	46,499,909	15,376,378	19,904,895
	1939	19,359,815	7,025,571	6,317,641
Vt.	1949	86,988,103	62,357,973	6,064,933
	1939	33,021,013	21,700,253	2,160,610
Mass.	1949	135,349,945	40,125,337	39,958,084
	1939	62,581,983	22,390,000	14,101,597
R. I.	1949	16,084,379	6,631,472	3,489,407
	1939	7,618,612	3,807,352	1,431,729
Conn.	1949	121,268,761	36,461,285	32,455,805
	1939	43,674,724	16,068,585	9,940,834

Source: *United States Census of Agriculture, 1950,* II, 752 ff.

The greatest specialization in poultry production is found in southeastern New Hampshire, eastern Massachusetts, southern Connecticut, and Rhode Island. In 1949 there were 13,131 poultry farms in New England, with the largest number, 4,202, in Massachusetts. In that state the value of poultry products sold was $39,-958,084, second to dairy products, which totaled only $167,000 more. In New Hampshire, income from poultry products consistently ranks *first* as a source of farm income. In Maine it exceeds

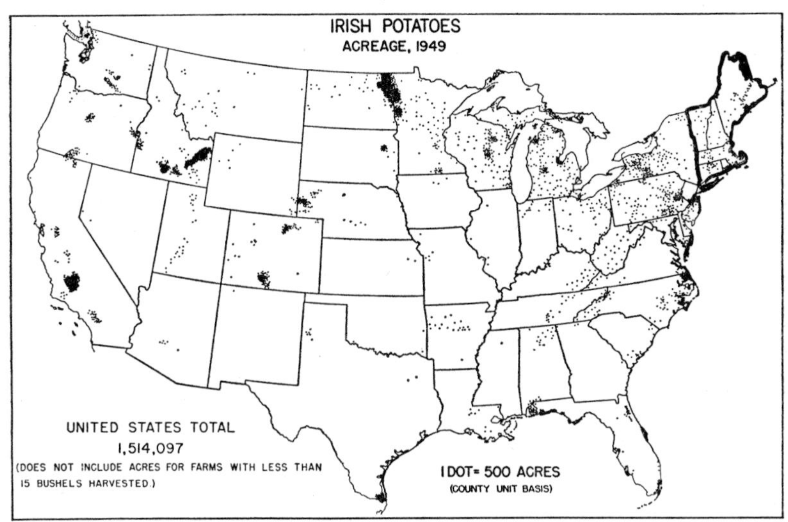

income from dairy products, but does not come up to the value of the potato crop there.

An effort has been made to improve the agriculture of Maine by increasing the number of beef cattle and by expanding dairying. Yet the state still depends on Aroostock potatoes and southern Maine sweet corn for a large share of its farm income. Potatoes alone furnished $55,580,305 of the value of farm products sold in Maine in 1949, or about 44 per cent of the $125,514,901 total. The climate, soil, and know-how have combined to give the famed Aroostock spuds a place of first rank. The best practices have been developed. New pesticides have done much to expand output. Long experience and hard work have resulted in the most modern

TABLE 12.—*Acreage and production of potatoes in Maine, 1899–1949.*

	Acreage	*Bushels produced*
1949	143,391	65,825,251
1929	162,396	47,441,580
1919	111,378	25,531,470
1899	71,765	9,813,748

Source: *United States Census of Agriculture, 1950,* II, 650–51.

mechanized operations and ventilated structures for storage. Although acreage only doubled between 1899 and 1949, production increased over six times.

The peculiar quality of southern Maine's sugar corn and its popularity with canner and consumer indicate that this is a fairly safe industry. But, as with potatoes, it is limited in area. Although acreage increased from 6,268 in 1939 to 9,807 ten years later, not much further expansion on a permanent basis seems likely.

The demand of near-by metropolitan markets for fresh vegetables besides potatoes has continued to make carrots, tomatoes, celery, green beans, onions, cabbage, lettuce, and other vegetables important in the farm economy of New England. Yet even vegetable production has not kept pace with the United States as a whole. Neither the acreage nor dollar value of vegetables, excluding potatoes, was as great in 1949 as in 1929. There were 79,809 acres of vegetables in 1929 and only 63,330 twenty years later. Even considering a cheaper dollar, the value of the 1929 crop was $13,578,874 compared to $12,315,787 in 1949. States farther south, and California, have become competitiors for the fresh home-grown vegetables in New England.

TABLE 13.—*Acreage and value of vegetables produced in New England, 1909–49.*

	Acreage	*Dollar value*
1949	63,330	$12,315,787
1939	64,430	7,246,441
1929	79,809	13,578,874
1919	54,482	12,757,966
1909	39,124	4,779,282

Source: *United States Census of Agriculture, 1950,* II, 658–59.

New England farms also produce a wide variety of fruits and nuts which add to the total income. In 1949 the value of small fruits, berries, and nuts sold totaled $15,996,729, about one-fifth of which came from Massachusetts cranberries. There have been some gains in small fruit production since 1920, probably due in part to the attempt to supply fresh fruits in season. Orchard production, however, has declined in importance since 1920.

In viewing the whole agricultural picture in New England, one sees the largest activity centering around hay and pasture and dairying, poultry, and vegetable and fruit farming, with a considerable sprinkling of specialty crops.

TABLE 14.—*Per cent of the commercial farms in the New England States which were classified as dairy, poultry, vegetable, or fruit and nut in 1949.**

	Total commercial farms	*Dairy*	*Poultry*	*Vegetable*	*Fruit and Nut*
Maine	52.0	31.7	17.6	2.1	3.7
N. H.	47.7	47.0	32.5	1.1	3.4
Vt.	68.7	82.7	5.8	0.2	0.6
Mass.	59.3	34.3	31.9	5.6	5.8
R. I.	60.8	37.5	33.6	6.0	2.2
Conn.	58.7	42.0	30.3	4.0	3.1

Source: *United States Census of Agriculture, 1950,* II, 1235.

* In the 1950 census a farm was classified by type if a particular product or group of products represented 50 per cent or more of the total sales from the farm. The 1950 data on types of farm are not comparable to those used in 1945, 1940, or 1930.

One angle gives promise of better times for the whole area. That is the growth of tourism and the desire of city people for products fresh from the farm. Over a decade ago, it was apparent even to the most rabid New England fan that not only was agriculture in an unhappy way, but that industry was tending to move southward to get a better tax situation and cheaper labor. With the lumber industry feeble, mining, (outside of quarrying) nonexistent, and industry departing, the future looked black indeed. Then, showing a flash of the resourcefulness that has always been so much a part of the Yankee character, the New Englanders took stock and found they had an abundance of something the American people with their new machine-permitting leisure were yearning for—playgrounds.

Here were beautiful lakes and rivers. As the forests grew, wild game had returned. History was everywhere, and Americans have a fanatic desire to gaze upon the places where history was made. The antique craze had developed and seemingly would not subside, even when roadside signs proclaimed "Antiques Made to Order." And while New England had always considered its snow a drawback to be minimized, now it became an asset as skiers flocked to the snow trains and winter sports became fully as important as summer sports.

This resource has brought millions of dollars to the area. Not only has it enriched resorts and transportation, it also has helped many a farmer. Now a man who used to work the year around with crops and livestock need only keep a fresh summer cow, grow a garden, make some maple sugar, and maybe carve a few knickknacks from wood for sale as souvenirs. In the summer he supplies the table while his wife cares for the seasonal boarders, to whom he sells everything, including the winter-made knickknacks. The work is easier and the returns much better than straight farming.

Another boon is the May-to-November stream of autoists. With a roadside stand, the farmer or his family can sell a large quantity of garden truck, along with eggs, broilers and turkeys, berries, jams, jellies, preserves, maple sugar and syrup, fruit, and antiques —new or third hand. It isn't farming in the old way, but it is a lot more profitable if one insists upon living on a New England farm.

Two quite typical New England items, cranberries and stones, deserve special mention. Now that turkey has become a year-round table item, the cranberry market has increased. This is good news for the relatively few cranberry growers, as is the announcement of a cranberry harvester that will save labor and lower costs. The Cape Cod area of Massachusetts is the country's greatest producer of cranberries. In 1949 this area harvested over 15,000 acres which produced 520,000 barrels of cranberries, one of the chief export crops of Massachusetts. And for that omnipresent past, the endless stones that each year work their way up out of a subsoil that seems to be nothing but stones, there has appeared a mechanical stone-picker in Massachusetts that painlessly clears off each year's stone crop.

The possibility of more tree culture in this area has been mentioned elsewhere. That thought should not be limited to nut trees. As the nation's total forest resources recede toward the danger point, it becomes more desirable than ever, if not mandatory, that those lands where forests once grew be returned to forest. This is particularly true if there is danger of serious erosion or if the highest land-use rating indicates a suitability for trees. The Northeastern States have great areas of land that come under this heading. The need is great and the opportunity is attractive. One thing stands in the way, and that is a tax policy in the states affected which places too much burden on the would-be tree farmer. Until New England recognizes and rectifies this mistake, the nation as a whole will suffer. Taxes should be levied on the forest product when it is converted to cash, not on its stumpage value while in growth.

No consideration of New England would be complete without mention of the part-time and residential farmer. With the exception of Virginia, West Virginia, Florida, and some areas in Washington and Oregon, New England has the highest percentage of part-time and residential farmers of any part of the United States. There is every reason to believe they are here to stay and will increase in numbers.

Usually the transformation of a full-time farmer to either a

TABLE 15.—*Part-time and residential farms in New England, 1950.*

	Total farms	*Part-time farms**	*Residential farms**	*Per cent of part-time and residential farms*
New England	103,191	14,287	29,489	42.4
Maine	30,368	4,642	9,901	47.9
N. H.	13,382	2,296	4,670	52.1
Vt.	19,043	1,952	3,991	31.3
Mass.	22,205	3,215	5,707	40.2
R. I.	2,606	350	670	39.1
Conn.	15,587	1,832	4,550	41.0

Source: *United States Census of Agriculture, 1950,* II, 1132–33.

* Part-time farms are those with a value of sales of farm products of from $250 to $1,199 a year, provided the operator worked 100 days or more off the farm, or if the nonfarm income received by the operator and his family was more than the value of farm products sold in 1949. Residential farms are defined as those whose total value of sales of farm products in 1949 was less than $250.

city man or a part-time farmer is the result of a wish to gain more security by making a personal balance of agriculture with industry. Agriculture's rewards, particularly in much of New England, are meagre at the best. This suggests that subsistence farming is about as far as one should, or could, go. But industrial work, on the other hand, is frequently seasonal and often subject to layoffs. Hence, if one has a small agricultural operation that can be handled by week-end work with help from the family, a roof overhead may be assured, with at least the provender of fruit trees and a garden, and possibly a few chickens and a cow, contributing to the support of the family. If the bulk of living expense can be gained this way, then any money from industry can provide clothing, education, medical service, and recreation. The proposition is so attractive that the 1950 census listed 43,776, or 42.4 per cent, of New England's farms as part-time or residential. Some of these have taken up this combination proposition.

As cities become more crowded, with possible threats to children's health and morals, and as the nervous strain of urban life grows harder to bear, it is possible that the combination city-country life will enlist even more practitioners. Another persuasive causative factor may be industry's own desire to get away from high urban taxes and labor trouble and to get nearer the rural market. This is causing decentralization of industrial areas and is widening the opportunity for more part-time farmers. The tendency of industry, as well as agriculture, to migrate to other climes, however, seems not to have run its course, and this will undoubtedly affect farming in New England.

On the bright side of New England agriculture is the possibility of combining numbers of small farms into larger operations. Also, by the expansion of grasslanding and livestock production, income might be raised. But taken all in all, the negative trends still overbalance the positive. It is not inconceivable that this area may sometime in the future become the equivalent of a gigantic national monument to history, culture, and recreation. The chief agricultural interest may be the lesson it teaches. Neither prosperity nor population will grow on poor soil and in an unfriendly climate when there is an alternative way or ways to make a living.

CHAPTER 3

The Middle Atlantic States: Prime Market

(New York, New Jersey, Pennsylvania)

THIS region is neither predominantly rich nor poor. It has some very good soils, some very poor, and a great many that are median. It possesses the typically flat sandy lands of the Coastal Plain, a piedmont region, a hilly and even mountainous portion, with many a fertile river valley thrown in to make almost a cross section of American agricultural lands. Some of the best soils are in the limestone region of southeastern Pennsylvania and the clay marl belt which extends from southwest to northeast through central New Jersey. Yet, on the whole, the land in crop production is generally poor and needs heavy applications of fertilizer to produce profitably. In the north this region has such a New England-like product as maple sugar. In the south it has the Dixie flavor of tobacco, fish, and side meat. Added to this is a strong dairy industry that brings to mind parts of New England, Shenandoah, and Washington, and truck farming and poultry that are being forced to meet competition from California, the Río Grande Valley, and Florida.

The land area of the Middle Atlantic States covers 64,327,040 acres, roughly the size of Wyoming. About half of this acreage, or

GENERAL PATTERN OF GREAT SOIL GROUPS

Middle Atlantic States

PODZOL SOILS

Light-colored leached soils of cool, humid forested regions.

BROWN PODZOLIC SOILS

Brown leached soils of cool-temperate, humid forested regions.

GRAY-BROWN PODZOLIC SOILS

Grayish-brown leached soils of temperate, humid forested regions.

WIESENBÖDEN (1), GROUND WATER PODZOL (2), AND HALF-BOG SOILS (3)

(1) Dark-brown to black soils developed with poor drainage under grasses in humid and subhumid regions.

(2) Gray sandy soils with brown cemented sandy subsoils developed under forests from nearly level imperfectly drained sand in humid regions.

(3) Poorly drained, shallow, dark peaty or mucky soils underlain by gray mineral soil, in humid regions, under swamp-forests.

LITHOSOLS AND SHALLOW SOILS (HUMID)

Shallow soils consisting largely of an imperfectly weathered mass of rock fragments, largely but not exclusively on steep slopes.

NEW YORK

PENNA.

N.J.

TABLE 16.—*Number of farms in the Middle Atlantic States, 1850–1950.*

	1950	1940	1930	1920	1910	1900	1880	1850
Total	296,694	348,100	357,603	425,147	468,379	485,618	488,907	322,103
N. Y.	124,977	153,238	159,806	193,195	215,597	226,720	241,058	170,621
N. J.	24,830	25,835	25,378	29,702	33,487	34,650	34,307	23,905
Pa.	146,887	169,027	172,419	202,250	219,295	224,248	213,542	127,577

Source: *United States Census of Agriculture, 1950,* 50.

31,855,003 acres, is in farms. Of the amount of land in farms, about 38 per cent of it is harvested cropland.

At first glance, it might be said that the outstanding characteristic of this region, agriculturally, is its middle-of-the-road policy, or cross-sectionalism. It has grown in the past, and still does grow, a wide variety of crops. Agriculture has been influenced by soil types, climate, and the racial and cultural background of the settlers. However, one of the most important influences in this area is the fact that it is contiguous to the greatest consumption and export markets in the world.

Wherever you go, from farmhouse to farmhouse, the chief topics of conversation are not so much farm practices as markets, prices, supply and demand, cost of distribution, and similar problems. Farther west or south, these same items enter into conversations, it is true, but not on the day-to-day, almost hour-to-hour basis that they do in the Middle Atlantic States. All over the nation, radio programs give reports on price fluctuations in the major markets once or twice a day. But in this region, the barn and house radio pours out the market news almost every hour. Even the big metropolitan stations such as WRCA in New York City give farm market news at six in the morning and again at twelve noon (when most trading for the day is over).

The price of wheat is important in Kansas, to be sure, but wheat is harvested only once a year, and it may be carried over still another year before it is sold. What happens in the hourly pit reports is not of such great interest. Long trends are. Cotton and tobacco have a similar story. The beef cattleman is particularly interested in markets in the fall, but the rest of the year that interest is secondary to the everyday business of breeding and feeding his herd. The feeder is more market-news dependent, but on a 60-, 90-, 120- day, or even an annual basis.

In the subject area, however, many crops will start or not go to market on a twelve-hour basis. If the sweet-corn market closes strong today, a farmer will hope that it will hold on the opening and start his truck rolling at midnight for the terminal. If the report states that broilers are in full supply and going into the cold-storage market, a poultryman will hold off for a few days in slaughtering that lot of five hundred which is about ready to go. Although milk prices are set at intervals, dairymen avidly follow their ups and downs by the day. A long trend downward may mean a meeting of farmers to protest to the milk administrator. It may mean a radical change in feeding and breeding. Likewise, the dairyman and poultryman want a daily report on the going price of feed.

Farmers farther west do a great deal of their selling to elevators, brokers, storage plants, canneries, packing companies, and, indirectly, to other farmers, particular eastern ones. But farmers around New York City, Jersey City, Philadelphia, and other urban areas are doing the bulk of their selling to people who will speed the products into rapid consumption. Certainly cold storage and

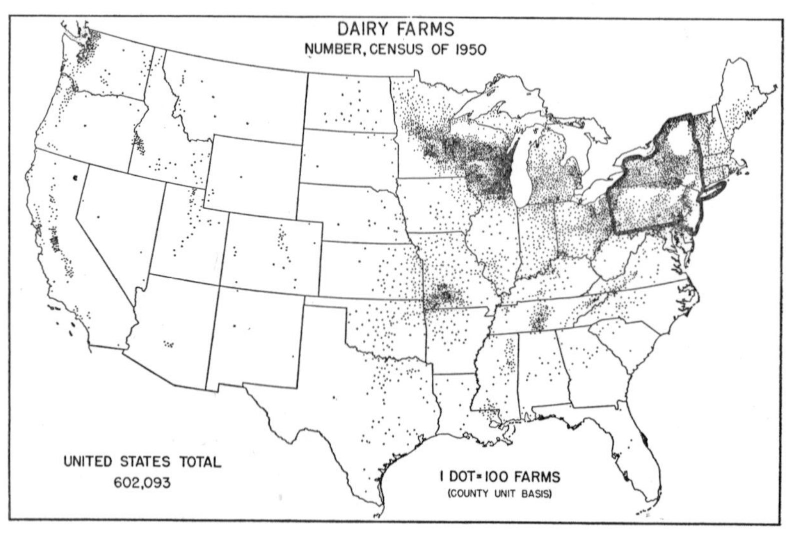

processing plants get huge quantities of products in this area, but only after the fresh market has refused them, usually by lowering the price.

Why these things are true can easily be seen from the figures on congestion. Seventy per cent of the population of New York State is along the old Erie Canal and the Hudson River from Buffalo to New York, inclusive. Farm population in this locality has dwindled to only 4.7 per cent of the total in the Middle Atlantic States. For the most part then, these people are consumers, not producers. The three states had slightly more than thirty million people in 1950, or about 20 per cent of the country's entire population. They consume farm products from every state. But to the fortunate group who live and produce close enough to enjoy a low transportation charge, the "strictly fresh" price is a great inducement in planning and marketing. The enormous "fresh" consumption capacity may be imagined when you realize that, on the average, New York City has only enough food at one time to feed its populace for a day or so. True, some foods would last longer, let us say salami, horse-radish, macaroni, *et al.* But a truckman's strike or a waterfront shutdown would bring acute shortages in the matter of a few meals after the stoppage was effective.

This gargantuan consumption naturally attracts farm products from everywhere. They may come in as an avalanche from Florida, Tidewater Virginia, or even Petaluma, California. If they do, then one wants to seek an alternate market quickly. Here again the area is favored. If Philadelphia is glutted, one may sell in Jersey City, Albany, or Baltimore. With modern highway trucking the farmer can change his market at will—and often does. For instance, a farmer eighty or one hundred miles north of New York may sell his fresh vegetables, poultry products, or fruit to markets in Albany, Troy, Kingston, Poughkeepsie, Newburgh, White Plains, Paterson, Hackensack, Newark, Jersey City, or New York City. This list could be much longer. Curiously enough, because of the importance and dominance of the big markets, very often the farmer overlooks the smaller but nonetheless good local markets.

There have been cases when fresh produce would bring more in the local farm villages of less than a thousand population than in one of the big markets. And in the summer of 1947 green corn was selling for a consumer price of eight cents an ear in New York and was going into the silos of the Hudson Valley because the cost of sacking and land transportation was more than the forty cents for a bag of fifty ears offered by the wholesale markets.

This market influence extends as far as the western borders of Pennsylvania and New York, where Pittsburgh and Buffalo offer enormous fresh markets. At the same time, fluid milk from just outside these cities is coming into New York and Philadelphia all day long. It is a marketing paradise—except when the other forty-five states upset the calculations. However, it makes cash marketing dominant and cash farming the accepted practice. Subsistence farming has declined to such a low level, notably in a few valleys in the Adirondacks, that it can be dismissed as a relatively unimportant subject.

As you might expect, intensive farming is the order of the day wherever the soil will take it. But because generations of farmers whose agronomic practices were brought from the gentler climate—and rainfall—of England did not perceive a difference, the acreage suitable for heavy cropping is not as large as it should be or once was. Considerable acreage has gone back to brush and rough pasture. In Pennsylvania, for example, every county in the state experienced a decline in farm-land acreage between 1900 and 1940. Considering the entire region, the cropland harvested dropped 1,146,436 acres between 1939 and 1949, and on the cropland areas on which intensive production continues, such as the Camden district in New Jersey, heavy applications of fertilizer are necessary to get a profitable output. Between 1939 and 1949 the amounts of commercial fertilizers put on New York and Pennsylvania farm lands nearly doubled; the increase was about one-third in New Jersey.

There has been, however, a steady increase in intensive livestock production, particularly dairying and poultry. Erosion is at a minimum on lands in pasture, hay, and poultry range. While there has been much abandonment along the southern tier of New York counties and northern Pennsylvania, the percentage never reached New England proportions, and some of this land is already coming back into production as pasture, but in much larger operations than on the original subsistence units. Today the fact that one does not see contour and strip cropping in this area on the scale that is seen in other areas might suggest that farmers in these states are not as progressive as their colleagues elsewhere. Actually this is not true. They know that a limited and fertilized pasture is in the very best conservation tradition.

TABLE 17.—*Size of farms in the Middle Atlantic States, 1850–1950. Average acreage per farm.*

	1950	1940	1930	1920	1910	1900	1880	1850
M. A. S.*	107.4	96.6	98	95.4	92.2	92.4	95.1	114.2
N. Y.	128.2	112.1	112.5	106.8	102.2	99.9	98.7	112.1
N. J.	69.5	72.6	69.3	76.8	76.9	82.0	85.4	115.2
Pa.	96.1	86.3	88.8	87.3	84.8	86.4	92.7	116.9

Source: *United States Census of Agriculture, 1950,* II, 799.

*Average acreage per farm in the entire Middle Atlantic States area.

As in most other sections of the country, the trend toward larger farms is characteristic in New York and Pennsylvania, although there has been little change in the size of farms in New Jersey since 1930. The census of 1950 showed that farms in New York averaged 128 acres. This was about the same as in Georgia and somewhat larger than in Indiana. In terms of cropland harvested, however, farm acreages are rather small. Sixteen per cent of New York farms in 1949 harvested less than 9 acres, while 21 and 31 per cent were in that category in Pennsylvania and New Jersey, respectively. On the other hand, 28, 25, and 20 per cent of the farms in New York, Pennsylvania, and New Jersey, respectively, harvested 59 to 99 acres. High capitalization per acre and per farm is characteristic of much of this area. The greatest capitalization per farm is in New Jersey, where in 1950 the value of land and buildings averaged $292.84 an acre, the highest for any state in the Union. Here the farms are small, the operations are very intensive, and the gross output per acre is high. For example, despite the small acreages of New Jersey farms, 39.6 per cent of the commercial farms in this state marketed farm products valued at over $10,000 per farm in 1949. This 39.6 per cent of the commercial farms also sold 76.7 per cent of the value of all farm products marketed.

TABLE 18.—*Value of land and buildings per acre of farms in the Middle Atlantic States, 1850–1950.*

	1950	1940	1930	1920	1910	1900	1880	1850
N. Y.	$ 91.62	55.16	73.19	69.07	53.78	39.21	44.41	29.00
N. J.	292.84	121.54	169.99	109.67	84.36	57.23	65.16	43.68
Pa.	107.19	59.22	78.58	75.14	56.01	46.37	49.30	27.33

Source: *United States Census of Agriculture, 1950,* II, 50.

Fewer and larger farm units in this region are able to produce a larger gross product than ever before. In 1949, for example, 62,522 New York farms reported selling 7,480,810,695 pounds of whole milk, while 83,891 reported selling only 5,869,537,247 pounds in 1930. Despite an increase of nearly 2,000,000,000 pounds of whole milk during these two decades, there was a decline in the number of dairy farms and only a small increase in the number of milk cows between 1930 and 1950. In 1950 there were 2,192,686 milk cows in the three Middle Atlantic States, compared to 2,039,150 twenty years before. There were fewer milk cows in 1950, however, than in either 1940 or 1945.

TABLE 19.—*Part-time and residential farms in the Middle Atlantic States, 1949.*

	Total farms	*Part-time farms*	*Residential farms*	*Per cent of total which is part-time and residential*
N. Y.	124,780	15,537	21,131	29.4
N. J.	24,779	2,990	3,656	26.8
Pa.	146,751	22,752	35,450	39.6

Source: *United States Census of Agriculture, 1950,* II, 1132–33.

Dairying is the leading agricultural industry in New York and Pennsylvania. It is much less important in New Jersey. On every basis New York is among the top states in dairy activity. The Empire State ranked third in the number of milk cows in 1949,

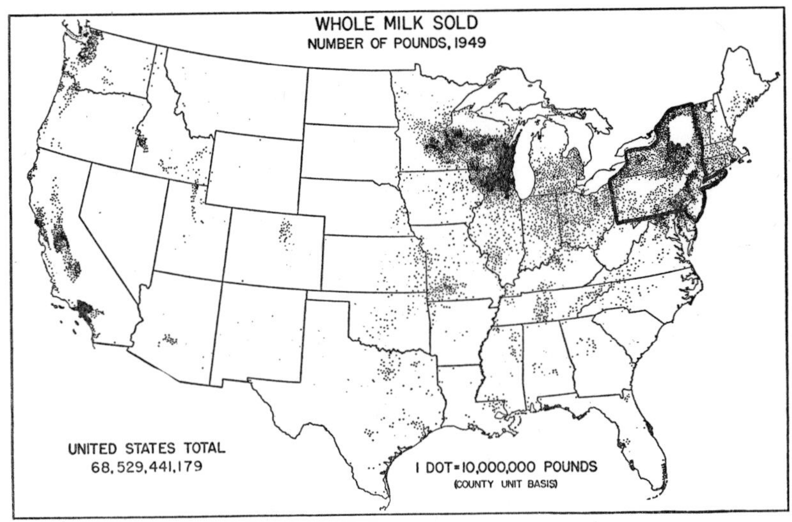

with 1,217,591 head, and was second in the pounds of whole milk sold. Wisconsin and Minnesota had a greater number of milk cows than New York, but only Wisconsin sold more milk. Total whole milk sold by farmers in the Middle Atlantic States in 1949 was 12,726,222,161 pounds, an increase of over 2,000,000,000 pounds compared to a decade earlier. The main emphasis in New York and Pennsylvania dairying is upon production for the fresh milk market. Practically the whole output goes into day-to-day consumption. In contrast, much of the production in the dairy belt of the upper Middle West is processed in cheese factories and condenseries.

TABLE 20.—*Value of principal farm products sold in the Middle Atlantic States, 1949 and 1939.*

		Value of all farm products sold	*Dairy products*	*Poultry and poultry products*	*Vegetables*
N. Y.	1949	$630,400,517	$319,323,051	$80,424,728	$37,154,197
	1939	242,417,196	111,656,707	32,198,786	17,153,313
N. J.	1949	214,319,270	50,146,294	72,840,884	26,324,569
	1939	74,449,535	22,976,065	16,500,577	11,047,276
Pa.	1949	545,926,998	200,416,348	115,251,596	15,795,747
	1939	198,024,370	68,219,850	36,432,359	7,314,402

Source: *United States Census of Agriculture, 1950,* II, 755 ff.

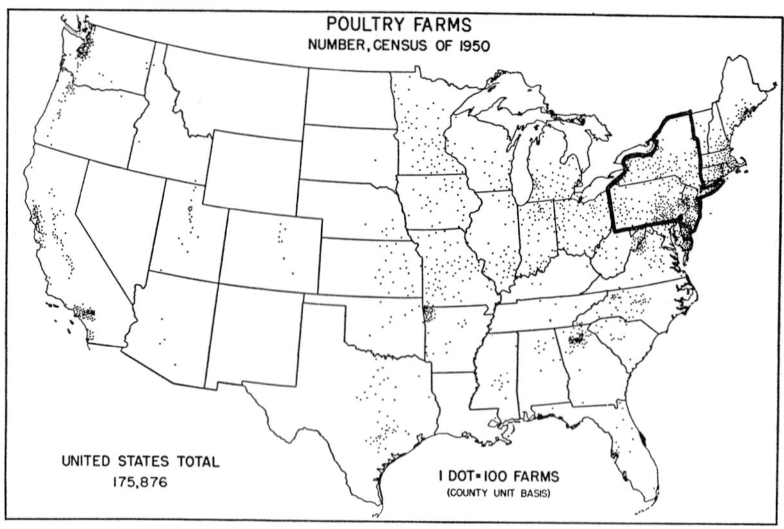

The importance of the dairy industry in New York can be further illustrated by the fact that about 55 per cent of the cropland is harvested for hay; and slightly over half of the total value of farm products sold in 1949 represented dairy products. The census of 1950 showed that 62 per cent of the commercial farms in New York and 49 per cent in Pennsylvania were classified as dairy farms. In New Jersey the figure was only 22.4 per cent. In most areas of New York and Pennsylvania, however, farmers combine dairying with some cash-crop or general farming operations. After hay, oats and corn rank next in cropland use in most of New York. In the northern parts of Pennsylvania and New York, corn is cut for silage and used for dairy feed. Much of the oats is grown as a nurse crop for hay seedlings. While dairying is relatively less important in New Jersey than in either of the other Middle Atlantic States, the dairy farms there are more highly capitalized, and have an unusually large gross product and total income. For instance, 45 per cent of New Jersey dairy farms sold products valued at between $10,000 and $25,000 in 1949. Although dairying is the most important farm business in both New York and Pennsylvania, poultry is second in importance. In New Jersey, poultry is the major agricultural activity and the largest single source of farm income. About 36 per cent of New Jersey's commercial farms are poultry farms. New Jersey farmers realized $55,000,000 from the sale of eggs alone in 1949. This was more than the income received from dairy products and about one-fourth of the value of all farm products sold. Actually, over half (51.6 per cent) of the value of New Jersey's livestock products came from poultry.

TABLE 21.—*Commercial farms by economic class in the Middle Atlantic States, 1950.**

	Per cent of total farms considered commercial	*Per cent of commercial farms in each economic class*					
		I	*II*	*III*	*IV*	*V*	*VI*
M. A. S.†	65.6	3.4	15.6	27.0	25.4	18.8	10.0
N. Y.	70.5	3.1	15.4	30.3	26.0	17.0	8.2
N. J.	72.9	10.3	29.3	22.9	16.2	13.7	7.7
Pa.	60.2	2.2	12.9	24.6	26.6	21.5	12.2

Source: *United States Census of Agriculture, 1950,* II, 1133.

* For a definition of the economic classes of farms, see Table 5.

† M. A. S. figures represent percentage for entire Middle Atlantic States area.

Besides dairying and poultry and poultry products, truck farming is vitally important in the agricultural economy of the Middle Atlantic States. Vegetables and horticultural specialties are raised in large quantities for the markets immediately at hand. The areas of greatest production are New Jersey, Long Island, the Hudson Valley, and parts of northwestern New York and southeastern Pennsylvania. In New Jersey, tomatoes, asparagus, sweet corn, and green beans, in that order, occupied the greatest acreages devoted to vegetables. In New York and Pennsylvania, sweet corn and tomatoes ranked in first and second place. In 1949 these states produced 48,743 and 31,139 acres of sweet corn, and 26,306 and 21,829 acres of tomatoes, respectively. Cabbage is a very important vegetable crop in New York. In 1949 the state's acreage was exceeded only by that of Texas.

One of the most intensive truck-gardening areas in the United States is the district around Camden, New Jersey. The level clay marl land both north and south of Camden produces vegetables

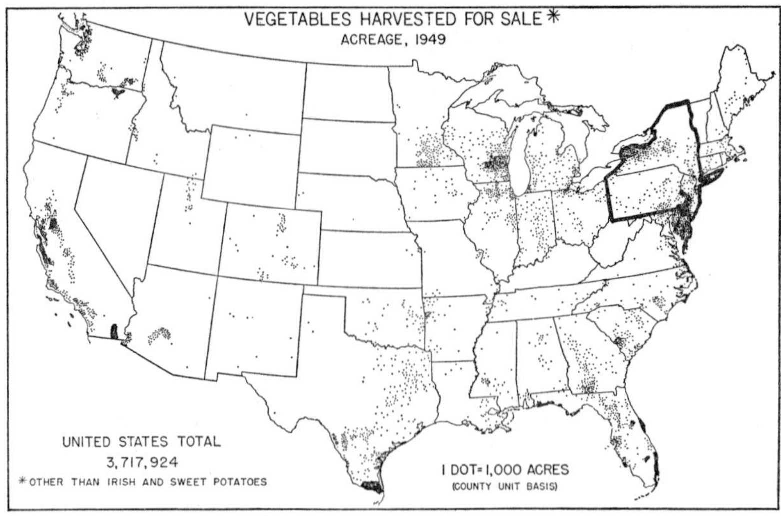

and small fruits in abundance. This is part of a trucking region which extends along the Atlantic Coast from South Carolina to New England. New Jersey had 143,590 acres of vegetables in 1949, not including potatoes and sweet potatoes. Canning plants process large quantities of vegetables which are not sold in the fresh markets, and the largest cannery in the world (Seabrook) is located here.

Omitting Irish potatoes, the value of vegetables produced and sold in the Middle Atlantic States in 1949 was $79,274,513. This was 21.5 per cent of the value of all farm crops sold in this area. Receipts from horticultural specialties were $87,115,601. The value of fruits and nuts added another $51,966,249 to farm income.

Here then is a region where many crops are grown, but where dairy, poultry, and vegetable farming are predominant. The total value of farm products sold in this area in 1949 amounted to $1,390,646,785. Of this amount, $917,677,414 came from dairy products, poultry and poultry products, and vegetables. Another important crop is Irish potatoes. New York ranks behind Maine, Idaho, and California in potato production, with a concentrated output on Long Island. Some tobacco is produced in Pennsylvania, mostly in Lancaster County, which produces more tobacco than any other county in the United States. Small grains are of some importance in both New York and Pennsylvania. Wheat acreage in 1949 was 861,000 in Pennsylvania, and this added $35,000,000 to the cash income of farmers there. The livestock industry, although small apart from dairying, adds considerably to the total farm income.

TABLE 22.—*Per cent of the commercial farms which were classified in 1949 as dairy, poultry, vegetable, or fruit and nut farms.**

	Per cent of total farms considered commercial	*Dairy*	*Poultry*	*Vegetable*	*Fruit and nut*
N. Y.	70.5	62.7	10.5	4.1	3.9
N. J.	72.9	22.4	36.4	16.0	4.8
Pa.	60.2	49.3	16.9	1.2	1.5

Source: *United States Census of Agriculture, 1950,* II, 1235.

* In the 1950 census a farm was classified by type if a particular product or group of products represented 50 per cent or more of the total sales from the farm. The 1950 data on types of farms are not comparable to those used in 1945, 1940, or 1930.

Despite the enormous advantage that contiguity to prime markets has given this region for generations, the future cannot be viewed with an equanimity based on the belief that such an advantage is eternal. Modern transportation, in part, but modern preservation even more so, are conspiring to bring new competitive threats to the farmers of this region. Such questions arise as how long will fresh-from-farm-to-you in the fresh form take precedence over fresh-from-farm-to-you in the processed form? Before the war, eviscerated poultry played a very small part, and that in a strictly luxury market. Housewives generally bought New York style (with entrails still in the bird) by an overwhelming percentage. But even today there are unmistakable signs that this preference was never really a preference, but a learned habit. Although figures presently available do not indicate a huge swing to the eviscerated, quick-frozen, ready-to-cook product, it is not foolhardy to predict that within possibly a decade New York style will be as unpopular as the big round cheese on the block, covered with flies and a damp cheesecloth, now is. Yet, only yesterday, wiseacres said that rattrap cheese would never be supplanted by the "new-fangled" individually packaged types.

Rather than looking to present consumption figures, let us take an example from the processors' angle of what the present writers consider the beginning of a trend. One of the greatest poultry supply houses, with a huge business in this country as well as abroad, is Carl A. Swanson & Sons, Omaha, Nebraska. This firm has been in business for half a century, with headquarters in Omaha, processing plants in six states, and outlets in forty. At one time they were the biggest handlers of New York style birds. Recently they went out of this line and switched entirely to the eviscerated, ready-to-cook item, in addition to packaged breasts, thighs, and other parts, chicken à la king, soups, and so on. They have also become one of the major turkey processors and producers in the country, with an annual pack in the seven-figure class. If such a house did not believe that the old-fashioned way was outmoded, they would not have made the huge investment necessary to set up a production line.[1]

Following the trend of quick-frozen, precooked products, ready to serve when thawed and heated, the C. A. Swanson firm has become the largest producer and distributor of frozen poultry products in the United States. Frozen chicken pies are one of their specialties. The tremendous potentiality of this business was demonstrated in late 1953, during a nationwide advertising campaign, when Swanson sold one million cases of frozen chicken pies in ninety days. As the number of women in business increases, and as apartment houses lend themselves less and less to traditional housekeeping, particularly cooking, the popularity of this type of service is bound to grow. Even television is making a change in dining habits, as witness the advent of precooked, frozen, whole meals in a disposable container, which the housewife can pop into the oven, heat, and serve—and never miss more than a few minutes of her favorite show. If this trend persists, will proximity to a large market continue to be a great advantage for the farmer?

[1] In eviscerating poultry, the work is done very much like the assembly of an automobile, only in reverse. The live bird is attached to a moving line and stays there until it is ready for cooking or freezing. It is killed, bled, plucked, singed, cleaned, drawn, and inspected, all the while moving slowly on an overhead track.

In general, poultry can be raised much more cheaply close to feed sources, as, for example, in Arkansas. Taxes are also lower in regions away from the metropolitan areas. Structural requirements are much less in the South and Southwest. Arkansas has become a huge broiler producer, ranking fifth in sales in 1949, with twenty-nine million chickens marketed, and Texas and Georgia sold twenty-six million and forty-five million respectively. If the bird is slaughtered where it is produced, and if all the waste is taken out, it is not too expensive to ship. If it is taken even further in processing, right to the finished meal, the savings become even greater. For the longer term, can a Middle Atlantic poultryman who has to ship in most of his feed pay the high terminal costs built up in recent years, pay high taxes, invest large sums in structures and working capital, and still compete with someone who will sell a full chicken dinner all ready to eat at a reasonable price?

The answer cannot be predicted with finality by anyone. But note that from the beginning of the twentieth century the outstanding trend in our everyday life has been for each of us to do less for himself and to rely more and more on the service trades. None of us any longer cobble our own shoes; few even shine them. We have seen privately owned diapers displaced in many homes by a diaper service. We have seen dried beans which were soaked all night, boiled all day, and baked the second day give way to a can in which the beans, the sauce, and the salt pork are all combined and precooked for us. Rice that used to require washing and boiling is now precooked and can be prepared in sixty seconds.

Any student of urban trends must recognize these things. And today, for the first time, the farmer is learning that he must study urban trends, as the farm seller is at last learning that he must study rural trends and practices. Small refrigerators and smaller urban families have just about spelled the death knell of the huge steak or roast (except in Lancaster and Philadelphia, two of the very few markets for large-sized cattle left in the United States). We have seen the coming of the Beltsville small white turkey to meet a similar situation. And now we see an even newer way to please the urban housewife and, incidentally, to expand the turkey market. That is, of course, the innovation of growing larger birds and turning their meat into individual steaks. This idea, again, is one that will probably favor the western range-raiser of turkeys rather than the near-to-market easterner. The cheap gains on the big birds raised under western practices are not duplicated in the confined raising of the East, where most feed is imported.

There is the matter of eggs, an item that has freshness for almost its entire sales appeal. A few short years ago, California was selling in the eastern metropolitan fresh egg market, topping it, and making a good profit, even though three thousand miles away. Then the northeasterners somewhat unwillingly learned what grading, packaging, and modern merchandizing methods could do. They made a comeback and recaptured their own market. New ideas in egg preservation such as the oil treatment have now been developed, and when these and other new techniques have been perfected, is there any reason to believe that the housewife cannot be sold on "preserved" fresh eggs as preferable to yard-fresh eggs? Anyone who would say "no" has not studied what advertising can do. After all, a quarter of a century ago citrus fruit was only a Christmas delicacy. Today even the most modest homes consider it a "must" for breakfast.

An unimpassioned consideration of the future of the eastern poultry industry, unless it modernizes many of its practices, its processing, and its merchandizing, does not seem to present a too optimistic picture. There is always the stickler that it is expensive to ship bulk feed to a finishing market. It is much cheaper to ship a finished product—IF you can compete in quality with the fresh, locally produced item. Everything seems to point to the quick realization of the latter proposition.

In dairying, the threats are not so great, but they are nevertheless far from nonexistent. Nothing in recent experience suggests that dried milk, or any other processed form has the taste appeal of fresh milk. The eastern milksheds, unlike those farther west, are mostly producers of fresh fluid milk. By-products are a secondary consideration, but for part of every year, during the flush season, the surplus milk must be marketed in processed forms, i.e. ice cream mix, dried or evaporated forms, cheese and cheese products, butter, and so on.

The price of blended milk and the stability of the price structure of whole milk in the eastern milksheds depend to a large extent on the price of butter in the flush period. The hope for a higher return to producers on the fluid product does not seem to be very well founded. As this is written, fluid milk has reached the point that any recession in wages would probably bring a quick decrease in its consumption. Distribution costs are so high that, even if the producer got nothing, milk would probably cost more than it did in the Depression, when farmers poured it down the drain rather than lose more money transporting it to town. Add to this highly dangerous position the fact that discrimination against oleomargarine is rapidly passing away. Even New York State has repealed its fifty-year-old law against colored margarine. When colored margarine, without the tax, can be sold for less than twenty-five cents a pound, the future of butter looks bad, at best.

Take the floor out from under butter, and the price of blended milk in the eastern milksheds in any surplus time is in grave danger, and the major farm enterprise of the Middle Atlantic States is threatened with bankruptcy. Again, nearness to market is important, but much less so than it was a few years ago.

Offsetting this threat is the possibility of doing more grasslanding and buying fewer concentrates from the Middle West. In Wisconsin, several milk producers stopped feeding concentrates entirely, and for years have fed only grass, grass silage, and hay. Admittedly, they do not get the gross production of their brothers who use concentrates, but, on the other hand, they have no cash outgo at all except for medicines, veterinary fees, and possibly some protein supplement. One man who has a quarter of a century record in this type of milk production, including the Depression years, showed a loss in only one year. That year he fed commercial feeds.

The eastern milksheds may possibly be driven to this type of milk production. This would entail larger acreages, managed pastures, grass silage, improved hay-making methods (possibly mow curing or dehydration of grasses), and improved grass strains which would increase protein content at harvesting time so that the need of a supplement would be eliminated. Such a shift would make a major change in farm patterns and economics, but we cannot be sure that the coming decade will not force it.

Truck gardening, the third big Middle Atlantic enterprise, seems no less in danger than poultry husbandry or dairying. Even now, Florida, the Middle South, Texas, the Mesilla Valley (New Mexico), the Salt River Valley (Arizona), California, and the northern Pacific Coast States all compete with local produce in the metropolitan markets. But their threat for the future does not seem to be so much in the strictly fresh market (via airplane as has been tried out successfully) as in the processed fresh market.

What will better canning, better quick-freezing, and even an edible dehydration[2] do to the fresh market? Standpatters say that no kind of processing can ever equal actual freshness. Maybe not, but few city people ever get actual freshness. The markets are so complex that at least many hours, often even days, come between field and table no matter how efficient the distribution is.

In reality, the urban consumer does not get what a farmer means by fresh vegetables even when the most modern and speedy techniques are employed. Anyone who has tried to match the field-fresh flavor of sweet corn by paying the premium prices asked in New York vegetable markets knows that it simply cannot be bought—at any price. That may account for the actual taste preference of many an urbanite for canned *petits pois* rather than unshelled peas, no matter how fresh they are. Peaches in the canned version are definite favorites of many people, even over the tree-ripened product.

This brings up a marketing quirk that all farmers who grow certain products must face sometime in the future: Not all consumers, in some cases not even the majority, actually *like* a true fresh flavor. Under modern advertising and promotion, taste preferences can be sold that have nothing to do with freshness. For instance, try to convince a lover of dried figs that the fresh product is better—or even edible. Here is a case in point of how taste

[2] Birdseye of frozen food fame is now reported at work in his laboratories to produce a new kind of dehydration that will excell even quick-freezing as a process for preserving the actual field-fresh taste. He might succeed as he did before.

habits can be built up to prefer a processed product rather than a fresh one.

One of the authors was educated in California and spent most of his college years working in the citrus orchards. There a love of the juice pressed from oranges dead ripe on the tree was acquired. For many years in the East, he often mourned that he could not get orange juice that was fit even for the cull pot. Then a brand new, homogenized, quick-frozen product was sent to him by a California manufacturer who hoped he had, at long last, been able to duplicate, or hold, the actual taste of tree-fresh orange juice. The author and his wife sampled this experiment, then went into ecstasies. It was the true, rich, full-bodied juice of the tree-ripened oranges pressed five minutes after gathering and properly chilled.

With great expectations, the product was tried out on a group of eastern friends in comparison with the best canned juice that could be procured. To a man, they turned down the new and superlative product. They wanted the juice their taste had been educated to. In other words, the manufacturer, now fully launched in business, would have to re-educate the consuming public, or else start with children, to gain acceptance of this truly remarkable product.

All of this argues that fresh vegetables tomorrow may have no edge at all. More and more, our foods come to us in combinations, semi- or fully cooked, spiced, herbed, mixed, and always with less work needed to get them to the table than the fresh item. These observers, at least (many a farmer to the contrary notwithstanding), think that the trend among consumers is toward "made" taste appeals and away from "natural" tastes. For one thing, and this is a cogent point, there is no particular reason why any national advertiser should sell fresh flavors. The advertiser's best profit comes from processed food. Farmers, being widely distributed and unorganized, have little opportunity to sell fresh as fresh. Recently the radio announced that hereafter you would not have to buy bacon and cheese separately to get a bacon and cheese sandwich, for now a spread is available that does the whole job for you. No work, no frying, just spread it on—again, labor has been taken out of food preparation.

The role of the working mother or homemaker in changing the tastes and mores of urban society is often overlooked, but it actually deserves a great deal of emphasis. After a day at office or factory, few women want to make anything "like mother used to make" if there is an economical, little-work substitute.

Another leading eastern product should be noted—fruit. New York is an especially heavy producer of apples. Its 18,000,000-bushel production in 1950 was exceeded only by Washington State. Surely, with nutritionists advocating more fruit consumption, this one classification has a bright future. So it would seem, but note that apple consumption per capita has been steadily declining. In 1929 the annual per capita consumption of apples was thirty-nine pounds. This had dropped to twenty-three pounds by 1950. Cherries and peaches show a little better history. Again we see processed forms making a new threat.

During World War II, the regional research laboratory at Albany, California, developed a frozen purée of fruit that received immediate and enthusiastic reception by the armed services, to which it was solely distributed. This new form of fruit flavor was found in the search for a use of culls, discards, and bruised products. The very best, selects, do not give any better result in the puréed form than off-sized and spotted fruit. Further, it is in a form that seems to be more popular than any fresh fruit, i.e. a sort of ice cream or frappé.

Perhaps the future of fruit in this section of the country will be more and more tied to manufactured products and less to fresh products (for instance, apple honey as a tobacco preservative). If so, then the high price of eastern orchards, high taxes, the need for expensive investment in coolers, and similar drawbacks will take away or equalize the last bit of the advantage of producing for a fresh market.

Among all these negative viewers is one outstanding and encouraging fact. Population is increasing much more than experts of the mid-forties thought it would. City population, despite much propaganda for decentralization, obtusely continues to grow. Most people would evidently rather put up with the drawbacks of the city to get its advantages than suffer the disadvantages of small town or rural living, with its undeniable values. This means, despite the drawbacks and despite the competition from other sectors and new forms of food, that the Eastern States can stay in business because our best agricultural land is decreasing in area even as consumption grows. Also, consumers are increasing elsewhere, nearer the sources of food products which in the past have competed in the East. The near-at-hand markets in California, for instance, may look better to West Coast farmers than the traditional metropolitan markets of the East.

The Middle Atlantic States, as well as New England, need not despair because long-held advantages are disappearing. But it is manifest that agriculture in these sections cannot sit comfortably on outworn shibboleths and expect to stay in a business that is becoming more highly competitive every day.

Farmers in this area must learn new processing, preservation, packaging, advertising, and all the other techniques of competitive business. In some cases they will have to change from an all "fresh" to a processed "fresh" market. Perhaps they will have to change their major enterprise. For instance, a man on a truck farm too small to economically utilize high-pressure, multi-row sprayers and dusters, and similar expensive tools, may find it advantageous to enter the cut-flower market. A dairyman with too small an acreage and no opportunity to expand to adopt a grassland program may have to switch to poultry or open a resort and market his products direct to his own guests.

The greatest of all threats to agriculture in this region is not the progress of other sectors, or new forms, or changing taste appeals, but the unwillingness to change that characterizes the older parts of the country. In the South it is as evident as a neon sign. In New England and the Middle Atlantic States, where farming has not been dramatized as it has in the Old South, it has not been so evident to students and certainly not to farmers. But it is here today—not in some far away tomorrow. The man who recognizes that fact and studies how he may change and adapt to meet new conditions will be the one who survives and prospers. If local people do not see these things, competition may come out of other regions and set up business in eastern communities. As an example, the fabulous Robert Kleberg of King Ranch fame recently bought ten thousand Pennsylvania acres on which he plans to feed out cattle raised in Texas. Others may follow his example—this is only a hint of what the future may bring.

CHAPTER 4

Delmarva: Intensive Region

(Delaware, Maryland, Tidewater Virginia)

SMALL in area, mostly flat in topography, basically sandy of soil, moderate in climate, and immensely productive under one of the most intensive systems of farming in the nation is the quick description of the area that has named itself Delmarva.[1] Historically, almost every kind of farming and nearly all crops with the exception of the subtropical have been seen in this demesne. For various reasons, sheet erosion and soil depletion being two important ones, the farming of yesterday has little more than romantic interest. The farming of today and tomorrow is the key to this area.

At the present time, there are about 69,000 farms in the Delmarva region. In the total farm economy, this area may seem relatively unimportant. In 1949 the value of all farm products sold here totaled only about $328,000,000 out of a national total of $22,000,000,000. Delaware and Tidewater Virginia each produced

[1] Technically, the Delmarva region includes only Delaware, the peninsular part of Maryland, the so-called Eastern Shore, and the two Virginia counties of Accomac and Northampton at the extreme southern end of the peninsula. For convenience, however, we have included the rest of Maryland and additional Virginia counties in the traditional Tidewater section. This entire area is a distinct marketing region with Norfolk on the south, Philadelphia on the north, and Baltimore and Washington, D. C., in between.

GENERAL PATTERN OF GREAT SOIL GROUPS

Delmarva

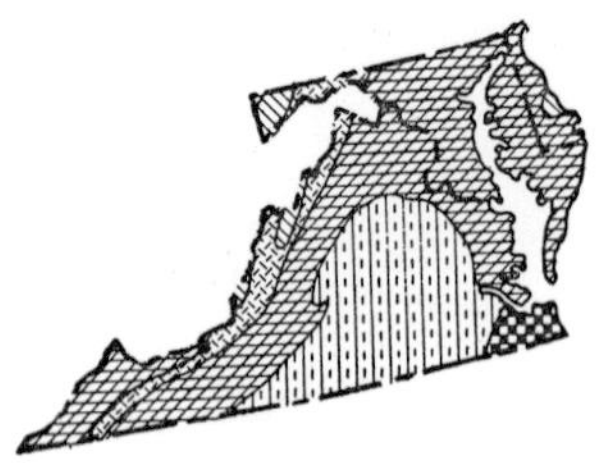

PODZOL SOILS

Light-colored leached soils of cool, humid forested regions.

GRAY-BROWN PODZOLIC SOILS

Grayish-brown leached soils of temperate, humid forested regions.

RED AND YELLOW PODZOLIC SOILS

Red or yellow leached soils of warm-temperate, humid forested regions.

WIESENBÖDEN (1), GROUND WATER PODZOL (2), AND HALF-BOG SOILS (3)

(1) Dark-brown to black soils developed with poor drainage under grasses in humid and subhumid regions.

(2) Gray sandy soils with brown cemented sandy subsoils developed under forests from nearly level imperfectly drained sand in humid regions.

(3) Poorly drained, shallow, dark peaty or mucky soils underlain by gray mineral soil, in humid regions, under swamp-forests.

LITHOSOLS AND SHALLOW SOILS (HUMID)

Shallow soils consisting largely of an imperfectly weathered mass of rock fragments, largely but not exclusively on steep slopes.

about 0.3 per cent of the total value of farm products sold in the United States, and Maryland produced 0.8 per cent.

TABLE 23.—*Number of farms in Delaware, Maryland, and Virginia, 1850–1950.*

	1950	1940	1930	1920	1910	1900	1880	1850
Del.	7,448	8,994	9,707	10,140	10,836	9,687	8,749	6,063
Md.	36,107	42,110	43,203	47,908	48,923	46,012	40,517	21,860
Va.	150,997*	174,885	170,610	186,242	184,018	167,886	118,517	77,013†

Source: *United States Census of Agriculture, 1950,* II, 52–53.

* The authors have included thirty-one Virginia counties in the Tidewater section which had 25,550 farms in 1950.

† This figure includes farms in what is now West Virginia.

Most of the farm income is derived from livestock and livestock products, and this percentage has been steadily increasing. In 1949 Delaware's farm income was divided thus: 15.9 per cent was from the sale of crops and 83.9 per cent was from the sale of livestock and livestock products. Ten years earlier the percentages were 30.6 per cent and 69.1 per cent in each category.

TABLE 24.—*Average number of acres per farm in Delaware, Maryland, and Virginia, 1850–1950.*

	1950	1940	1930	1920	1910	1900	1880	1850
Del.	114.3	99.6	92.8	93.1	95.9	110.1	124.6	157.7
Md.	112.3	99.7	101.3	99.3	103.4	112.4	126.4	212.0
Va.	103.1*	94.0	98.1	99.7	105.9	118.6	167.4	339.6†

Source: *United States Census of Agriculture, 1950,* II, 799.

* The average size of farms in Tidewater Virginia was 107 acres in 1950.

† This figure includes farms in what is now West Virginia.

Poultrying and dairying are the leading agricultural pursuits in Delaware and Maryland. These are also important in Tidewater Virginia, but are not predominant. Most of Virginia's dairying is in the counties west of Washington, D. C. When one thinks of Kansas, he thinks of wheat. When one thinks of Delaware in agricultural terms, he should think of chickens. This little state, which

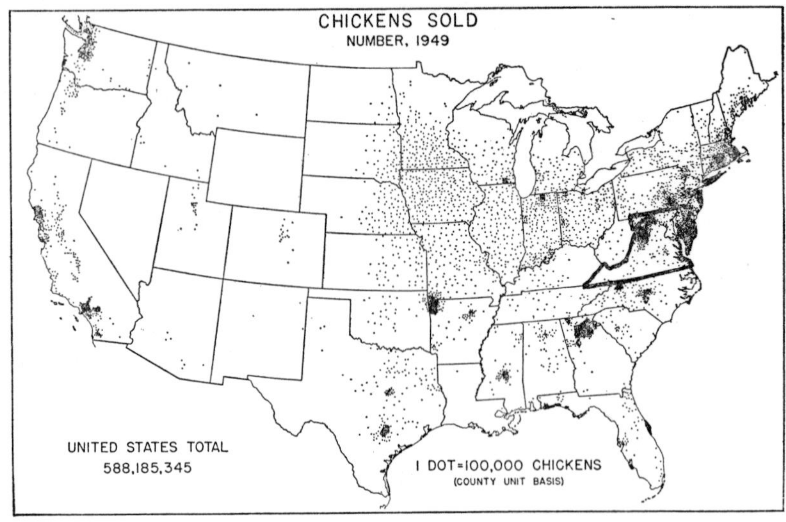

harvested only 389,000 acres of cropland in 1949, much less than Lubbock County, Texas, is the nation's outstanding chicken producer. In 1949, Delaware poultrymen sold 59,304,111 chickens, or 10 per cent of the total sold in the entire United States. Ten years before, they marketed only 5.5 per cent of the total, indicating a major change which is occurring in Delaware's agriculture.

TABLE 25.—*Number of chickens sold in Delaware, Maryland, and Virginia, 1919–49.*

	1949	1939	1929	1919
Del.	59,304,111	16,615,137	2,070,702	434,970
Md.	39,672,298	8,449,787	3,563,273	1,618,774
Va.	24,604,324*	13,492,384	7,647,829	4,700,493

Source: *United States Census of Agriculture, 1950,* II, 448–49.

* Tidewater Virginia: 6,667,536.

Over 44 per cent of Delaware's commercial farms are classified as poultry farms, but poultry and poultry products brought 85 per cent of the value of all livestock and livestock products sold in 1949. Income from chickens was $50,502,000, or nearly 71 per cent of the total farm income. Most Delaware chickens are sold as broilers in the nearby metropolitan markets. Very few chickens are kept throughout the year and not many eggs are sold. Although Maryland ranked third in number of chickens sold in 1949, this source of income played a much smaller part in the total farm economy than in Delaware. Poultry farms in Maryland sold 24.4 per cent of the total value of farm products in 1949.

The emphasis upon poultry in this area would seem to predict a healthy agricultural economy. Comparing the period of 1935–39 with 1950–53, the per capita use of poultry and eggs has jumped 46 per cent, while the consumption of red meats has grown only 14 per cent. However, an ever present problem is the relation between feed costs and poultry prices. In 1949, poultry farmers in both Delaware and Maryland spent between 52 and 55 per cent of the total value of farm products for feed. Thus an unfavorable relationship between feed and poultry prices could be very damaging to farm income in Delmarva.

Dairying is the ranking agricultural industry in Maryland and is a very weak second in Delaware. In Maryland, 28 per cent of the commercial farms were classified as dairy farms by the 1950 census; 22.1 per cent were so classified in Delaware. A total of

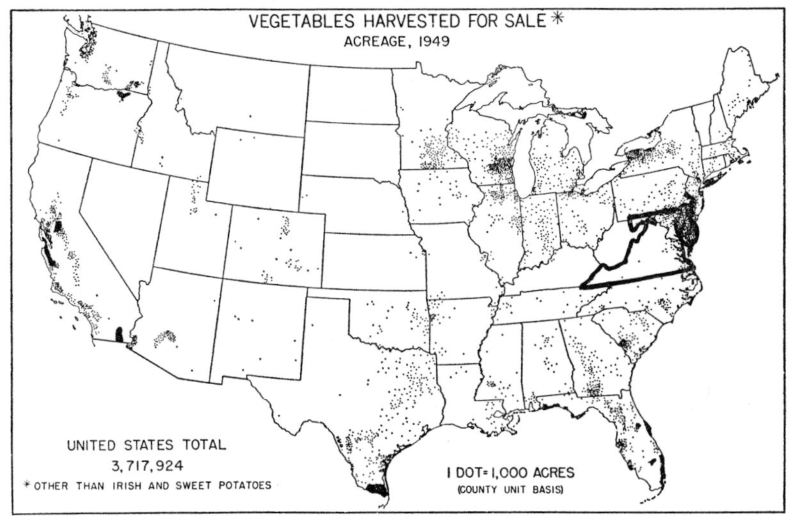

$47,000,000, a little more than 25 per cent, of Maryland's farm income came from dairy products. Dairying is concentrated in the Piedmont region northwest of Baltimore.

Much of the Delmarva region is in the Atlantic Coast truck-farming belt which runs from South Carolina to New England. Most of Delaware and Maryland's lower Eastern Shore is the region where fruit and truck farming is most important. Further south in the Virginia counties of Accomac, Northampton, Princess Anne, and Norfolk, the same situation prevails. Sweet corn and tomatoes are the leading truck crops in this area. Maryland grew 34,105 acres of sweet corn and 23,224 acres of tomatoes in 1949. Delaware had 3,582 and 3,784 acres, respectively, of these crops. Other important vegetables are cucumbers and English peas.

To a person from the Corn Belt or the Wheat Belt, farm operations in the Delmarva region might seem insignificant. Yet many farmers in this area are in big business. More than half of Delaware's commercial farmers are in the top three economic classes, which means that in 1949 they sold more than $5,000 worth of farm produce. Of the poultry farmers, 23 per cent sold products in excess of $25,000, and another 35 per cent marketed produce valued at between $10,000 and $24,999. Considering all of Delaware's commercial farmers, 12.3 per cent sold products of $25,000 or more. This percentage of high-income farmers was surpassed by only two other states, California and Arizona. However, this class of farmers made up only 4 per cent of the total commercial farmers in Maryland and about the same percentage in Tidewater Virginia.

TABLE 26.—*Percentage of commercial farms by economic class in Delaware, Maryland, and Virginia, 1949.**

	Per cent of farms considered commercial	*Per cent of commercial farms in each economic class*					
		I	*II*	*III*	*IV*	*V*	*VI*
Del.	74.6	12.3	23.0	18.1	17.4	14.4	14.7
Md.	65.4	4.0	15.2	24.3	23.0	20.2	13.4
Va.	51.8	2.0	5.3	9.1	21.1	31.3	31.2

Source: *United States Census of Agriculture, 1950,* II, 1133.

* For the definition of the economic classes of farms, see Table 5.

On flat lands, one does not ordinarily think of conservation as a prime consideration. But if those flat lands are of easily leachable soils and if the precipitation is high, one of the most insidious types of erosion takes place—the erosion of nutrients. It is insidious because there is nothing visually dramatic about it like the gullying of Utah or the Deep South. In this case, the outward manifestation of erosion is the story told by sickly plants, low yields, and abandoned fields.

In the early thirties, when depression was brooding over all the nation, one of the authors started farming in this region for the first time. Then land could be bought for a song, or less. The average value per acre as shown in the accompanying chart gives no hint of the price depths to which some of the land had fallen. Much of the soil was gray, inert, and seemed without life or vitality. The condition was described locally as "soil sour" and was thought to come from overcropping plus heroic dosages of patent fertilizer. It was obvious that the humus content was from low to nil. Earthworms were noticeable by their absence.

The roads were semideserted. Abandoned canning plants were everywhere. Fields were weed infested where they were not rapidly returning to woods. There was much abandonment, while fishing was doing more to make a living for the local folks than the onetime rich farming of the region.

Since about 1940, however, a great change has taken place. Now this whole region has become one of the most populous broiler-producing areas in the world. As previously shown, little Delaware sold over 59,000,000 chickens in 1949, more than any state in the Union. At the southern end of Delmarva, in Tidewater Virginia, the little town of Suffolk boasts of being "The Peanut Capital of the World." Nansemond County grew 19,382 acres in 1949, and produced 24,632,000 pounds of peanuts with a value of $2,709,520. In 1947 the first big livestock breeders' show was held near Baltimore. And once again both canned and fresh truck—as well as a considerable cut-flower business—flourish from the North Carolina border to Wilmington.

Certainly part of the present-day prosperity is war inspired. But much of it comes from a change in farming practices. Not a little

TABLE 27.—*Value of farm products sold in Delaware, Maryland, and Virginia, and the percentage represented by crops and by livestock and livestock products, 1939–49.*

	Value of farm products sold		*Per cent of value of farm products sold*			
			Crops		*Livestock and livestock products*	
	1949	1939	1949	1939	1949	1939
Del.	$ 76,227,871	$ 16,241,779	15.9	30.6	83.9	69.1
Md.	172,157,401	55,076,468	31.6	44.8	67.8	54.6
Va.	309,644,442	108,374,161	43.1	49.3	54.7	48.5

Source: *United States Census of Agriculture, 1950,* II, 752–54.

of the change is due to the city men who bought farms along the Eastern Shore, made huge investments, practiced good cropping, and—highly important—brought in livestock. Income shifts describe this situation. In 1939, for example, 30.6 and 44.8 per cent of the value of Delaware's and Maryland's farm products came from crops, and 69.1 and 54.6 per cent from livestock and livestock products. At mid-century, however, the value of crops had dropped to 15.9 and 31.6 per cent, respectively, in the two states, and the value of livestock and livestock products had increased to 83.9 per cent in Delaware and 67.8 per cent in Maryland.

Today manure goes on the fields by many tons per acre. Green-manure crops are common. Fertilizer is again used in quantities,[2] but coupled with humus applications. The soil is alive once more and the earthworms have returned.

Better understanding of the agronomy of their region has changed the outlook of Delmarva folks from one of despair to one of confidence. There is no reason for this area to sink into an agricultural waste, as it seemed bound to do such a short time ago. The wisdom of practicing reasonable rotations, of returning nutrients to the land, and of keeping up drainage where advisable is so apparent that it is unlikely a return to yesterday's bad practices will ever occur. Also, it cannot be denied that the better fiscal

[2] Baltimore, Maryland, is noted, among other things, for being the birthplace of the American fertilizer industry. Here were started the first mills and mixing plants. Today, besides providing the standard fertilizers, Baltimore is also a large producer of tankage, fish meal, and other protein supplements.

Courtesy Standard Oil Company of New Jersey

The universal, idealized picture of the American farmer, who has given way to a newer, more modern master of mechanization.

Courtesy Standard Oil Company of New Jersey

The average American farm, once a small operation, has become increasingly larger and more complex. (Aroostook potato country near Presque Isle, Maine.)

Spraying Maine potatoes with an eight-row power spray equipped with a dropped-nozzle boom.

Courtesy United States Department of Agriculture

Courtesy Seabrook Farms

This mechanical spinach harvester, developed at Seabrook Farms, New Jersey, cuts and loads a ton of high-quality leaves in about ten minutes.

In addition to planting lima beans, this piece of equipment at Seabrook Farms also fertilizes them and treats them with liquid herbicide to retard weed growth.

Courtesy Seabrook Farms

Courtesy Standard Oil Company of California

A modern egg-production plant near St. Helena, California, in which a 50,000-bird flock is maintained. Light, humidity, and feeding are automatically controlled. Note the production cards on each cage.

A once-familiar scene in some parts of the South which is now being replaced by progressive and far more productive conditions.

Courtesy Standard Oil Company of California

These two fields in Madison County, North Carolina, were once equally gullied. By using phosphate and lime, the owner of the field on the left produced cover crops that halted erosion and permitted livestock grazing.

Courtesy United States
Department of Agriculture

A South Carolina tobacco grower examines some flue-cured tobacco from his drying shed.

In recent years, the South has become increasingly cattle-conscious. Here, a commercial herd grazes in a pasture of white clover and Dallis grass.

Courtesy Soil Conservation Service

position of the landowners, the coming of new capital, and the realization of the importance of livestock are solid, positive factors in predicting a successful future.

TABLE 28.—*Part-time and residential farmers in Delaware, Maryland, and Virginia, 1949.*

	Total farms	*Part-time farms*	*Residential farms*	*Per cent of part-time and residential farms*
Del.	7,452	720	1,170	25.4
Md.	36,162	4,792	7,647	34.4
Va.	150,823	20,908	51,693	48.2
Tidewater Va.	25,550	3,276	7,705	43.5

Source: *United States Census of Agriculture, 1950,* I, 261 ff.; II, 1132–33.

The area lends itself to a wide diversification and a quick change in pattern. For instance, if spinach, let us say, seems to offer good market possibilities, a man may put some of his land into this very chancy crop. If he hits right in his marketing, he may come out with a killing, as many have done. He may, on the other hand, as one neighbor on the Nansemond River did, make $60,000 in one year from a quarter section, then lose that and considerably more in the next three years trying to repeat his successful venture.

But if he is not trying to make a fortune overnight, he may balance that spinach with a canning crop such as sweet corn. The sweet corn may make good money or none at all, but he will plan to take the residue back from the canning plant to put on the land or to feed to beef cattle. Or he may ensile the material and use it in the winter for his dairy cows. Winter barley will be an added help in his feeding and will cut down his cash outgo. Field corn grows well and yields highly under the new hybrids. And he may, as have quite a few in this region, go in for contract raising of hybrid seed. In fact, he can quite easily work out a plan that will give him a chance at big money, maintain his position if that chance does not come off, and still make a living from other enterprises. Best of all, in this region he can plan out a full year's employment with peak labor load not too onerous (providing he has invested in machines) and winter low not too expensive to carry if his plan was carefully thought out.

An example of the change-over from the old cash-cropping to the new diversified cropping comes from one of the author's records. The area is the Eastern Shore, just about in the middle between Cape May and Wilmington. Originally, the lands in the operation were eight farms of about 125 acres each. Of this acreage, each had from 60 to 80 acres of arable ground; the balance was in woods. All but two of the farms had been abandoned when the prices of canning vegetables went below the cost of production. The two still inhabited were worked after a fashion, but the owners depended on the oyster beds and on doing day work for their neighbors for the bulk of their living.

As fertility was low, drainage poor, and possible returns meager, it was at once apparent that previous farm sizes were inadequate to provide for changed conditions. A period of extensive farming while land rehabilitation was going on was mandatory. Acreage prices were so low and the condition of fences and structures so bad that it was not difficult to assemble a number of tracts into the roughly one thousand acres finally purchased by one of the authors. Of this one thousand acres, less than half was set up in workable fields.

At first almost the whole place was put into grass. Where there was some hope of cropping, soybeans and barley were planted. When the soybeans flowered, they were plowed under for green manure with a fertilizer "starter" to aid in breaking them down. Beef cattle were bought as four-hundred-pound calves in the West and shipped in. Pound yards were roofed and floored to save every bit of manure. A drainage program was instituted to un-waterlog some fields that showed promise.

While these beginning rebuilding jobs were under way, some of the less sorry lands were put into experimental crops. For instance, in those days there were no recommendations of which strain of hybrid corn was best suited for certain known conditions, so twenty-six strains were put into experimental plots. The strains chosen from the vast number available were selected because they fared best on the same isotherm in other regions. Admittedly, this was "playing by ear," but no one had any other suggestions.

Herbs, row crops, and cereals also were tried out. From this work, two strains of hybrid corn were selected, not because of highest yield, but largely because they showed the most thrift and standability. The latter attribute is vital in an area where heavy, smashing rainstorms are liable to come in September.

There were not enough feedstuffs and even the grasses were too poor to permit as large a herd of manure-makers as was desired. Then the question became whether to give a light treatment all over or concentrate on a few fields. The choice was made for the latter alternative.

Manure was piled on the land until is was a gamble whether the soil could absorb the quantities applied. A five-component pasture mix with a companion crop of barley was planted. Liming had preceded the planting, but it also followed as a top dressing. Soil tests both for *p*H and for available nutrients were made frequently.

The August-planted barley was pastured lightly. In the spring it was harvested and gave around fourteen to sixteen bushels per acre. Then as the pasture mix took over, the beef cattle were turned back into the fields, but on a twenty-one-day rotation of pasture. The object was to get a four-inch growth before the cows did the mowing job, and to keep down weed infestation. Droppings were broken up with a homemade Scotch harrow.

The rotation worked out was three years of grass, one year of a row crop, and one year of grain. After the first time around, the new hybrid corn produced sixty-five bushels against a previous top of twenty-five. Barley went from fourteen or fifteen to thirty or thirty-five bushels an acre. Corn for ensilage went up to around twenty-five tons. As corn had not previously been grown for this purpose, there were no figures with which to compare this tonnage.

The first several years saw little except red ink, but at the end of eight years the operation was in the black. Herbs produced well and made money. The beef cattle were topping the market readily in Baltimore and Wilmington. Corn yields were rising each year. Hay made around two tons regularly. And where truck crops (sweet corn and peas) were reinstituted, it was not uncommon to gross three to five hundred dollars per acre.

Best of all, that soil was alive. Its depth of humus color increased every year. Its friability rose to where it was a pleasure to work it. And although the temptation to open up more land or break it into the rotation was great, the owner kept on the safe and sane side. His was an intensive kind of outgo with a limited but highly intensive input. In other words, he prepared for three years at relatively low cost for the two years when he expected the land to give back almost explosively. Yet he was maintaining and building his basic capital, i.e. fertility reserve.

This type of farming, in a dozen variations but with the same basic thinking, now characterizes a goodly part of the region. Where chickens or turkeys (important newcomers) are the cash crop, manure and litter are looked upon as being as important as money from the market. If truck is the money-maker, then beef or dairy cattle are hard at work in the background providing replacement nutrients. If hogs and peanuts are making the money, dairy cattle are probably maintaining the soil. In many of these operations, the input of capital, plus better management of the land, has paid big dividends.

A facet of this territory's business that is similar to an important aspect of agriculture in the Middle Atlantic States must be stressed. When the only transportation to the metropolitan markets was by sea or rail, Delmarva did not fare so well. The coming of truck transportation and the new turnpikes must be given high credit for helping in the rehabilitation of the area.

Now a farmer south of Norfolk can load a truck at nightfall and expect it to hit Jersey City by dawn. Of course, neighborhoods farther north are even better off. This circumstance, plus the reopening of the canning plants with their new process of quick-freezing, tends to stabilize the agro-economy of the whole region. The quick and efficient transportation in refrigerated trucks also makes possible the wide diversification of risk now practiced. It has been a big factor in the growth of the cut-flower and ornamental-plant industry, another diversifier which is reaching respectable dollar volumes. In 1949 the income from this industry amounted to $607,765 in Delaware and $3,455,580 in Maryland.

It should be noted well that this happy change has brought one big new factor into the picture, namely, a high capital requirement.

TABLE 29.—*Value of land and buildings per acre in Delaware, Maryland, and Virginia, 1850–1950.*

	1950	1940	1930	1920	1910	1900	1880	1850
Del.	$114.11	$ 61.30	$ 74.31	$ 68.56	$ 51.17	$ 32.30	$ 33.74	$ 19.75
Md.	125.07	65.27	81.42	81.25	47.80	33.88	32.33	18.81
Va.	82.01*	41.04	51.16	55.19	27.29	13.64	10.89	8.27†

Source: *United States Census of Agriculture, 1950,* II, 52–53.

* Value of land and buildings in Tidewater Virginia was $99.33 in 1949, somewhat higher than for the state as a whole.

† This figure includes farms in what is now West Virginia.

Lands now bring prices comparable to the high-cost truck lands of New Jersey or Long Island. Machinery requirement likewise has gone up into the many thousands of dollars. And working capital has become an important tool of production, for the heavy fertilization program alone may require an outlay of several hundred dollars per acre. Farming in the Delmarva region is no longer cheap, or even modest. To succeed, the entrepreneur must think in terms that are fairly comparable to so-called "Small Business." Given the cash and the know-how, however, this area is well favored and doubtless will adapt without disaster when the inevitable readjustment in farm values takes place.

CHAPTER 5

The Middle South: Reorganizing Belt

(Piedmont Virginia, West Virginia, North Carolina, Kentucky, and Tennessee)

CONSIDERED as a whole, this is one of the poorest agricultural regions in the entire United States. To be sure, there are parts of this area which can boast of their agricultural riches, of heavy production and high incomes. Some of the tobacco farms in the Kentucky bluegrass region or the large cotton farms in southwestern Tennessee rank high in value of products sold. But too much of this area is an agricultural slum, a "Land of Do Without." The Middle South had about 20 per cent of the country's farm population in 1950, but sold only about 7.7 per cent of the total value

TABLE 30.—*Number of farms in the Middle South, 1850–1950.*

	1950	1940	1930	1920	1910	1900	1880	1850
Va.	150,997	174,885	170,610	186,242	184,018	167,886	118,517	77,013*
W. Va.	81,434	99,282	82,641	87,289	96,685	92,874	62,674	——
N. C.	288,508	278,276	279,708	269,763	253,725	224,637	157,609	56,963
Ky.	218,476	252,894	246,499	270,626	259,185	234,667	166,453	74,777
Tenn.	231,631	247,617	245,657	252,774	246,012	224,623	165,650	72,735

Source: *United States Census of Agriculture, 1950,* II, 53–54.

* This figure includes farms in the area which became West Virginia.

GENERAL PATTERN OF GREAT SOIL GROUPS

The Middle South

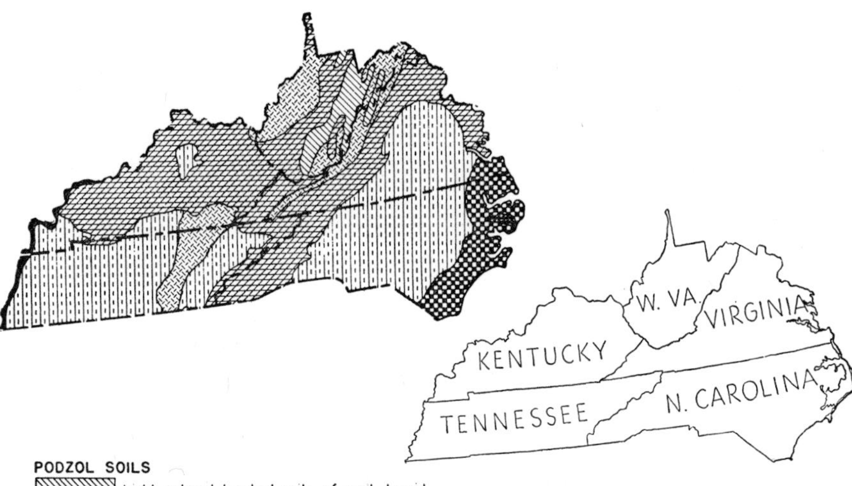

PODZOL SOILS

Light-colored leached soils of cool, humid forested regions.

GRAY-BROWN PODZOLIC SOILS

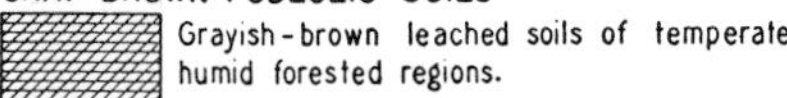

Grayish-brown leached soils of temperate, humid forested regions.

RED AND YELLOW PODZOLIC SOILS

Red or yellow leached soils of warm-temperate, humid forested regions.

WIESENBÖDEN (1), GROUND WATER PODZOL (2), AND HALF-BOG SOILS (3)

(1) Dark-brown to black soils developed with poor drainage under grasses in humid and subhumid regions.

(2) Gray sandy soils with brown cemented sandy subsoils developed under forests from nearly level imperfectly drained sand in humid regions.

(3) Poorly drained, shallow, dark peaty or mucky soils underlain by gray mineral soil, in humid regions, under swamp-forests.

BOG SOILS

Poorly drained dark peat or muck soils underlain by peat, mostly in humid regions, under swamp or marsh types of vegetation.

LITHOSOLS AND SHALLOW SOILS (HUMID)

Shallow soils consisting largely of an imperfectly weathered mass of rock fragments, largely but not exclusively on steep slopes.

ALLUVIAL SOILS

Soils developing from recently deposited alluvium that have had little or no modification by processes of soil formation.

of farm products. The 4,527,586 farm people in this region sold only $1,706,020,683 worth of agricultural products, which was slightly less than the value of farm products sold in California, where the farm population was only 617,367.

There are many problems in this region, but two stand out. One is the pressure of farm population upon the land resources. This accounts for the small farms and the low incomes in much of the area. The average size of farms in the five states is a little over eighty-nine acres. However, about 32 per cent of the farms had

TABLE 31.—*Average number of acres per farm in the Middle South, 1850–1950.*

	1950	1940	1930	1920	1910	1900	1880	1850
Va.	103.1	94.0	98.1	99.7	105.9	118.6	167.4	339.6*
W. Va.	100.9	89.7	106.5	109.6	103.7	114.7	162.6	——
N. C.	67.0	67.7	64.5	74.2	88.4	101.3	141.9	368.6
Ky.	89.0	80.2	80.8	79.9	85.6	93.7	129.1	226.7
Tenn.	80.0	74.7	73.3	77.2	81.5	90.6	124.8	261.0

Source: *United States Census of Agriculture, 1950,* II, 799.

* Includes the area which became West Virginia.

less than twenty-nine acres in 1950. The percentage of farms under twenty-nine acres for West Virginia, Virginia, North Carolina, Kentucky, and Tennessee, respectively, was 27.6, 33.2, 39.2, 28.4, and 33.6. In much of the region, however, the percentage of small farms is even greater. In seventy-five counties located in eastern Tennessee and Kentucky, western North Carolina, and south-

TABLE 32.—*Percentage of farms under ten acres in the Middle South, 1920–50.*

	1950	1930	1920
Va.	12.7	8.0	7.8
W. Va.	10.8	6.6	5.3
N. C.	9.9	6.6	5.1
Ky.	11.2	8.7	9.1
Tenn.	10.5	5.9	4.9

Source: *United States Census of Agriculture, 1950,* II, 837–38.

TABLE 33.—*Total farms, and farms under thirty acres in the Middle South, 1950.*

	Total number of farms	*Number and percentage of farms under thirty acres*	
Va.	150,823	50,130	33.4%
W. Va.	81,418	22,454	27.6
N. C.	288,473	112,996	39.4
Ky.	218,237	61,937	28.5
Tenn.	231,524	77,720	33.8

Source: *United States Census of Agriculture, 1950,* II, 810–14, and 837–38.

western Virginia, 70,612 farms out of a total of 177,057, or nearly 40 per cent, had less than thirty acres. The small operations are emphasized even more by looking at the cropland harvested per farm. Out of 25,026 southeastern Kentucky farms reporting cropland harvested in 1949 less than ten acres were harvested by 19,759.

In the second place, since the land is mostly hilly or mountainous, soil erosion has been in the past, and still is, a serious deterrent to farm prosperity. For example, in West Virginia it was estimated in the late nineteen thirties that from 25 to 75 per cent of the topsoil had been lost on 64 per cent of the farm land. For the state as a whole, only about 7.2 per cent of the land is classified as average to good, which means that it can be farmed without serious erosion. In southwestern Virginia, western North Carolina, and the eastern parts of Kentucky and Tennessee, the story is not much different.

In this region which is characterized by hills and valleys and then more hills and valleys, conservation is mandatory. It has taken a long time for that fact to sink in. No matter how one may deplore some of the acrobatic bookkeeping of the TVA, that organization deserves large credit for its teaching and exposition by precept of the whys and wherefores of saving the land. But the many rivers of the region running from the Appalachians to the coast or to the Mississippi are still red to brown in color. There is little clear water except in the smallest streams in the dry season. Too much of this region is still being carried futilely away to the ocean. However, changes can be noted by the student who is not too discouraged by the past. There is enough evidence of progress now to give hope for the future. The 4-H clubs and the Future Farmers of America should probably share with the agricultural colleges, the state departments of agriculture, and the TVA in taking credit for the changing present.

If anything characterizes the Middle South, it is the wide variety of crops raised, the high degree of subsistence farming which still exists, and the low standard of living for a great majority of the farm families. The Piedmont region of Virginia gives an impression of grassy rolling country, stone walls, some orchards, and relatively little cropland. This is the area where possibly the last of the country gentry in the United States still hold forth. Fox hunts are common. General farming typifies the region. Corn, small grains, dairying, livestock, and quite a bit of tobacco occupy most of the farm activities.

Next, moving westward, is the Shenandoah Valley, a garden of Eden bordered on both sides by an outworn agricultural system. Almost anything can grow here and does. Grains, forage crops, fruits, and livestock thrive on the good soil and under the gentle climate. A great fruit-growing industry exists in and on both sides

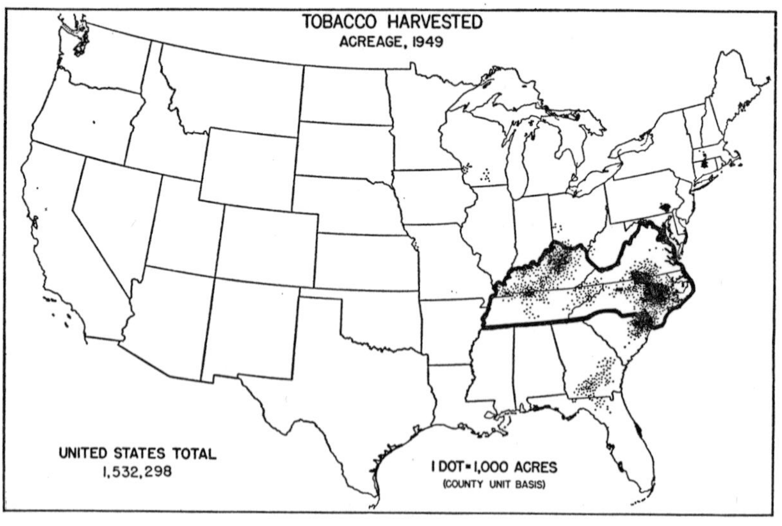

of the valley. This area harvested 4,797,160 bushels of apples and 429,000 bushels of peaches in 1949. But market saturation seems to indicate this positive factor has about reached its peak of expansion. While many crops are grown in the valley, most of the farm income is derived from livestock and livestock products. Dairying and poultry are especially important. In Augusta County, which is completely crossed by the Shenandoah Valley, $8,457,553 of the $9,822,361 worth of farm products marketed in 1949 came from livestock and livestock products.

Then we come to the agricultural slums of the nation. The Appalachians, beautiful to look at in mass, famed in song and story, become on close examination almost brutal in what little they provide and what they have done to man. When the land was first opened to settlement, a hardy race of Scotch-Irish-English immigrants came in. Many of them were heading farther west where there was better land, but some families stopped off and built primitive homes. Farming was started on land that was mostly up and down and seldom on the level for more than a few feet. From almost the beginning of settlement down to the present time, this area provided a poor living for its people. With the passage of many rainstorms, poor cropping practices, and a stubborn unwillingness and financial inability to make changes, the poor living became poorer and poorer until in the nineteen thirties it reached a state of painful subsistence hardly as good as a displaced person in Europe could expect in the terrible winter of 1946–47.

Even in the relatively prosperous nineteen forties, most of the

TABLE 34.—*Value of land and buildings per acre in the Middle South, 1850–1950.*

	1950	1940	1930	1920	1910	1900	1880	1850
Va.	$ 82.01	$ 41.04	$ 51.65	$ 55.19	$ 27.29	$ 13.64	$ 10.89	$ 8.27*
W. Va.	59.31	30.29	38.85	42.93	26.37	15.80	13.06	——
N. C.	98.65	39.09	46.75	53.76	20.35	8.56	6.07	3.23
Ky.	80.87	38.26	43.73	60.39	28.64	17.38	13.92	9.15
Tenn.	77.26	35.93	41.28	52.53	23.98	13.03	10.00	5.15

Source: *United States Census of Agriculture, 1950,* II, 53–54.

* Includes the area which became West Virginia.

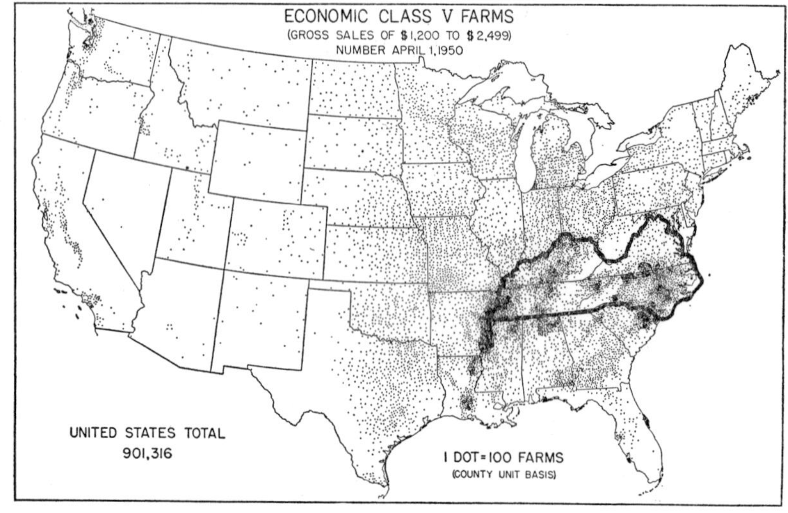

farmers in this region were in economic Classes V and VI, which meant their sales of farm products were less than $2,500. In 1949 the commercial farms in Class VI in this locale sold an average of about $700 worth of products; Class V farms sold $1,758 worth. In fact, only a very small percentage of the farms in this region are even classified as commercial farms. The *United States Census of Agriculture, 1950* defined a commercial farm as one which sold over $1,200 worth of farm products, or between $250 and $1,199 worth, providing the operator did not work more than one hundred days a year off the farm or make more from off-farm work than he did from the sale of his own farm products. Out of 28,294 farms in southeastern Kentucky, only 2,338 were classed as commercial farms in 1949. Of these, 1,616 were in Class VI. Kentucky families in this class sold an average of only $732 worth of farm products. They might have made nearly that much more from nonfarm employment and still have been considered commercial farmers. But as a matter of fact they did not, as 1,146 of the 1,616 reported no off-farm work whatsoever. In other words, the total income for many of these farmers was less than $750 a year.

Erosion has taken a terrible toll of the land. It has taken a worse toll in human values. Ignorance, poverty, intolerance of out-

TABLE 35.—*Economic classification of commercial farms in the Middle South, 1949.**

	Per cent of farms considered commercial	*Per cent of commercial farms in each economic class*					
		I	*II*	*III*	*IV*	*V*	*VI*
Va.	51.8	2.0	5.3	9.1	21.1	31.3	31.2
W. Va.	28.7	1.0	4.9	8.5	15.9	27.9	41.8
N. C.	67.1	0.2	1.4	8.7	32.0	35.9	21.8
Ky.	61.7	0.7	3.5	9.7	21.3	32.5	32.4
Tenn.	59.7	0.5	2.0	5.6	16.2	35.1	40.6

Source: *United States Census of Agriculture, 1950,* II, 1133.

* For the definition of the economic classes of farms, see Table 5.

siders and outside ideas were its results. A glance at Table 35 will show that subsistence and low-income farms are dominant in this region. About 40 per cent of the farms in the hill and mountain country of the Middle South are under thirty acres, and this is too small for adequate farming in any place but on the richest lands of the coast, in a highly productive irrigated region, or close to big metropolitan centers. It should be noted, too, that no big or even very good markets are close at hand, even if the land and the type of farming were productive. And there is a high percentage

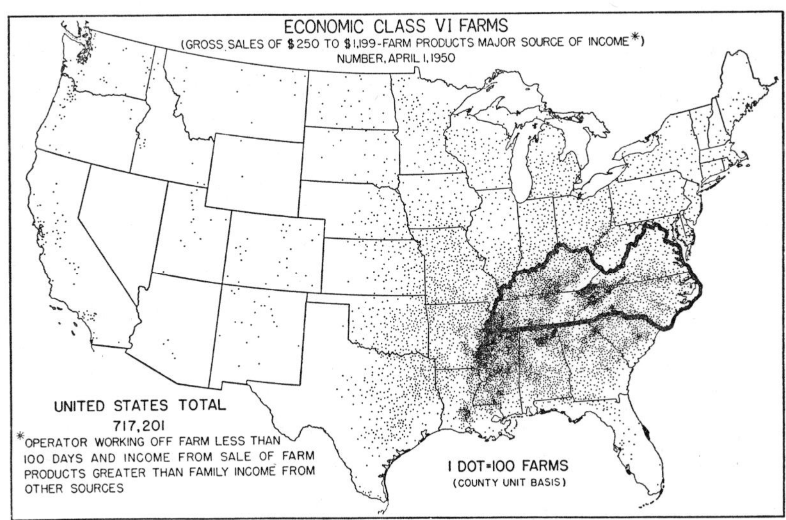

of part-time farmers in this area. Over 71 per cent of West Virginia farms are classified as part-time or residential. The figure is 47.5 per cent in Virginia, 32.8 per cent in North Carolina, 38.3 per cent in Kentucky, and 40.3 per cent in Tennessee.

But all of this area has not been, and is not today, an agricultural slum. Far from it, for as the land slopes toward the Mississippi or the Ohio, there are large livestock farms, profitable cotton plantations, and good tobacco farms. And the valley of the Tennessee River is being enriched by improved farming practices.

The major crop in the Middle South so far as acreage is concerned is corn. In North Carolina, Tennessee, and Kentucky, corn was grown on 36, 37, and 43 per cent, respectively, of all cropland harvested in 1949. Over 82 per cent of North Carolina farmers reported growing corn. In Virginia and West Virginia, corn acreage was second only to hay. But in the entire region, corn acreages are small and production is meager on the eroded fields. Out of 29,205 farmers in western North Carolina who in 1949 reported growing corn, 19,920 grew less than five acres. Most farmers in the eastern counties of Kentucky and Tennessee grew only five or ten acres. Most of the corn is used to feed a few head of livestock or a small poultry flock and is part of the subsistence farming so common in

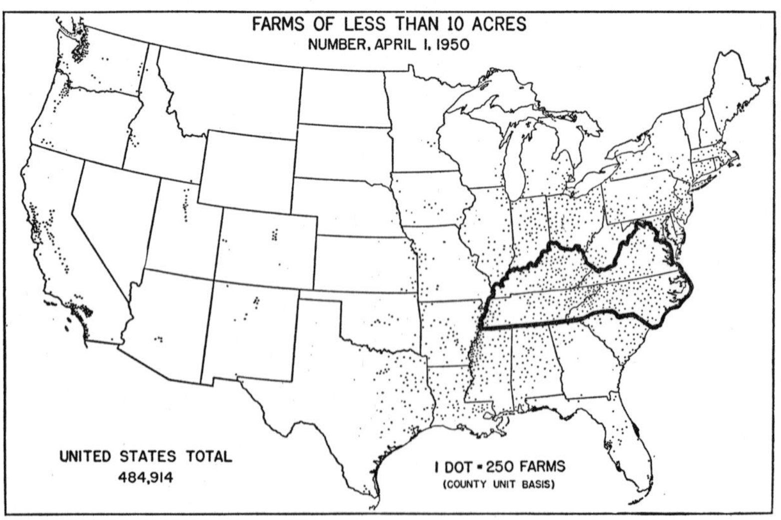

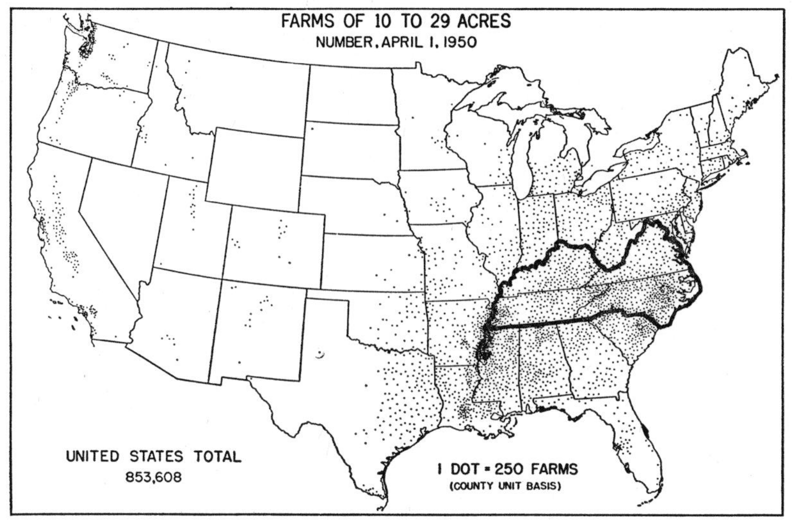

the area. In 1839 Tennessee was the leading corn-producing state in the Union, but 110 years later it had dropped to sixteenth.

In Virginia and West Virginia, hay occupies the greatest acreage of cropland harvested. It ranks second in Kentucky and Tennessee, and is becoming more important in North Carolina. In all of the states of the Middle South, the percentage of cropland harvested in hay increased between 1939 and 1949. This reflects better use of the soil and the growing importance of livestock production in the region.

But the two chief crops acreage-wise bring relatively little cash income to farmers. The main cash crops are tobacco and cotton. Tobacco production is of outstanding importance in North Carolina and Kentucky, where in 1949 its value made up 53 and 48.9 per cent, respectively, of all farm crops sold. Of the twenty-five first-ranking counties in tobacco acreage, twenty of them were in North Carolina. In Virginia and Tennessee, tobacco brought 23 and 15 per cent of the value of all crops sold.

The areas of greatest tobacco production are in the "Bright Tobacco Belt" of the Piedmont, which also extends to the Coastal Plain in North Carolina. In 1949 the census of agriculture classified 69 per cent of North Carolina's commercial farms as producers

TABLE 36.—*Acreage and production of tobacco in Virginia, North Carolina, Kentucky, and Tennessee, 1909–49.*

	1949	1939	1929	1919	1909
			Virginia		
Acreage	115,400	160,686	172,134	225,504	185,427
Production (lbs.)	124,904,164	136,753,568	115,825,610	102,391,226	132,979,390
			North Carolina		
Acreage	604,909	774,598	685,074	459,011	221,890
Production (lbs.)	661,981,561	715,616,397	454,222,610	280,163,432	138,813,163
			Kentucky		
Acreage	323,680	361,005	466,118	631,438	469,795
Production (lbs.)	404,881,235	324,518,411	376,648,533	504,661,592	398,482,301
			Tennessee		
Acreage	103,888	118,206	129,973	138,561	90,468
Production (lbs.)	127,324,176	109,422,777	112,236,961	112,367,567	68,756,599

Source: *United States Census of Agriculture, 1950,* II, 634–35.

of "other field crops" (a category which includes tobacco). Most of these were really farms on which tobacco was the main crop. Another large tobacco belt extends from northwestern Tennessee in a northeastern direction across Kentucky. The major area of production is the Kentucky bluegrass region, and in recent years

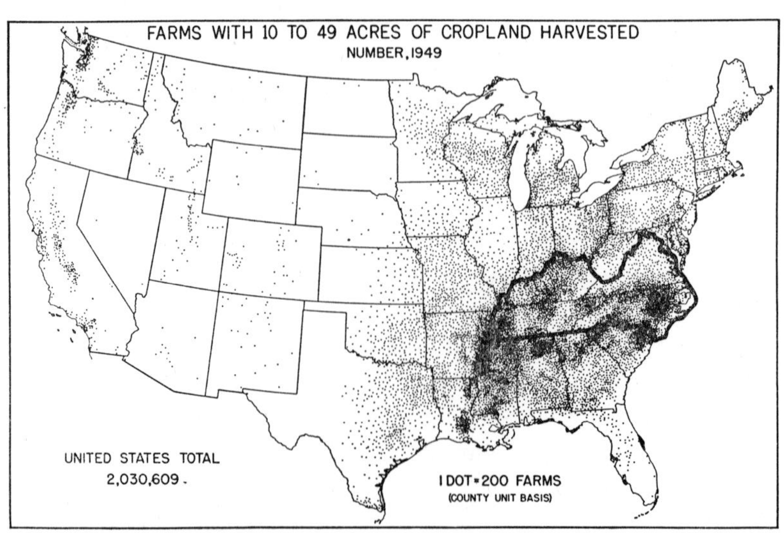

tobacco production has been expanding in eastern Tennessee. Greenville is the heart of the East Tennessee burley tobacco area. Tobacco is the most important cash crop on many of the small East Tennessee farms. In Carter County, a mountainous county, the average planting of tobacco, however, was only seven-eighths of an acre per farm in 1945. In Watauga County, North Carolina, many of the twenty- and thirty-acre farms, mostly on mountain slopes, each raised from three- to five-tenths of an acre of tobacco.

In the southwestern part of Tennessee, and throughout a considerable part of North Carolina, the principal cash crop is cotton. In 1949 Tennessee and North Carolina produced 616,742 and 472,000 bales, respectively, realizing an income of $91,255,535 and $67,372,079 from their cotton sales. Cotton was the largest cash crop in Tennessee, and over 32 per cent of her commercial farms were classified as cotton farms by the census of 1950. The state then ranked sixth in cotton production. Many of the cotton

TABLE 37.—*Value of crops and livestock sold in the Middle South, 1939–49.*

	Value of crops sold		*Per cent of farm products sold represented by crops*	
	1949	1939	1949	1939
Va.	$133,575,360	$ 53,401,637	43.1	49.3
W. Va.	12,717,433	6,354,766	15.5	20.9
N. C.	455,712,714	171,028,891	81.9	85.9
Ky.	207,462,772	67,084,043	49.7	52.3
Tenn.	178,463,226	57,284,587	52.4	53.4
	Value of livestock and livestock products sold		*Per cent of farm products sold represented by livestock and livestock products*	
	1949	1939	1949	1939
Va.	$169,518,829	$ 52,589,167	54.7	48.5
W. Va.	67,173,286	23,296,364	81.8	76.6
N. C.	91,040,465	25,763,530	16.4	12.9
Ky.	206,399,056	60,280,339	49.5	47.0
Tenn.	157,608,437	48,613,035	46.3	45.3

Source: *United States Census of Agriculture, 1950,* II, 753–54.

farmers are sharecroppers who are part of larger managerial units. The acreage of cotton per farm has been increasing. In 1939 the average number of acres of cotton per cotton farm reporting was 8.7, in 1944 it was 9.8, and in 1949 it was 13.2 acres. Large acreage increases in 1949 were due largely to the fact that farmers were preparing for acreage allotments and wanted to have as large a base acreage as possible, but, nonetheless, more acres per farm has been the trend. Cotton acreage and production in North Carolina have decreased considerably over what they were in the nineteen twenties, and, while acreage has also declined in Tennessee, production is up. In both states, cotton will undoubtedly continue to play an important role in the farm economy.

In the entire region, mechanization has lagged far behind most other parts of the nation. Consequently, labor productivity on a great majority of the farms has been extremely low. Lack of capital, small acreages, and the difficulty of adapting machines to cotton and tobacco production have all militated against mechanization of farm production in the Middle South. Although important progress has been made in this regard since 1940, only 21.7, 22.6, and 21.9 per cent of the farms in North Carolina, Kentucky, and Tennessee, respectively, had tractors in 1950. Out of 10,231 farms of less than thirty acres located southwest of Knoxville, Tennessee, only 846 had tractors.

Perhaps the most encouraging thing about the agriculture of this region is that change is coming to the hills. Possibly the first break in the pattern came during and after World War I when the

TABLE 38.—*Number of farms reporting tractors, and percentage of farmers reporting tractors in the Middle South, 1920–1950.*

	Number of farms reporting tractors				*Per cent of all farms reporting tractors*			
	1950	1940	1930	1920	1950	1940	1930	1920
Va.	36,515	10,808	9,142	2,206	24.2	6.2	5.4	1.2
W. Va.	11,602	3,437	2,641	541	14.2	3.5	3.2	0.6
N. C.	62,686	11,983	11,034	2,184	21.7	4.3	3.9	0.8
Ky.	49,342	11,246	6,951	1,913	22.6	4.4	2.8	0.7
Tenn.	50,797	10,967	6,556	1,796	21.9	4.4	2.7	0.7

Source: *United States Census of Agriculture, 1950,* II, 226.

mountaineers came down out of their fastnesses and away from the endless fights with the "Revenoors" to take work in the industries of the Ohio Valley. They spread out from here to work as far north as Detroit. At one time, it was said that the bulk of all Akron's rubber workers were from the hills, and even now many of the Akronites are hill people who did not go back. At first, however, it was common for them to work to get a stake and then return to their wild, free life, the hunting and fishing and the simple dances and song fests which have characterized their lives almost without change from the coming of the first of their ancestors from overseas.

As time went on, more and more of the younger people sampled industrial life. The older folks slowly died off. Abandoned hill farms became more common. Healing grasses and trees covered over the awful hillside scars. But during the Depression there was a tremendous reversal of the tide. When factories closed, the hill folk returned to a life of independence, even though it was on a pay scale much lower than they had known as unskilled laborers in the city. As business picked up and World War II came closer, the tide flowed downward and back to the workbench.

While these movements were going on, education was being sent in, chiefly by the home missionary societies of the various churches. Early educational efforts were misdirected. The well-meaning northerners who provided the educational funds also stipulated training in the classics—hardly a curriculum to make a mountaineer in consonance with his environment. But this error was seen and corrected, and education became more vocational and less academic. Domestic science, hygiene, and animal husbandry, agronomy, and handcrafts were taught.

One of the ironies that came to the American Indian also occurred in the lives of the hill people. Once the mountaineer was very much of a handcraftsman. He could make almost anything out of wood that wood was adaptable to. His womenfolk were skilled weavers, spinners, quilters, and seamstresses. These arts provided for the simple wants and tools of their lives, but brought precious little cash. The modern teachers not only revived and expanded these almost-forgotten crafts, but, what is more, found markets for the products. Cash from something besides whiskey started flowing back to the hills.

In 1947 one of the authors investigated a co-operative in North Carolina. Its members were engaged almost wholly in making carpets. A study of their patronage slips showed they were averaging from four to sixty dollars a week. Much depended on how many children of working age were in the family. They still had their little patches of farm land and did some farming on them. But they were taking the county agent's advice: contouring, strip cropping, and terracing were getting some attention. The too steep slopes were abandoned. Gardens for home use and a little feed for chickens were being raised; the family cow was being tended. Little if anything edible came to town for sale. But here was the biggest surprise of all—an enormous poundage of foodstuff was coming into the co-operative cold-freezer. The growth of this business was such that the manager had expanded the plant twice before the author's visit and was making preparations to expand again.

Poultry, hogs, berries, vegetables, and game were brought to town for processing and freezing at the time the mountain folk brought in their carpets. Moreover, although their automobiles were fourth or fifth hand, still they were coming to town, over modern roads for most of the way, in autos, and not on muleback or on foot, which had been their way until just a few years ago.

There is a long way to go yet. More roads, more education, more abandonment of impossible agricultural situations must come along before the region gets out of the slum class. But the World War II training of the young men has had a decided bearing, repeating the experience following World War I. Then a break was made. This period has seen that break widened into a definite trend. A project such as Oak Ridge can have a positive social value in this respect, no matter how terrible its orginal purposes may have been.

Another helpful factor is the educational work of the newspapers in Tennessee, as well as elsewhere in the South. Some years ago, an editor who did not hide his head in the sand and who was therefore sick at heart over the conditions in the Middle South started a campaign called "Plant-to-Prosper." Other communities made similar steps calling their programs "Live-at-Home" farming. The idea was simply that the first goal of the people on the land who did not own big commercial farms was to get their own living, and a good one, from the land.

County agents and social workers had been trying for years to educate the people away from cash farming, away from dependence on cotton and tobacco alone or (without much fanfare) reliance on corn in the liquid form as a source of livelihood. Their efforts had met with a notable lack of success. But the dynamic newspaper campaign, coupled with the offering of cash prizes and tying in with the 4-H and Future Farmers, turned the trick.

Housewives competing against each other at fairs took pride in the number and quality of their canned-goods entries. They expanded their family's diet by putting up chicken, hog meat (besides the traditional ham and bacon), black-eyed peas, greens, and such crops that grow easily and well. This pride then was expanded to cover the house, buildings, and grounds of the contestants. For the first time, shiftless, "I-don't-care" shacks got a face lifting. Flowers appeared in dooryards. The children were active in helping to turn their homes into places with some degree of loveliness and livability. Pictures of prize winners in the press did much to speed this social advance.

Healthy change is also coming in the better agricultural parts of the region. State agricultural departments and colleges have been doing outstanding and effective work. Perhaps the information and know-how had been available all along, but farmers in the cotton, tobacco, and livestock-farming areas have recently been able to instigate improved practices, at least partly because of more prosperous times. Tennessee, for instance, stepped out ahead in such research work as the mow curing of hay. Another assist of vital importance was given by the agricultural departments of the railroads. The Illinois Central, for one, has made a brilliant record in speeding up livestock and crop development.

Today the annual agricultural report from Kentucky, Tennessee, and, to a lesser degree, North Carolina and Virginia makes inspiring reading to anyone who knew this borderland just a few years ago. The number of cattle in Kentucky, for example, increased about half a million between 1930 and 1950. In Tennessee the increase was nearly as great, and cattle numbers have grown significantly in North Carolina and Virginia. Many beef-cattle farms whose purebreds make headlines in the nation's sales rings call this area home.

Tennessee and Kentucky farmers are milking more cows than they did twenty-five or thirty years ago. The increase in these states was 210,000 and 162,000, respectively, between 1930 and 1950. In both states the amount of marketed whole milk more than doubled between 1929 and 1949. In 1929, Tennessee farmers sold only 375,030,245 pounds of whole milk; in 1949 they sold 1,061,982,877 pounds.

Sheep production is important in Virginia, West Virginia, Kentucky, and Tennessee. Kentucky had 700,000 head in 1950, giving it a ranking of twelfth among all the states. Hog production is also becoming increasingly important. The value of livestock and livestock products is growing in the total farm economy of the region. For example, in North Carolina only 12.7 per cent of the value of all farm products sold in 1939 came from livestock and livestock products. A decade later this had grown to 16.4 per cent. In Tennessee and Kentucky the value of crops sold and the value of livestock and livestock products sold was nearly in balance in 1949. Livestock and livestock products brought Kentucky farmers 49.5 per cent of the value of all farm products sold in 1949.

Conservation is not a city-man folderol, but a matter of everyday concern to practical farmers. In Kentucky, 110 soil conservation districts were organized between 1940 and 1950. Over seventeen million acres of farm land were included within the organized districts. The other states in this area have also made outstanding progress in curbing erosion and restoring the land. This is especially true in the areas which come within the activities of the TVA. Smart diversification, plus excellent use of home-raised products, is bringing new stability to agriculture.

And what of the future of tobacco? It is hard to find a crop that takes more from the soil. It is a crop that needs, or has needed in the past, huge amounts of cheap, almost peon, labor. Like cotton, tobacco is afflicted by the vagaries of international markets. Outside of government stabilizing policies, it is a feast-and-famine proposition. And, with such a blow as the cutting off of imports by Great Britain and the low buying that other foreign countries are forced to, its future certainly does not look too bright.

On the other hand, tobacco does not have to ruin the land it is raised on. The Amish in Lancaster County have handled the crop for generations without killing the land. The new electric hotbeds for plant starting take some of the high labor requirement away. Electric curing sheds are another technical advance. The new insecticides and fungicides promise great help. Chemicals that can control the ripening, much as hormones control apple drop, are in the experimental stage and may be successful. If they are, it is not too Jules Vernish to dream of a tobacco harvester.

Balancing off the pros and cons, it may be surmised that a smaller international requirement would bring a smaller acreage but a better crop. Possibly then, more lands that are not ideally suited to tobacco will be changed to other and less damaging crops. Strict rotation, returning humus and nutrients to the soil, and the help of the new technical advances, taken all together, might put tobacco in a position both economically and agronomically such as it has never been in during all its history. In any case, it is a fair bet that the crop will be fitted better into new rotations that will provide diversity with safety, of both income and capital maintenance.

Of course, it is not possible to turn from this region without some consideration of the TVA. Probably no other New Deal innovation has caused so much comment, constructive and destructive criticism, and downright conflict. Out of the compost heap of statistic, claim, and counterclaim, some facts seem to deserve that name.

Beginning near Knoxville on the Tennessee River and extending downstream to that river's confluence with the Ohio at Paducah, Kentucky, this social experiment in controlling a whole river valley aims to take in 40,600 square miles of land lying in seven states (Virginia, North Carolina, Georgia, Alabama, Mississippi, Tennessee, and Kentucky). It provides flood control, navigation, cheap power for manufacturing, soil and forest conservation, education, better farming, and general social advance of the people who come under its paternalistic hand.

It can be said truthfully that it has done all these things. Where floods were disastrous before the TVA, they have been held under control very well in such a year as 1947. According to the TVA report, if its dams had not been in existence, the valley would have had one of the worst floods in the memory of man in that year.

It is true that electricity has been brought to thousands of farms, as well as small towns, at very low rates. In 1933 only one farmer out of twenty-eight in the area had electricity. By 1953, seven out of eight farms were electrified. Also, it is true that the annual usage of electricity by consumers in this area is higher than the national average. Of special importance to farmers is the fact that cheap power has stimulated a remarkable growth of industry in the Tennessee Valley, although there is a pressing need for even greater industrialization. With resulting job opportunities, many rural people have left the farm. This has lessened the pressure of population upon the land and has permitted larger farm operations, greater mechanization, and improved farm practices. The result has been a decrease in row crops and an increase in pasture and hay. There has been a significant increase in dairying.

TVA fertilizer has gone on thousands of farms to the benefit of the farmer. And the project's conservationists have done a good job of teaching the needed principles, both on field and forest.

Perhaps these, and the many more deeds of righteousness that the TVA can claim, are right and proper functions of a federal government. Possibly the other half-dozen valley authorities that some people want should be federalized and built. But there is at least one item the student should keep in mind before making his decision. That is the matter of bookkeeping. The TVA pays no taxes, but does make payments in lieu of taxes. There is room for large argument here concerning whether those payments are realistic and comparable to what private industry must pay. Then there is the matter of interest and amortization of the original loans. Here again, accountants from private business claim grave errors of omission occur. One last item the reporter gets in interviewing in the Tennessee Valley, and that is that not *all* of the folks who supposedly have been benefited so greatly are grateful or even placid about the paternalism. In fact, some are volubly unhappy. There is also the question of whether we should make all taxpayers liable for the benefit of a few.

Whatever judgment the citizens may make, it is certain that the TVA is here to stay. Possibly the grandiose plans for further—and seemingly endless—government development and expansion will not be approved. Whether they are or not, the TVA must be given some credit for helping in the great reorganization of an area that sadly needed attention. Now that the initial push has been given, perhaps the people themselves will be better able to solve their many remaining problems.

CHAPTER 6

The Deep South: The Shifting Cotton Belt

(South Carolina, Georgia, Alabama, Mississippi, Louisiana, Arkansas, Texas, and Florida)

IN ALL the thousands of years of agricultural history, probably no crop, except the grape, has been eulogized so lushly and so fanatically as cotton. And in all that history, with no exception, has any crop been so damned, so deplored as the white lint. It has been no aid to the comity of peoples that the defense of cotton has come mostly from those who grow it and the bulk of criticism from outsiders.

Cotton built the South, and cotton tore it down. Cotton created one of the most gracious civilizations on this continent, and the same crop produced our worst rural slums. One of the factors that contributed to cotton's ascendancy was its inedibility. Fieldworkers would not pilfer it for food, and it was worth little without being ginned. Hence, in the slave and post-slave economy of the South, cotton had a peculiar value. But to carry out the endless paradox of the plant, it may be that in a near tomorrow cotton's greatest value will be as a food from the edible oil of the seed. And a final paradox is that cotton was doomed long ago by a parasite, the boll weevil, which in turn helped to save the South from bankruptcy by causing a curtailment in cotton acreages and a geographical shift of the crop to other lands farther west.

The case for cotton is persuasive—up to a point. It flourishes particularly well on most of the soils and in the general climate of the South. When the price is right, the cash return is probably higher than for any other crop. It was our prime export for many years, which was an important consideration when we were primarily a debtor nation. It has long been our greatest cash crop, making up slightly over 15 per cent of the value of all crops sold in 1949. (Corn, the crop we grow in the greatest volume, did not produce as much cash, for most of it is fed to livestock.) A peculiarity of the southern climate gave cotton another virtue in that it is a 200-growing-day crop. In a land where the mere act of living can be onerous because of the heat, six months of work and six months of "settin'" seem just about the proper balance to many natives of the region. Finally, cotton is a crop of such uncomplex culture that its raising presents no intellectual chore for the predominantly Negro and poor-white field labor of the South.[1]

TABLE 39.—*Cotton production (number of bales) in the Deep South, 1899–1949.*

	1949	1939	1929	1919	1899
S. C.	543,936	849,982	835,963	1,476,645	881,422
Ga.	609,967	905,088	1,344,488	1,681,907	1,287,992
Fla.	17,502	11,424	34,426	19,538	61,856
Ala.	824,290	772,711	1,312,963	718,163	1,106,840
Miss.	1,496,902	1,533,092	1,875,108	957,527	1,313,798
La.	607,186	717,713	798,828	306,791	709,041
Ark.	1,584,307	1,351,209	1,398,475	869,350	709,880
Tex.	5,549,667	2,724,442	3,793,392	2,971,757	2,506,212

Source: *United States Census of Agriculture, 1950,* II, 628.

The agricultural case against cotton is ominous. The crop is one of the worst of soil robbers. It not only exhausts soil nutrients but vitiates humus. There is little doubt that we have exported to other

[1] This does not decry the intelligence of Negroes and poor whites as such, but rather it takes into consideration that, until recently, Negro education was from slim to not-at-all. Obviously, it is a harder job to teach an illiterate how to grow hybrid seed corn, for instance, than to teach him wheat growing. Cotton, in its simplicity, is much like wheat.

GENERAL PATTERN OF GREAT SOIL GROUPS

The Deep South

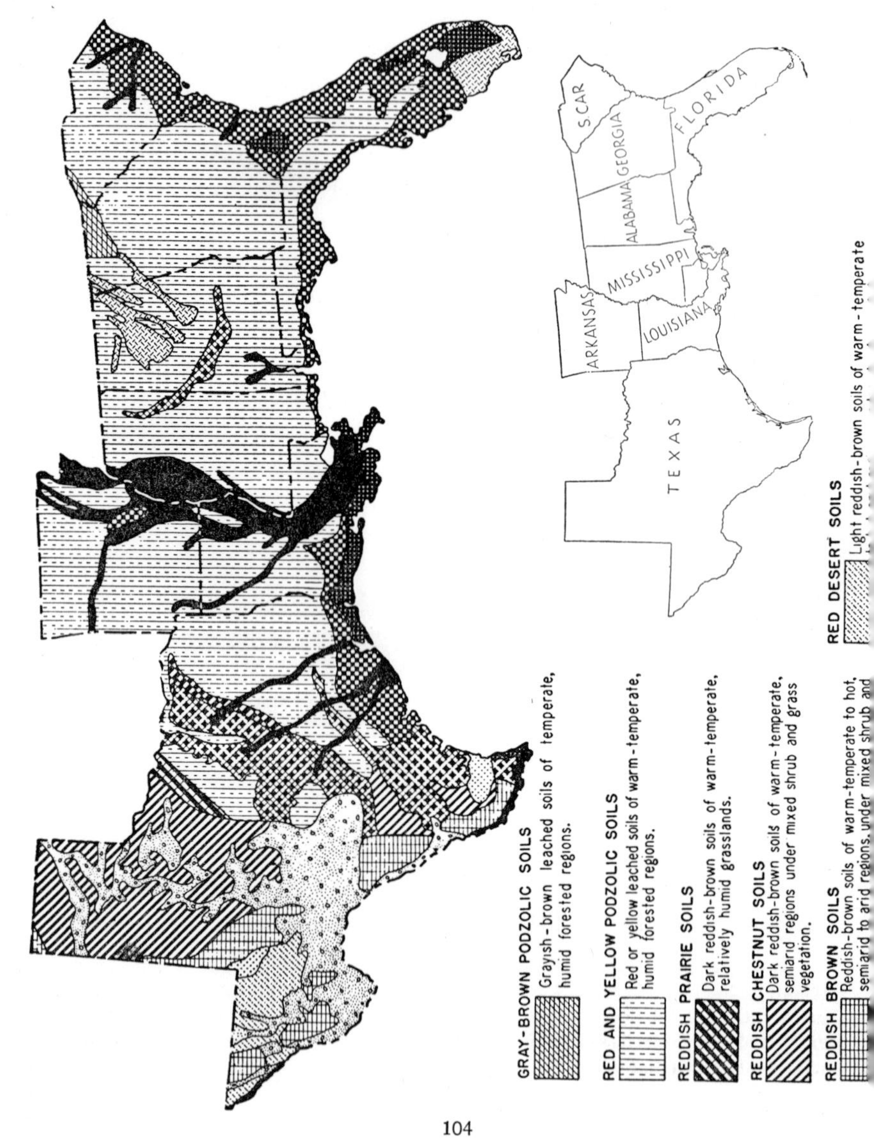
S. CAR
GEORGIA
FLORIDA
ALABAMA
MISSISSIPPI
ARKANSAS
LOUISIANA
TEXAS
GRAY-BROWN PODZOLIC SOILS
Grayish-brown leached soils of temperate, humid forested regions.
RED AND YELLOW PODZOLIC SOILS
Red or yellow leached soils of warm-temperate, humid forested regions.
REDDISH PRAIRIE SOILS
Dark reddish-brown soils of warm-temperate, relatively humid grasslands.
REDDISH CHESTNUT SOILS
Dark reddish-brown soils of warm-temperate, semiarid regions under mixed shrub and grass vegetation.
REDDISH BROWN SOILS
Reddish-brown soils of warm-temperate to hot, semiarid to arid regions, under mixed shrub and
RED DESERT SOILS
Light reddish-brown soils of warm-temperate

countries in the form of cotton a great dollar value of our original soil heritage.

It is a crop that particularly lends itself to absentee ownership with all the attendant evils. Around it grew up an economic system that to all intents and purposes carried on the evils of slave days without even the precarious safety of food and shelter given the slaves. Under the tenant or share-crop system, the southern worker was rarely out of debt.

Because only cotton land made owner-profits, even the kitchen garden for the hands, a "must" in all other portions of the country, was not allowed. The rule was that cotton came right up to the cabin door. While some planters claimed it was futile to offer kitchen-garden space because the hands were too shiftless to take advantage of it, critics have surmised that any food, home grown and not bought on credit from the plantation commissary, might give the workers a feeling of independence that could result in their refusal to work.

Cotton's worst fault, at least as it was handled by man, was its effect on the southern diet. In a land which could produce probably the finest diet in the world, malnutrition in some form or

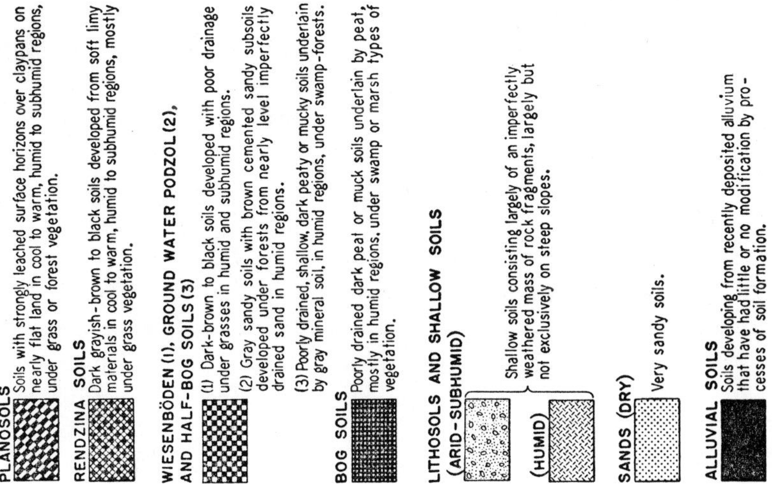
PLANOSOLS
Soils with strongly leached surface horizons over claypans on nearly flat land in cool to warm, humid to subhumid regions, under grass or forest vegetation.
RENDZINA SOILS
Dark grayish-brown to black soils developed from soft limy materials in cool to warm, humid to subhumid regions, mostly under grass vegetation.
WIESENBÖDEN (1), GROUND WATER PODZOL (2), AND HALF-BOG SOILS (3)
(1) Dark-brown to black soils developed with poor drainage under grasses in humid and subhumid regions.
(2) Gray sandy soils with brown cemented sandy subsoils developed under forests from nearly level imperfectly drained sand in humid regions.
(3) Poorly drained, shallow, dark peaty or mucky soils underlain by gray mineral soil, in humid regions, under swamp-forests.
BOG SOILS
Poorly drained dark peat or muck soils underlain by peat, mostly in humid regions, under swamp or marsh types of vegetation.
LITHOSOLS AND SHALLOW SOILS
(ARID-SUBHUMID)
(HUMID)
Shallow soils consisting largely of an imperfectly weathered mass of rock fragments, largely but not exclusively on steep slopes.
SANDS (DRY)
Very sandy soils.
ALLUVIAL SOILS
Soils developing from recently deposited alluvium that have had little or no modification by processes of soil formation.

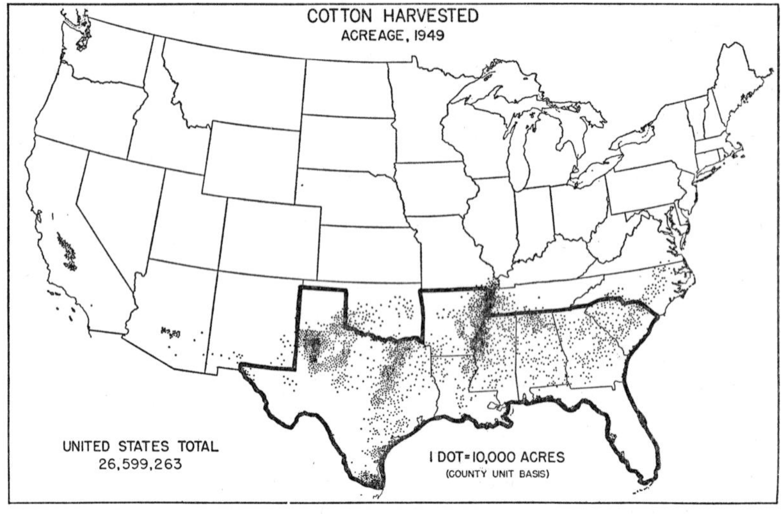

other was actually the lot of both master and man. Nobody worried about building a better diet. It was easier to grow only a cash crop, cotton, and then buy from the North much of the sketchy foods which were necessary. Such buying, in combination with the inadequate status of food preservation, as well as the traditional taste desires, almost eliminated dairy products from the diet.

The far-famed southern cookery may have been as tasty in the mansion as many literary travelers found it. Certainly it was not as widespread among all the people as the same writers would have one believe. But, in any case, it was never nutritionally sound. The meals featured fried breads, fried greens, fried meats, and even fried desserts. Salt pork, bacon, ham, side meat, back meat, and "bones" were the standard meats. The various portions of the hog indicated the financial and social standing of the eater, and from this social convention came the expression "livin' high on the hawg." The ribs ("bones") of the prevalent razorback were the lot of the laborer. And "bones" from a razorback, be it known parenthetically, carry mighty little eating, for the swamp-runner of the South never saw corn.

This diet was so inadequate that an old saying is still heard in the Delta States that for every child she bears, a mother loses a tooth. It has been only too true. A calcium-deficient diet from calcium-less soils put such a strain on the lime reserves of the pregnant mother that, in fact, teeth did fall out. It was not uncommon a few years ago, and it still unfortunately true in too many areas, that a woman of thirty would be toothless. Fortunately, however, the present South is awakening to what human nutrition means.

Economically, a one-crop cash-farming pattern carried all of the price jeopardy that one could rightly expect. If the world price of cotton went down, depression stalked southern fields. When the New Deal sought to help the South by raising the price of cotton above the world price, one of the effects was to give Brazil, Egypt, and India a prominent place in cotton culture from which they are not likely to budge. Between 1916 and the beginning of World War II, the percentage of the world's cotton produced in the United States declined from 60 to 40 per cent. By 1950 it was less than 40 per cent. Because of cheaper overseas wages and lower living costs, most of our cotton growers find it difficult to compete. For example, E. D. White of the United States Department of Agriculture, who visited the Nile Valley in 1948, reported that even though Egyptians were planting cotton by hand, they were doing it as cheaply as an American grower with his most efficient four-row tractor-mounted planter.

But when cotton's price was firm, great was the South's joy. Planters bought new automobiles. Field hands ate higher on the hog. Bankers saw their loans and interest return satisfactorily. Tradesmen had a field day as new building and old bill paying coincided. This is one of the dangers of this chancy crop. Just one good season and prosperity seems to be everywhere, even though lean years of sickening effect have been the lot of everyone for half a decade.

This feast-and-famine routine, probably with some help from the climate, has not been conducive to thrift. When cotton money is good, cotton spending is better. Nobody seems to remember the bad years and nobody seems to fear they will ever return. "Eat, drink, and be merry today, for next year we'll make a bale to the acre at a good price" becomes the unspoken but obvious feeling of the populace.

An example comes to mind from the territory around Halls, Tennessee. For some years, a friend of the writer, out of sheer charity, helped support a family of cotton farmers who had a piece of land in the flood bottoms. If the price was good, the flood took the crop, or the boll weevil was particularly bad. If the crop was good, the price was bad. During the later thirties, practically no money came from the land. But each year the farmer scraped together enough money and credit to buy seed. What time was not put into the cotton, he spent as a wholly unnecessary yard boy, or, more correctly, pensioner, on the grounds of the friend's house.

Then war shot the price of cotton up. At the same time, weather and boll weevil were kind. In just one season, the near-pauper farmer became a man of substance, thin though it was. Did he repair his house, see to the belated education of his children, get dental and medical service so long needed, or lay away a dollar against a rainy day? Not at all. He got a "store-boughten" suit, a new automobile, and had a really herculean series of bouts with the bottle. When cotton prices break, or when flood, insect, or

TABLE 40.—*Per cent of cropland harvested in the Deep South which was devoted to cotton and corn, 1939 and 1949.*

	*Cotton**		*Corn*	
	1949	1939	1949	1939
S. C.	30.2	27.2	34.1	40.8
Ga.	21.9	21.1	41.9	48.1
Fla.	2.5	3.5	30.6	41.9
Ala.	32.3	27.1	43.1	48.5
Miss.	45.1	35.2	32.6	42.5
La.	29.1	26.9	22.9	40.2
Ark.	43.4	31.1	18.8	33.8
Tex.	37.6	31.1	8.2	18.0

Source: *United States Census of Agriculture, 1950,* II, 533, 629.

* It must be kept in mind that in 1949 many farmers planted an extra large acreage in anticipation of government acreage controls. They wanted as large a base acreage as possible.

frost ruins his crop, he will be exactly where he was the last year of the Depression.

Perhaps cotton alone should not be blamed for the pervading shiftlessness that afflicts so many of the followers of the crop. Perhaps the bankers should come in for some onus too. Because cotton in the bale is not subject to quick deterioration, has a known grading, a future market, and a sales value of some amount, no matter how low, and because it can be held safely for a rise in the market, it has always been the one southern product that could be used as collateral. Other crops and livestock and livestock products enjoyed no such privilege. Some southerners allege the reason for this is that a 500-pound bale of cotton is not stolen easily and cannot be eaten, while all other crops, particularly food crops, have a way of deteriorating in the heat or disappearing in the mouths of an always hungry populace. Whatever the reasons, it is certain that the southern economy did not begin to perk up until lenders became willing to take collateral other than cotton for their loans, and that is mostly a modern phenomenon.

It would be unsocial to say that human erosion could be in any way less shocking than the erosion of natural resources. Yet when one travels through the South, the latter strikes the outlander with such force, particularly if he has been taught a more rational husbandry, that it is almost impossible to see the human side for the thousands of miles of gullies, of topsoil gone forever, even of subsoil running away ceaselessly to the ocean.

Not only whole farms, but even whole townships have been farmed out and eroded away until nothing fit for human usage is left. Everywhere there are thousands of acres of brush and some scrawny trees on land which once raised cotton. Gullies ten, twenty, and thirty feet deep are common. As the land receives fifty to sixty inches of rainfall annually, the gullying becomes worse each year. The forests have been cleared or burned away to make fields, and with them has gone the cover that kept the soil in place. Abandonment does not halt the destruction, although it does impede it, for in that lush climate some kind of weed will grow on any piece of land not cultivated, except of course in the gullies. But when the worst scars are healed over, out of sight is not out of danger, then comes the burner who wants to make better browse for his cattle or to grow a better crop of wild berries, or one who burns his adjoining cotton fields to keep down the boll weevil. In a few hours, the brush and weeds are gone and the process of erosion begins its destruction anew.

In the fall of the year, from Richmond south to Tampa, the auto roads are hazy with blue smoke. The air is saturated with the pungent odor of burning pine. The night is lighted from a thousand fires. Too many Southerners are still convinced that this is the proper way to farm. Truly, in few places in the world does the heart of the lover of the land lie more heavy than in our own Deep South.

Happily, that picture is growing somewhat dimmer. Here and there, little islands of a new kind of agriculture are appearing. More and more, you meet southerners who are quite as alive to the dangers of the traditional ways of doing things, to the almost cosmic cost of yesterday's methods, and to the tragic loss of soil as the most rabid northern conservationist. And despite the incalculable waste, so great is the potential of this once-rich and still-rich land with its twelve-month agricultural year that it is not inconceivable it alone might one day feed a nation of the present population.

TABLE 41.—*Number of farms in the Deep South, 1850–1950.*

	1950	1940	1930	1920	1910	1900	1880	1850
S. C.	139,364	137,558	157,931	192,693	176,434	155,355	93,864	29,967
Ga.	198,191	216,033	255,598	310,732	291,027	224,691	138,626	51,759
Fla.	56,921	62,248	58,966	54,005	50,016	40,814	23,438	4,304
Ala.	211,512	231,746	257,395	256,099	262,901	223,220	135,864	41,964
Miss.	251,383	291,092	312,663	272,101	274,382	220,803	101,772	33,960
La.	124,181	150,007	161,445	135,463	120,546	115,969	48,292	13,422
Ark.	182,429	216,674	242,334	232,604	214,678	178,694	94,433	17,758
Tex.	331,567	418,002	495,489	436,033	417,770	352,190	174,184	12,198

Source: *United States Census of Agriculture, 1950,* II, 53–55.

To assay the Cotton Belt as it is and as it may be, one should start with the crop that gave it its name, for it is still the most dramatic, if not potentially the most valuable, crop in the area.

First of all, it should be emphasized that the term "Cotton Belt" is really a misnomer, despite its historic and current use. Although cotton is the main crop in the South, the commonly held idea that the Cotton Belt was, and is, a fairly continuous area from the Carolinas to West Texas has always been incorrect. It is especially erroneous today. The so-called Cotton Belt is not a continuous area. There are large sections within the region in which little or no cotton is grown. The principal cotton-growing areas of the South are the inner Coastal Plain of Georgia and the Carolinas; the Georgia and Carolina Piedmont, running from south-central North Carolina through South Carolina and Georgia to eastern Alabama; northern Alabama; the Mississippi alluvial valley; the south Texas Coastal Plains; the black, waxy prairies in north Texas; and, finally, the High Plains of West Texas and southwestern Oklahoma. Major differences exist among the cotton-producing sections of the South. There is little comparison between the large irrigated fields around Lubbock, Texas, where production is highly mechanized, and the small ten-acre patches in Alabama, Georgia, and South Carolina.

TABLE 42.—*Average size of farms (acres) in the Deep South, 1850–1950.*

	1950	1940	1930	1920	1910	1900	1880	1850
S. C.	85.2	81.7	65.8	64.5	76.6	90.0	143.4	541.2
Ga.	129.9	109.6	86.4	81.9	92.6	117.5	187.9	440.9
Fla.	290.4	133.9	85.2	112.0	105.0	106.9	140.7	370.7
Ala.	98.8	82.6	68.2	76.4	78.9	92.7	138.8	289.2
Miss.	82.4	65.8	55.4	66.9	67.6	82.6	155.8	308.9
La.	90.2	66.6	57.9	74.0	86.6	95.4	171.3	371.7
Ark.	103.4	83.3	66.2	75.0	81.1	93.1	127.7	146.3
Tex.	438.5	329.4	251.7	261.5	269.1	357.2	208.4	942.5

Source: *United States Census of Agriculture, 1950,* II, 799.

Tremendous changes are taking place in the South today, changes which mean a less dominant position for cotton. For years there have been those who deplored placing so much emphasis on production of the white lint. Henry Grady's famous obituary in the *Atlanta Constitution* pointed out how sadly dependent the South was on others when it did not need to be at all, only if cotton

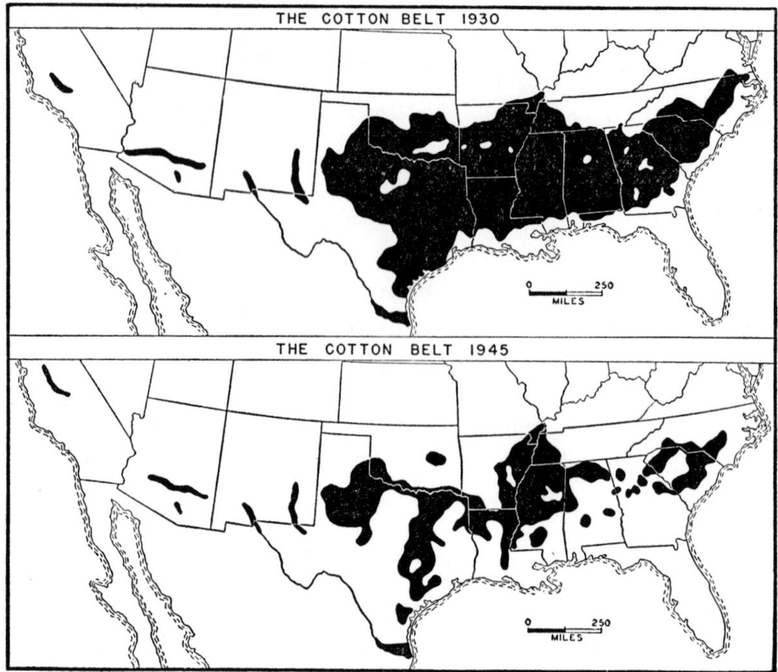

From Franklin C. Erickson, "The Broken Cotton Belt," *Economic Geography,* Vol. XXIV, No. 4 (October, 1948), 264.

were not king.[2] But despite these few voices crying in the wilderness, cotton might have gone its terrible way if the boll weevil had not shown up in the eighteen nineties. It came to Texas, then slowly spread eastward. The boll weevil arrived in Alabama, for example, in 1912 and was responsible for a yield decline per acre of 27 per cent in the period from 1915 to 1923. Field after field of cotton was eaten away. Some farms were abandoned. Some of the displaced persons left agriculture entirely. A dent had been made in

[2] "The grave was dug through solid marble, but the marble headstone came from Vermont. It was in a pine wilderness, but the coffin nails, screws, and shovels came from Pittsburgh. With hardwoods and metals abounding, the corpse was hauled on a wagon that came from South Bend, Indiana. A hickory grove grew near by, but the pick and shovels came from New York. The cotton shirt on the dead man came from Cincinnati; the coat and breeches from Chicago; the shoes from Boston, the folded hands were incased in white gloves from New York, and round the poor neck, that had borne all its living days the bondage of lost opportunity, was twisted a cheap cravat from Philadelphia."

the solidarity of cotton's rule over the South, even though weevil control measures were partially successful. By sheer force of necessity, some livestock came into the picture. The peanut found more popularity. Sweet potatoes got added attention. And peaches in some sections were found to be money-makers.

The boll weevil put a cost bar in cotton's way. The lack of new land suitable for cotton culture constituted another deterrent, and farmers were forced to put fertilizer on that in cultivation, thereby adding still more to the cost of production. The steadily rising costs made the competitive position weaker. But rather than resulting in any significant crop curtailment as such factors should, it seemed that the shrinking margin of profit came out of the hides of the people. In fact, as happened in the case of so many other crops, as the margin narrowed, production was raised to cover fixed costs that did not change with the market.

Then came the reprieve of World War I—and cotton was king again. After a short postwar slump, prices were relatively good until 1926, when the record-breaking 17,300,000-bale crop wrecked markets. Yet even then acreage continued large, amounting to over 43,000,000 acres in 1929. But the king's throne started to wobble. Rayon came along, at first only a cloud as big as a man's hand. However, that cloud was blotted out momentarily by a bigger cloud, the Depression. At last acreage curtailment really meant something. From 43,000,000 acres in 1929, the crop went down to 29,000,000 acres in 1933. Under further government restriction programs, it declined even more and reached a low of 16,200,000 acres in 1945. Now people began to ask: Can cotton ever come back?

Cotton did come back after World War II. By 1949 the acreage reached 26,599,000, and it grew larger until checked by federal controls in 1954. Although cotton acreage declined about 17,000,000 acres between 1926 and 1950, production remained high. The 43,500,000 acres in 1926 produced 17,300,000 bales, while 26,500,000 acres twenty-three years later had an output of 15,500,000 bales.

But all the time the synthetics were moving quietly ahead, circumscribing the domestic and foreign markets. In 1942 the world's production of rayon equaled approximately 8,172,000 bales of cotton. United States production alone was the equivalent of 1,700,000 bales. An equally serious blow was the pricing of the United States out of the world cotton market. Exports had been dropping even before 1933 and the Agricultural Adjustment Act, but higher domestic prices made it more and more difficult to hold our once-supreme position in the markets abroad. Now the strongest cotton men became queasy. Cotton was suggested as road material. It was offered for every purpose any dreamer could dig up. Yet, as it was a prime source of cellulose, one of its biggest new uses was to make the very synthetics that were helping to kill it. And hovering over the scene was the threat, only a whisper at first, that Brazil could sell cotton for eight cents, at which price a vast United States acreage would have to go out of production.

The fight was on to find a way to produce cotton at a price that could compete with that of foreign growers, whom we had, in effect, held an umbrella over until they could get into business. Just before World War II, which granted cotton another reprieve, there started to be hints that Yankee mechanical genius might find the way to keep us in the world market. That way was total mechanization of cotton production.

Cotton has been notoriously resistant to mechanization. This has been partly due to the peculiar nature of the cotton plant and the specialized labor requirements it demands during the growing season. Both of these factors have created mechanical and technical problems not found in wheat or corn. Furthermore, a shortage of labor, which has been so important in stimulating labor-saving machines in American agriculture, generally has not been present in the cotton-growing regions. An adequate and cheap supply of Negro labor has reduced the pressure to mechanize. Also important is the fact that much of the country's cotton crop is produced on small, irregularly-shaped rolling farms of less than thirty acres. Tractors and related machinery cannot perform efficiently in such circumstances and are not practical for the production of only a few bales of cotton. Tradition and custom, too, have been important factors in retarding mechanization of cotton production.

The major obstacle confronting mechanization, however, has

been the extraordinary amount of hand labor necessary for chopping and picking. How to apply machines successfully to these operations has perplexed many an ingenious inventor. Complete mechanization was blocked until these technical problems could be solved. Even with primitive, one-mule, half-row equipment, a man can plant and cultivate more cotton than he can pick by hand. Consequently, there has been little demand until recently for two-, three-, or four-bottom plows and two- and four-row planters and cultivators. There was little or no economic advantage in adopting these labor-saving machines when hand labor had to be maintained on the plantation the year round to provide an adequate force for hoeing and picking. The sharecropper or tenant might as well be kept busy the rest of the season, and so the planter clung to simple equipment.

Furthermore, suitable power was not readily available until the introduction of the Farmall general-purpose-type tractor with detachable and specialized equipment in the middle twenties. Only then did tractors begin to increase in popularity in the Cotton South. Cotton mechanization in Texas, for example, really began around 1925, when the first two-row Farmall-type tractor was introduced in the Corpus Christi area.

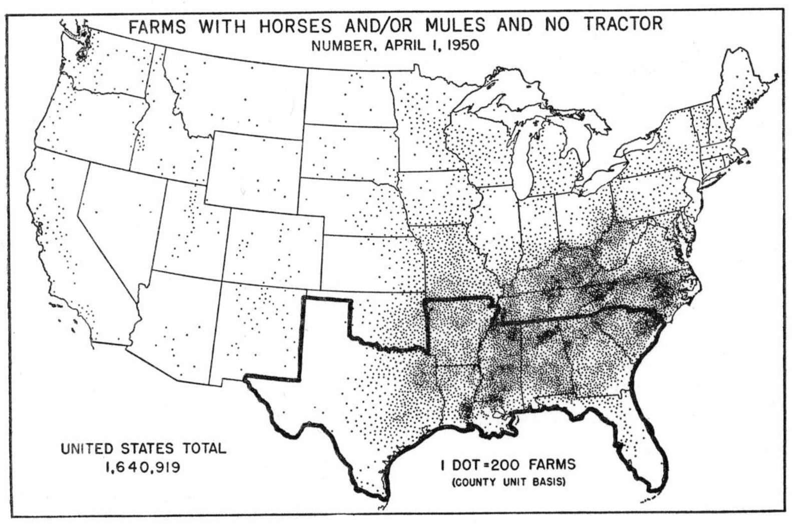

The number of tractors in the cotton states grew rather slowly until about 1940, when tremendous increases began to be made. In Alabama the number of tractors increased 168 per cent between 1945 and 1950, and in some other southern states the increase was nearly as great. Although the percentage increases were very impressive, the South was still far behind in absolute terms. In 1950 only 17.9 per cent of Alabama's farms had tractors, compared to 81.7 for Nebraska and 63.9 for Ohio. So far as cotton was concerned, the greatest deterrent to complete mechanization was the lack of a successful mechanical picker. But by World War II this problem, too, had been pretty well solved.

TABLE 43.—*Number of tractors on farms in the Deep South, and the per cent of farms reporting tractors, 1920–50.*

	1950		1940		1930		1920	
S. C.	30,282	16.8	4,791	3.1	3,462	2.0	1,304	0.6
G.	60,269	24.4	9,327	3.8	5,870	2.1	2,252	0.7
Fla.	22,018	26.9	7,703	10.2	5,244	7.4	680	1.1
Ala	45,751	17.9	7,638	2.9	4,664	1.7	811	0.3
Miss.	51,698	13.3	10,577	2.7	5,542	1.5	667	0.2
La.	35,735	18.9	9,476	4.6	5,016	2.4	2,812	1.6
Ark.	60,308	22.7	12,564	4.3	5,684	1.8	1,812	0.6
Texas	232,328	49.1	98,923	20.6	37,348	6.4	9,048	1.9

Source: *United States Census of Agriculture, 1950,* II, 226.

Ever since 1850, serious attempts had been made to develop a mechanical cotton picker, although progress was slow until the nineteen thirties.[3] At that time John and Mack Rust developed a picker which had limited success. It was the International Harvester Company, however, which produced the first pickers on a commercial scale. It had a few for sale in 1941. About 100 of these machines were manufactured and sold between 1941 and 1943. Then after World War II production jumped. In 1949 International Harvester manufactured 1,100 pickers at its Memphis plant. Other companies entered the field, and by 1953 the National Cotton Council estimated that there were about 16,000 mechanical

[3] Part of the following discussion has been taken from Gilbert C. Fite's article, "Recent Progress in the Mechanization of Cotton Production in the United States," *Agricultural History,* Vol., XXIV (January, 1950), 19–28.

pickers in the United States. Most of them were in the Mississippi Delta and California.

In the same year, there were about 20,000 mechanical strippers in use. These machines strip the entire boll from the cotton stalk, rather than just pick the lint, as is done by the spindle-type machines. Most strippers were first used in southwestern Oklahoma and West Texas. Since 1944, cotton has been grown and processed, from planting through harvesting, on a completely mechanized basis. This means preparing the seed bed by tractor instead of with mules. Seeding is done by new precision planters, tractor drawn. Weeding is done by flame and chemicals. The Dixie chopper does any thinning or chopping necessary. Pests are controlled by spraying chemicals over cotton fields from airplanes, and similar techniques are used to rid the cotton plants of their leaves prematurely, a process called defoliation. This reduces the "green-leaf trash" in mechanically picked cotton.

But now what would happen to southern farmers mechanized out of their jobs? An answer came to this problem before mechanization was scarcely out of the laboratory. Former sharecroppers and tenants began to move to northern factories during World War I, and the flow continued between Versailles and Pearl Harbor and grew into an avalanche during World War II. One authority estimated that 1,600,000 workers left southern farms between 1940 and 1945. The about-to-be displaced laborers had, in most cases, already deserted the cotton fields before mechanization became very widespread. In fact, it was the lack of adequate labor which caused many southern landowners to turn to mechanization. Oscar Johnston of Scott, Mississippi, manager of the largest cotton plantation in the United States, said in 1947: "Mechanization is not the cause, but the result of economic change in the area. Most if not all of the migration of farmers and farm workers which has taken place during the past few years has resulted from factors other than mechanization itself. All over the South, tenant houses now stand vacant on farms where mechanization has not yet achieved considerable development." From 1935 to 1944, there were about 850 tenant families on Johnston's plantation, but by 1947 the number had dropped to 525. More than 300 tenants had gone, never to return.

The question of whether the mechanical and chemical revolution in cotton production will put the United States back into a more favorable position in world markets cannot yet be definitely answered. It can be said with certainty, however, that it offers one of the best hopes. To be sure, there are many problems which need to be solved before cotton production can be completely mechanized. A major handicap is the lower grade of machine-picked cotton. It is usually about one grade below hand-picked cotton. Furthermore, mechanical picking is made more difficult because all bolls do not ripen at the same time. Another technical problem is that of mechanical weed-control. Chemical and flame weeding have not been universally successful.

Perhaps the greatest deterrent to complete mechanization is the high expense. Only big operators can afford the necessary equipment. It was estimated in 1947 that it would take about $35 an acre to mechanize the farms in the Clay Hills of Mississippi. Tractors and tractor-drawn equipment are expensive, and this is especially true of the mechanical pickers which have so far been put on the market. The price of a spindle-type picker and tractor was about $10,000 in 1950. "The primary need in harvesting equipment," said O. B. Wooten, agricultural engineer at Stoneville, Mississippi, "is a smaller, less expensive machine, particularly for farms of small acreages." Indeed, this is the heart of the mechanization problem on southern cotton farms. Particularly in the Southeast, many cotton farms are too small to warrant the expense of machines and equipment. In Alabama, about 69 per cent of the farms produce cotton, but the average acreage in 1952 was 10.6 acres. Heavy and expensive multiple-row equipment simply does not meet the needs of these farmers.

A study of harvesting costs in California's San Joaquín Valley between 1946 and 1951 showed that when a mechanical picker harvested less than one hundred acres costs rose very sharply. Since this is true, most progress in mechanization in the old cotton-producing regions of the Southeast has taken place on the larger and more fertile farms. These farmers had adequate resources and acreages to change to mechanically powered harvesters, as well as to other machines. Smaller and cheaper mechanical harvesters could partially meet the problems of the small-acreage cotton farmers, and custom harvesting or co-operative ownership of harvesting equipment is a possible solution. Southerners are vitally aware of this whole problem of mechanizing small farms. This was the major theme of the Seventh Beltwide Mechanization Conference held at Gadsden, Alabama, in October, 1953.

More efficient production on southern farms, including cotton farms, will be gradually brought about by combining the small acreages into larger production units. In fact, this trend has been going on for some time. On these larger operations, machinery will then become more economical and efficient, and the standard of living of the remaining farmers will be raised. Undoubtedly, mechanization will be helpful in forcing inadequate-size units out of production, thereby hitting at one of the South's sore spots. In other words, while many tears may be shed by sentimentalists over driving little people from the land, a long-range judgment is that they have no chance under modern competitive agricultural conditions on their inadequate acres ever to progress much beyond Tobacco Road status. A change of employment might well be a change for the better. It could scarcely be worse.

TABLE 44.—*Dollar value of land and buildings (per acre) of farms in the Deep South, 1850–1950.*

	1950	1940	1930	1920	1910	1900	1880	1850
S. C.	$69.06	$30.12	$36.48	$65.46	$24.64	$ 9.06	$ 5.10	$ 5.08
Ga.	43.28	20.28	26.15	44.74	17.78	6.95	4.30	4.20
Fla.	57.23	38.90	84.22	46.55	22.49	9.35	6.15	3.96
Ala.	48.69	21.35	28.62	27.77	13.90	6.51	4.19	5.30
Miss.	55.42	24.80	32.79	43.41	18.01	8.33	5.86	5.22
La.	82.21	35.40	44.70	47.31	22.75	12.76	7.13	15.20
Ark.	60.18	25.32	34.13	43.14	17.75	8.13	6.16	5.88
Tex.	46.21	18.81	28.85	32.45	16.39	5.50	4.70	1.44

Source: *United States Census of Agriculture, 1950,* II, 53–55.

Besides the significant changes in costs of production that mechanization will bring, there is the even more important effect it can have on conservation. Some southerners have recognized the problem for many years, but little has been done about it until recently. For example, Solon Robinson, at a meeting of the Farmers' Club of the American Institute held in New York City, July 11, 1854, said: "Travel through all the Southern states, and you will see millions of acres that have been ruined. . . . The land has been washed away by the system of plowing up and down hill, till waters that were once navigable have been filled up and changed to dry land. . . . We should devise a system of tillage that will prevent the land from washing away. It should be a rule in all hilly countries that every slope should always be plowed level—no matter how long or how crooked the rows are; let them wind round the hill and always plow by the thumb and level."[4] Today the South is becoming quite alert to the costs of soil wastage. The little "ten-acres-and-a-mule" places make a poor congregation to receive the doctrine of humus replacement, contour and strip planting, rotation, and all the rest. The economy of the little places is so rigidly circumscribed there is little chance to apply the new methods. But the wisdom and eventual profit of conservation farming can and is being sold to the bigger operators.

For instance, one farm in the rich Black Belt of Alabama traditionally planted 1,000 acres a year to cotton. The fertilizer bill was terrific. After the philosophy of soil conservation was sold to the owners, the cotton fields were limited to 250 acres. Hogs, dairy cattle, crimson clover, kudzu, and crotalaria were added to the farm program. All manure was returned to the land, and a green-manure crop preceded the opening of any ground to be put into cotton. The owners reported that after three years of this system the smaller acreage of cotton produced as much as the larger acreage ever had, while the humus content and general tilth went up, and erosion losses were reduced to a negligible amount. Best of all, they were farming the year round instead of only part of the year, and the annual income reflected that change satisfactorily.

No doubt cotton acreage east of the Mississippi will continue to diminish as mechanization and conservation progress. But even without those two weighty factors, the geographical center of cotton has moved steadily westward because of abandonment and the boll weevil. For instance, in 1952 Texas had a crop of 3,808,000 bales out of a total national crop of about 15,000,000 bales. Thus

[4] Quoted in *Harper's,* Vol. CXLV (December, 1947), 514.

Texas maintained her record of recent years of producing between one-fourth and one-third of the national cotton product. And a goodly percentage of the Texas crop comes from the High Plains region of West Texas, where operations are highly mechanized and production costs are low. For example, in recent years the man-hours required to produce and harvest an acre of cotton have been reduced to as low as six in the High Plains of Texas, where four-row equipment and mechanical strippers are used in harvesting. Thus, even though Texas production per acre is generally lower than in the Southeast, Texas cotton farmers have lower costs and can out-compete the southeastern cotton growers because of larger acreages and an economical use of machines. And boll weevil infestation is not as bad as it is in the humid Southeast.

Going still farther west, although acreage goes down, yields start to mount fabulously. Thus it is not uncommon for New Mexico and Arizona to show average returns of from 500 to 700 pounds of lint per acre, or more, while California production is also in the 700-pounds-per-acre category. And the total of bales that are coming from these states has increased greatly in the last few years. When the total national crop that can find a market is far under present production, what will be the effect on growers' distribution? Without getting into the fanciful, it is safe to say that the steady shift of the center of cotton to the West will continue unless prohibited by national agricultural policy and political considerations. California can easily make one-third of national production, given sufficient water supply. And note that the traditional evils of cotton are largely left behind in the new territories.

If it is true, as we suggest here, that cotton never again will be king in the South, what will then fill the vacuum left behind? The answer to that is a story more exciting than the mechanization of one of the last of the slave-labor crops.

Indeed, a revolution in southern agriculture has been going on during the last twenty or thirty years and is progressing with increased rapidity today. Changes in land use have been of utmost significance. As already pointed out, millions of acres have been taken out of cotton production. New crops have been introduced and expanded, and the yields of old ones greatly increased. There were more soybeans, peanuts, rice, and grain sorghums in 1950 than twenty years before. Hay and pasture acreage is increasing, reflecting a greater and more profitable livestock industry. And progress is being made in sustained-yield tree growing. Numbers of livestock have changed radically. There were 54 per cent fewer horses and mules on southern farms in 1950 than in 1930. But there were more cattle, and in some areas the number of milk cows has increased. Sales of whole milk climbed way up in all southern states between 1939 and 1949, but the most notable development was in the growth of beef production. Conservation is making important strides forward. Cover crops are being planted in ever increasing amounts and soils are being preserved and restored. Generally, productivity on southern farms is making great advances. One must be careful, of course, not to overstress the process of agricultural change. It is not taking place uniformly throughout the South. For example, in Marion County in northeastern Alabama, one-third of the farms were operated with one mule as late as 1942. But the change is becoming more and more characteristic of farming operations.

Alabama agriculture reflects some of the vast changes which are occurring in the South. In 1909 a little over 30 per cent of Alabama's Black Belt was in cotton. By 1944 only 3.5 per cent of the land was planted to this traditional crop. Cotton acreage in Montgomery County dropped from 83,593 in 1929 to 21,547 acres in 1949. Montgomery County got 75 per cent of its farm income from livestock and livestock products in 1949, and only about 12 per cent from cotton. For the state as a whole, 73.4 per cent of the value of all farm products sold in 1939 came from crops, but by 1949 this had declined to 65.4 per cent. The value of livestock and livestock products increased from 24.8 per cent of the total value of farm products sold in 1939 to 30.9 per cent ten years later.

Not only has there been an important shift to livestock production in some areas of the state, but crop changes are significant. In southeastern Alabama, cotton has generally been replaced by peanuts. In 1949, on 415,115 acres, Alabama produced 279,809,580 pounds of peanuts, which had a total value of $28,000,000—nearly one-fourth the value of the state's cotton crop. Most cotton in Ala-

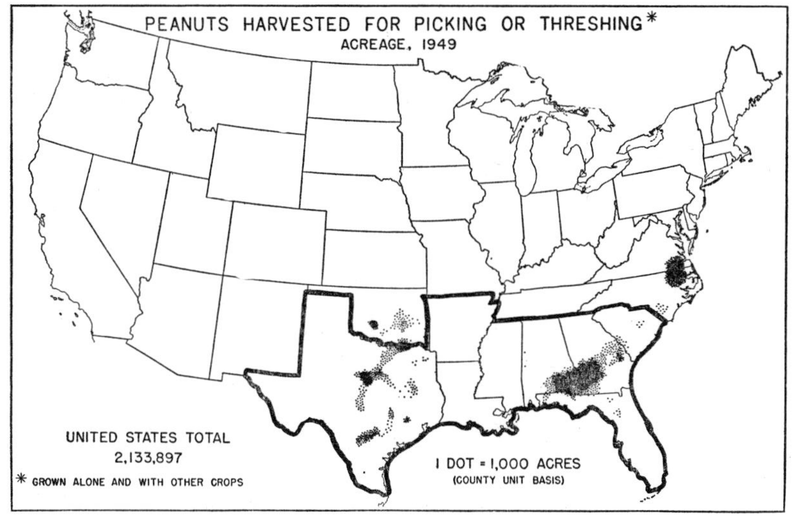

bama today is being produced in the northern sections of the state rather than in the south or central portions. The acreage of legumes has been greatly expanded. Broiler production jumped from less than 2,000,000 in 1940 to over 17,000,000 in 1951.

Similar dramatic changes have been going on over much of the South. Georgia is the ranking peanut state. Farmers there grew 860,000 acres in 1951 and produced 698,000,000 pounds, more than twice as many as either Texas, Alabama, or North Carolina, the other leading producers. Cotton brought over $90,000,000 to Georgia farmers in 1949, but it seemed less significant when compared to $58,685,000 for peanuts.

In Arkansas and Texas, and to a lesser extent in Louisiana, there has been a great increase in rice production. Arkansas acreage jumped from 153,095 in 1939 to 411,040 in 1949, and that of Texas from 186,236 to 541,769 during the same period. In recent years, Texas has been producing a little more than 25 per cent of the nation's rice. The Texas rice belt stretches along the Gulf Coast. Production is highly mechanized, and the self-propelled combine harvester is one of the most notable developments. Seeding from airplanes is becoming increasingly common: about 110,000 acres were planted by plane in 1953.

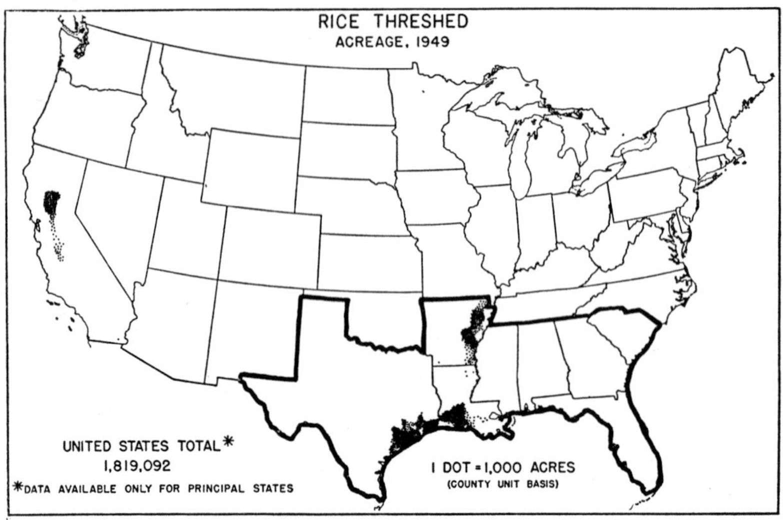

Soybeans, once grown mostly in the South, have come back. Arkansas produced over 12,000,000 bushels in 1951, mainly in the northeastern part of the state. In a few counties soybeans occupied more cropland space than cotton. Mississippi is also becoming an important grower of soybeans. This crop has found favor in the South because production is easily mechanized and it fits into the share-crop and tenant system. Like cotton, soybeans cannot be eaten and must be sold through an oil mill. And sugar cane, not long ago thought to be on the way out, has seen an increase of about 100,000 acres in Louisiana between 1929 and 1952.

Vegetable and fruit production is receiving more intensive attention in some parts of the modern-day South. Increased industrialization is providing better nearby markets. Arkansas and Louisiana strawberries are sold fresh and frozen all over the United States. Arkansas is also a heavy apple-producer, while South Carolina and Georgia have long been famous for their peaches. It has been in the lower Río Grande Valley of Texas, however, along with Florida (which will be considered later), that the greatest advances in vegetable and fruit output have occurred. From 1929 to 1949, the vegetable acreage in Texas grew from 191,470 to 436,235 acres. Among the leading crops were green beans, cabbage, carrots, dry

TABLE 45.—*Value of farm products sold in the Deep South, and per cent of value of all farm products sold represented by sales of crops and by sales of livestock and livestock products, 1939–49.*

	Value of all farm products sold		*Per cent of value represented by*			
			Crops		*Livestock & prod.*	
	1949	1939	1949	1939	1949	1939
S. C.	$ 213,561,714	$ 87,370,250	78.8	87.1	18.9	12.0
Ga.	375,151,595	122,279,684	62.2	77.8	32.0	19.8
Fla.	338,645,416	80,430,764	73.7	75.9	25.2	23.6
Ala.	274,037,437	76,952,670	65.4	73.4	30.9	24.8
Miss.	339,660,853	115,426,273	73.9	84.1	24.0	14.7
La.	245,730,002	90,093,721	75.2	84.0	24.0	15.4
Ark.	392,850,799	118,284,687	74.8	77.6	24.3	21.3
Tex.	1,753,052,010	439,063,949	64.7	48.8	35.1	50.9

Source: *United States Census of Agriculture, 1950,* II, 752–54.

onions, spinach, and tomatoes. Texas produces much more cabbage than its nearest competitor, New York. And despite the claim of Rush Springs, Oklahoma, to being the watermelon capital of the world, Texas had more than twice as many acres of watermelons as any other state in 1949. (This crop has also found high favor in Georgia and South Carolina.) Moreover, the citrus growers of

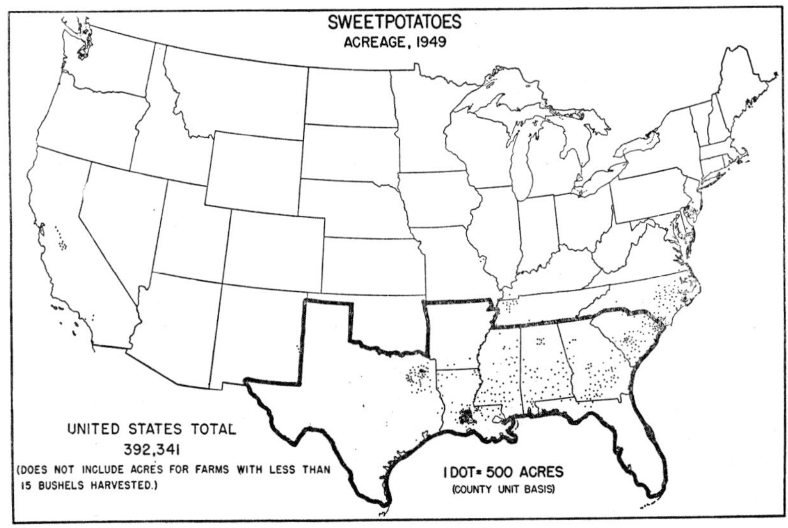

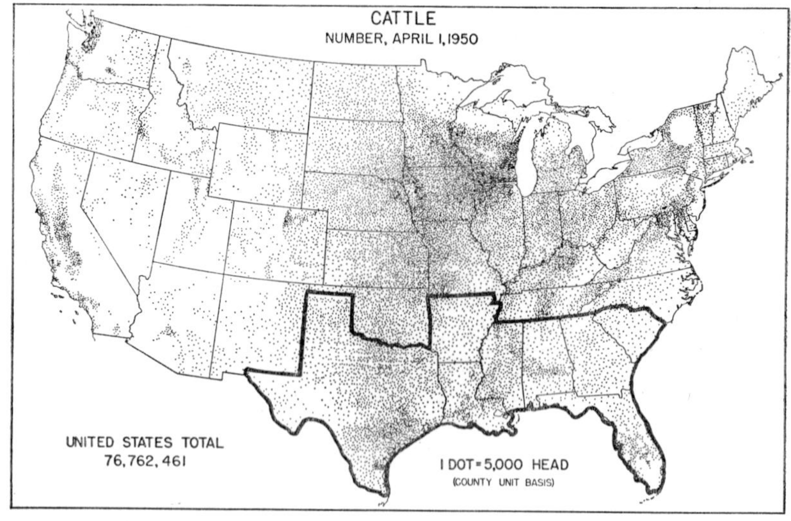

California and Florida are finding increasing competition from the fruit farmers of the Río Grande Valley.

Perhaps what is happening in the South today can be told better by recounting one of the most outstanding examples of the new farming rather than by quoting mountains of statistics. Besides, the current statistics do not accurately reflect the truly fundamental shift which is taking place. In the late nineteen thirties, Cason Callaway retired from the textile-manufacturing business and bought some 30,000 acres in the Georgia Piedmont near Hamilton. The land was badly eroded, suffering from decades of cotton production. It cost from $3 to $10 an acre. Callaway cleared areas of useless brush and timber, contoured the land, applied lime and phosphate, and planted gully-healing crops such as kudzu. All of this cost him from $40 to $60 an acre.

Next, livestock were added and forage crops expanded. To get a high-quality feed, Callaway began dehydrating kudzu and lespedeza. He added scuppernong grapes (native to the South), blueberries, all perennials. Then he increased the number of chickens, geese, ducks, and quail. With vegetables, small fruit, poultry, and livestock, Callaway was able to produce most of what he and the families who lived on his land needed. As a result of this planning, the Callaway farms produced $300,000 worth of food for man and livestock in 1944. Seventy families were living in abundance on land that previously supported only fifteen in a very meager way. Obviously, such agricultural operations require huge amounts of capital. But experience has shown that many smaller farmers can bring about similar changes on a lesser scale, and with profit to themselves. Some landlords have at last broken with tradition and are furnishing capital for dairying and livestock enterprises, as well as for cotton or other cash crops. Today, in many areas of the old Southeast, dairying has been enlarged when landlords put up land and capital for dairy operations on a fifty-fifty basis with tenants. In many cases this arrangement has proved highly successful and has meant more income for both tenant and landlord.

Today the Callaway plans are not dreams, but realities that have attracted the attention of agriculturalists in all parts of the country. Every few months some new outgrowth of the plans comes into the news to indicate that the changes are not temporary or a slight awakening in a long sleep. For instance, it is probable that Georgia now leads all of the country in the business of custom rehabilitation of fields. Young Georgians back from World War II got the newly awakened bankers interested in the solid values of restoring the land. The bankers put up the credit. Youth brought in surplus army supplies of the land-moving type. Now some hundreds of young fellows are applying the lessons learned in the Seabees on Pacific islands to literally remake the face of Georgia. This instance has its collateral effect, too, for farm-equipment sales show a greater percentage of increase in the Southeast than most anywhere else in the country. It is clear that ten acres and a mule and the sorry life that goes with them are headed for oblivion.

True, the blue haze of burning woods still hangs over the South, but just the same, millions of forest acres of loblolly pine and hardwoods are now in tree farms. Paper mills are humming and expanding. The gifts of Charles Holmes Herty to his native area are at long last appreciated. Lands whose nutrients were once depleted by cotton or tobacco are now producing a better, and permanent, living for their owners as silvicultural enterprises.

True, you still see gullies, washing, land destruction, and cotton rows running up and down the slopes. But you also see luxuriant growths of kudzu healing other erosion-scarred lands. As previously shown, forage crops are increasing at an amazing pace. Livestock numbers and quality are going up. Northern Mississippi and Alabama, for instance, comprise an area now looked upon as a leading Polled Hereford section of the nation.

TABLE 46.—*Number of cattle and calves in the Deep South, 1900–50.*

	1950 April 1	1940 April 1	1930 April 1	1920 January 1	1900 June 1
S. C.	369,560	274,586	270,171	434,097	342,898
Ga.	1,002,771	803,357	783,063	1,156,738	899,491
Fla.	1,101,239	721,015	431,448	638,981	751,261
Ala.	1,269,389	889,983	799,523	1,044,008	799,734
Miss.	1,569,327	1,139,660	1,008,672	1,250,479	873,356
La.	1,284,616	1,051,901	729,690	804,241	670,295
Ark.	1,153,027	982,173	812,590	1,072,966	894,535
Tex.	7,825,007	6,281,537	6,602,702	6,156,715	9,428,196

Source: *United States Census of Agriculture, 1950,* II, 401.

The South's standard of living still needs an elevator to get on par with the rest of the country. And until the older generation, with its stubbornly held convictions, is gathered to its fathers, the general nutritional level will not be all or even partially what it should be. But the conservationists are getting such a hearing as they never had before. Youth is learning. Tomorrow, the South may present not the traditional dining table, but one that will deserve fame far more than the fabled table ever did.

In this modern world where machines do the work of men, where probably no more than 10 per cent of our population need be engaged in agriculture to fill all our needs, what will the predominantly agricultural South do, not only to achieve what the rest of the nation achieved yesterday, but to keep up with the parade of progress? The leaders of the old Cotton Belt have known for many years that reliance on agriculture alone kept them in an unstable position. Especially since World War I, they have sought

TABLE 47.—*Per cent of commercial farms by economic class, 1949.**

	Per cent of farms considered commercial	*Economic class*					
		I	*II*	*III*	*IV*	*V*	*VI*
S. C.	60.5	0.6	1.8	4.6	19.8	35.6	37.6
Ga.	61.8	0.7	3.3	7.9	20.5	34.4	33.2
Fla.	52.9	7.7	8.9	12.3	19.1	28.3	23.7
Ala.	55.9	0.6	1.8	4.0	12.9	32.1	48.7
Miss.	62.4	0.7	1.3	2.6	10.1	33.2	52.1
La.	56.8	1.7	3.6	6.2	15.7	37.4	35.3
Ark.	62.1	1.5	4.1	8.0	17.5	33.8	35.0
Tex.	68.4	5.6	13.4	18.3	23.1	23.1	16.6

Source: *United States Census of Agriculture, 1950,* II, 1133.

* Based on a sample of farms only. See Table 5 for basis of classification.

manufacturing from other parts of the country by offering sites, cheap labor, and low taxes. But industry was slow to take up the offers. Southern workers did not have the know-how. Their output was lower than trained northern workers. And freight rates were discriminatory against the South.

However, World War II helped out with some of these difficulties. For one thing, the repetitive pattern of modern mass production does not require too much know-how or mechanical training. For another, the vast number of war plants in the South trained millions of workers in factory methods. As the cost of operating a factory in the North skyrocketed, southern tax and wage rate differentials looked even better to industry. Hence, there has been a fairly steady migration out of New England and the great industrial concentration centers such as Pittsburgh and Detroit to southern sites. The Gulf Coast of Texas and Louisiana has experienced an industrial revolution seldom seen in our history.

This general development was not enough, and it was not spread around as southerners wished. Hence, a reversal of previous planning was necessary. If northern industry would not move fast enough or far enough, southern promotion would get into the fight. From this thinking came a new plan and a new slogan, "Balance Agriculture with Industry," or, for short, the "BAWI Plan." An article in *Fortune* magazine has explained what this plan did in Mississippi: In the late nineteen thirties "farmers were unable to sell their produce profitably, and small towns were disintegrating under the joint pressure of low farm prices and unemployment. A state commission was set up; public funds were made available for building low-rent factories; and twenty industries were brought to the small towns of the state. Some inevitably died a-borning, and when the war came on some were closed down for lack of labor and materials; but twelve remain (1944). They manufacture hosiery, rubber tires, woolen goods, shirts, chenille products, plywood and steel ships. According to a study published by the Federal Reserve Bank of Atlanta, the twelve B.A.W.I. plants in the middle of 1943 had 14 per cent of the employment and 24 per cent of the payrolls of all Mississippi's manufacturing."[5]

The rate of progress in the balancing of agriculture with industry is updated by a story in the *Wall Street Journal* for January 5, 1948, which reported, among other things, that Louisiana had over 260 new businesses signed up. Mississippi got a new million-dollar Sterling Drug plant to make milk of magnesia. North Carolina could count 406 new plants in construction in 1948, and 262 were in line for expansion. Promoters in Georgia reported that ground had been broken for 455 new plants in just ten months' time. Tennessee obtained International Harvester's new $30,000,000 cotton-picker plant at Memphis which hired 3,000 workers. Now, Alabama boasts of new Goodrich and Goodyear tire plants. Arkansas has a new Welch grape juice factory. Georgia points to both a General Motors and a Ford assembly plant, plus a Lily Cup plant that is expected to become the biggest of that company's string. Winston-Salem, North Carolina, is proud of a huge Sears Roebuck store. And, of course, there is the H-bomb plant in South Carolina.

Not all of these new developments will succeed. Somewhere along the line the whole South may suffer a recession, but even if it comes during the life of this book, the underlying change is positive. Despite the ups and downs which are bound to happen as a purely agricultural economy starts to divide its allegiance and its dependence, the basic drive to get more industry into the picture will continue and in the long run succeed. Over the longer term, secular

[5] Ladd Haystead, in the farm column of *Fortune*, Vol. XXX (October, 1944), 174.

growth and better nutrition at home should bring a whole new processing industry into the South.

Add it all up, subtract the negatives, give full weight to the problems, and the picture of tomorrow's former Cotton Belt may be something close to this outline. There will be many fewer cotton farms, and in all likelihood considerably less cotton acreage. There will be more local processing of cotton and cottonseed meal and oil. The meal will stay at home, largely as a protein supplement for the South's new livestock industry.

Hay and forage crops will increase greatly in acreage and number. Already the per cent of cropland harvested for hay is showing great increases. In 1939 only 6.5 per cent of Mississippi's cropland was harvested for hay; ten years later it was 10.2 per cent. In South Carolina the increase was from 2.6 to 9.4 per cent in the same period. Where alfalfa, timothy, and other northern forage crops made little progress because of their inadaptability, new crops such as kudzu, crimson clover, crotalaria (hybrid corn adapted specially to southern soil and climate), and probably several others not yet out of the plant breeders' hands will take over. Where high humidity makes the curing of forage crops difficult, dehydration and silage will do the preserving job. And for the bulk of the entire area, pasturing will be carried on from ten months to a year.

Sweet potatoes as a cattle feed are here to stay. Peanuts for dozens of purposes are now firmly established. Tung orchards along the Gulf Coast seem to be permanent residents if the world picture on fats and oils does not make too radical a change. Specialty crops in the category of Callaway's scuppernongs and berries will increase. Vegetable acreage will increase for local use, but what it will do for national consumption is impossible to foresee at this time, for it already appears that we have more truck-crop potential than we have a market for, even with the new preservation processes.

Beef cattle will become a bigger factor, particularly now that we have chemical sprays to give fly relief. The long pasture season of the South seems to offer a particularly good opportunity here. Where the weather is too hot, or tick threat is present, the crossing of Brahmans with the English breeds to make Brafords, Brahorns, and Brangus, already successfully done by the King Ranch of Texas, will get around these difficulties.

Dairying will increase for local fluid consumption, if not for sale in the national market. The increase will probably be steady rather than rapid, for, despite the fact that nutritionists are now trying to change it, the southern diet has always been lamentably low in dairy products. Furthermore, basic changes in farm organization are needed if dairying is to thrive. Farms in much of the Cotton South are too small to diversify to livestock and dairying. One study of southern Mississippi farms showed that, if dairying were added to cotton farming, feed and pasture land would have to be increased about three times on most small farms. Another problem is the need for capital to change from cash-crop production to dairying. Studies made of twenty-four farms in the Waco, Texas, area between 1949 and 1953 showed that the cost of converting to grade A milk production ran from $10,000 to $12,600 per farm.

Poultry has always been in the picture, and will continue to increase in importance. Georgia, Arkansas, and Texas sold 45,000,000; 29,000,000; and 26,000,000 chickens, respectively, in 1949. The increase in Georgia was from 4,200,000 in 1939 to 45,700,000 in 1949. This is little short of revolutionary.

Throughout the South, there will be a steady increase in part-time farming as little places go on a "live-at-home" philosophy while one or more of the family works seasonally, part time, or full time in the factories that grow up from the BAWI Plan.

Sherman E. Johnson of the United States Department of Agriculture has written that "material increases in production and net income for southern farm workers largely depend on (1) providing more land, livestock, machinery, fertilizer, and other capital items per worker and (2) opportunities for nonfarm work for the young people who grow up on farms but who will not be needed in farm occupations, and for the workers who will be released from agriculture as mechanization and other improvements gain momentum. These changes are inevitable. They are already under way. . . . Readjustments of this kind will create opportunities for farm workers in the South to equal the per capita production and income of farm workers in other regions. But on many farms the change involves shifting from a simple cash-crop type of farming, with hand-and-mule operations, to relatively complex soil-conserving types, that involve forage, pasture, winter cover crops, livestock, mechanical power, and larger farms. This kind of farming requires more management and more mechanical skill for successful operation."[6] It is the kind of farming which is gradually coming to the South.

The South does not have to be the nation's No. 1 economic problem. It need not be the Limehouse of agriculture, the nadir of rural slums. Great as its problems are, reluctant though it is to change, there are ferments now at work that promise this area may well become a steady bolster to the whole economy rather than the drag it has been in the past. These writers (who have no southern background and only a student's interest) believe the old Cotton Belt's best days are before it.

A recent announcement comes from the Department of Agriculture of the establishment of a new dairy breeding-program in the South which may mark a historic change. The Department has imported Sindhi bulls from India to cross with American Jerseys. The Sindhi, like the Brahmans, have sweat glands which our domestic cattle lack. The imported animals therefore are able to stand extremes of heat that curtail the thrift, milk production, and general welfare of the Jerseys. The experimenters hope to produce a crossbreed that will have the Sindhi's heat resistance and the Jersey's milk-producing qualities. The fact that the crossing of Brahmans with beef cattle is now considered a success suggests that this experiment has much to recommend it. Such an animal on the year-round pastures of the South may literally bring about a revolution in dairy production and marketing. If to this possible success is added a truly tasty and safely preserved milk powder, easily reconstituted, or a frozen concentrate, the implications to the current fluid-producers and to the hot Caribbean countries where little or no milk is now available are almost fantastic in scope. Theoretically, processed milk could be sold in New York stores for a fraction of the cost of fluid milk produced right out-

[6] Sherman E. Johnson, *Changes in American Farming* (USDA *Miscellaneous Publication 707* [December, 1949]), 71.

side the door. The success of margarine in stealing butter's market indicates the possibility. At the same time, a milk that would keep in the tropics might add several million new export customers to our market.

Because it is not properly a part of the Cotton Belt and because it has the inconclusive and difficult-to-define agricultural status of a tourist state, Florida is included here as an appendage. Despite the many millions of dollars that come from Florida sugar cane, beef cattle, citrus fruits, vegetables, tung, and such new crops as ramie, the tourist crop is actually so overwhelmingly dominant that the agronomic contribution to state income is unreasonably dwarfed.

For hundreds of years since the first tourist, Ponce de León, explored this land, Florida has found people from elsewhere more important than crops at home. Until the late nineteenth century, agriculture progressed hardly at all. Indeed, even the tourists weren't very productive, or numerous. The geographer-agriculturist J. Russell Smith looks upon Florida as a frontier only starting toward a relatively adult economy in very recent years. Historically, he seems to be on sound ground.

In the post-Civil War years, citrus made a fairly respectable start in the subtropical regions of the state. Previously, a little cotton, some livestock, tobacco, and vegetables had been raised in the northern or panhandle section. The first citrus boom seemed to promise a real healthy move toward a prosperous agricultural economy. Then the freezes of the nineties blighted not only crops but hopes and long-term expectations. Production dropped from over five million boxes to a little over two hundred thousand in four years.

The danger of frost is only one of the deterrents to a successful subtropical agriculture. Actually, despite the boosters, Florida soils are some of the poorest on the continent. They lack basic nutrients to a large extent. Even worse, in recent years we have found that application of heroic quantities of the classic NPK does not do the whole job. Absent also are the trace minerals. In fact, much of the interest in, and study of, the place and function of such elements as copper, magnesium, cobalt, and boron (to list but a few) probably stemmed out of the troubles of Florida soils.

Since the original citrus-and-tourist boom and bust of the last century, Florida has moved ahead in a series of jerky, stair-step progressions. There have been big booms and big busts, with little booms and little busts coming along regularly in between. The national citrus industry faced bankruptcy from overproduction in the winter of 1946–47, to cite a recent example. A "providential" freeze killed off a good portion of the Florida crop, strengthening prices and giving surcease to Texas, California, and those Floridians who escaped the cold blast. The same thing is often true of the prolific vegetable industry. Northern markets become glutted. Then the only way to make shipping costs on the crops is for a climatic or pathologic disaster to take place. When enough production is destroyed or made unmarketable, the surviving growers manage to stay in business. The unfortunates, like their nonfarming colleagues who lose in the horse and dog races or at the gaming tables for which the state is famous, either wangle a new stake or else go back north, from whence they have usually come. Gambling, in short, is the proper description of most Florida agriculture.

Besides poor soils throughout most of the state and danger of freezes, Florida also has a water problem. Usually there is too much rather than not enough water. Most of the state has a water table so near the surface that fence-post holes become wells. This means that drainage, always an expensive job, looms importantly in the plannings and economy of the farmers. Then if the drainage is done too enthusiastically, as it has been done in the Everglades, the rich peat lands dry out sufficiently to ignite. As a result, Florida has literally had large areas of its most valuable land burned away to ash.

Even though the desire of the present authors is to be completely objective and not let the too strident broadcastings of the Florida boosters sway us into a negative attitude, there are still a few more deterrents to farming progress that must be mentioned. One is the prevalence of mosquitoes, flies, and dozens of insect pests that make life unhappy for man and beast. So little of Florida is more than a few feet above water, so much is actually swamp or lake, and so few are the freezes that this area is a veritable heaven for entymological specimens.

As if this were not enough, the herpetologists also find the region a rich one, but their chosen genera hardly appeal to farmers. In fact, Florida highways usually are liberally sprinkled with dead water moccasins. Rattlesnakes and copperheads add to the risks.

Such a catalogue of unfavorable factors would seem to argue against much, if any, future for agriculture. But the factual statistics on production show that Florida has become one of the greatest expansion areas in the nation in recent years, possibly surpassed only by a few far western regions.

The positive side of the picture shows a citrus industry beaten down again and again, but coming back each time. Growers now know how to supply trace elements to the trees. Through better cultural practices and better processing and merchandizing methods, they have raised the quality and output of the crop. Almost every day brings some new frost-fighter, so that hazard is being brought ever nearer to control. The chemical weeders and insect killers will find wide usage in this area. The "quick decline" disease that is threatening to destroy California as a competitor has made little inroads in Florida. Florida farmers get the majority of their total income from fruits. The value of all fruits and nuts sold in 1949 was $129,931,152, or about 52 per cent of the total value of all farm products sold. Over 24 per cent of the farms were classified as fruit farms by the 1950 census.

In Florida's other great money-maker, the vegetable industry, the old hit-or-miss methods of the past are disappearing, as trained agronomists and plant pathologists have come into the industry in recent years. Production has gone up phenomenally. Acreage reclaimed from the Everglades is constantly setting new records. Modern transportation and preservation methods have been big helps. In fact, Florida's boast that it could supply all the vegetables needed by the entire nation probably would not be far from correct if more Everglades muck were brought into production. Florida vegetable acreage increased from 60,250 in 1919 to 256,355 in 1949. And the value of the vegetable crops rose from less than

$14,000,000 to nearly $60,000,000 in the same period. Vegetables represented 19.4 per cent of all crops sold in 1949.

Both citrus and vegetables, however, are threatened by something worse than pests, frosts, or lack of fertilizers. Both groups of crops very easily slide into surplus position, even under the abnormal demands of war years. During World War II, Florida growers overplanted thousands of acres of citrus. In previous years there had been a constant surplus of the fruit and its products. In the same way, more vegetable land was opened up on the grand scale. Today, few realists, even giving full weight to population growth, can see how the citrus and vegetable people have any hope of staying in business unless an acreage shift is made on a voluntary and large-scale basis.

The question becomes: Into what could these acres be changed? Beef cattle on Florida range land have been expanding at a terrific rate since the discovery that an infusion of Brahman blood would help combat both the tick and the heat. Today, on a beef-cattle count, Florida is an important cattle state. The number of cattle and calves in 1952 was 1,539,000, over 500,000 head more than in 1930. But land expensively capitalized for vegetables and citrus is not the kind a cattleman wants or can economically use.

Sugar cane is grown successfully south of Lake Okeechobee, and about 36,000 acres were reported under cultivation in 1949. But again the surplus threat is present, the amount of land suitable for cane is not great, and this crop can hardly take over the citrus and vegetable lands farther north because of climatic limitations. Lemon grass is a recent experiment, but at this writing its future is vague indeed. High hopes are held for ramie, the crop that may cause hemp its greatest headaches in the future. Again, as of the moment, the future of this crop is obscure. A few acres, probably not many more than are in production now, can be turned to tung culture. However, this oil crop has very specific demands for water, soil, and a cold spell to induce dormancy (but not too long a cold spell or the dormancy changes to death). That limits the amount of Florida land this crop can take.

The only bright possibilities are in the highly problematic field. If a tremendous change, induced by advertising, in the nation's dietary habits could be brought about, as was done with breakfast orange juice after World War I, maybe this citrus crop could be saved. But most observers believe that citrus products for human consumption are somewhere close to their top per capita consumption now. And the potential production, which will soon be a reality, as the young plantings are presently maturing, seems to be far beyond any possible consumption capacity, even considering the population growth expected in the immediate future.

Although vegetables, unlike citrus fruits, cannot be widely grown in the winter in this country, it is apparent that the California, Arizona, New Mexico, Texas, and Florida fields have a potential clearly greater than any reasonable consumption levels for years to come. To make matters worse, the newer preservation processes and the slow swing which some students think they see to a processed rather than a fresh taste militate against high-cost production and transportation.

Vegetables, even though they spout from the earth in huge yields per acre, are not grown cheaply in Florida. The fertilizer cost alone is immense. Florida used 984,000 tons of fertilizer in 1949, and the total cropland harvested amounted to only 1,728,232 acres. Spraying and dusting are other big items. Yet even when these large costs are encompassed, there remains the long and costly shipment to the metropolitan northern markets. And freight rates are going up rather than down.

Search the possibilities as one will, it seems difficult, if not impossible, to view the future of either citrus or vegetables in Florida as bright. Because the state is not self-sufficient in beef cattle, the possibilities here seem somewhat brighter. As mentioned above, the two great historic deterrents, ticks and heat, are now on their way to being liquidated. The native grasses of the Florida hummock are known to be deficient in total digestible nutrients, but salt that has trace minerals in it, chiefly copper, is helping. Better grasses no doubt will come along too. Of course, the pasture season is year-round. What the beef-cattle industry lacks is a concentrate, such as corn, to finish the animals.

Peanut hay has been tried and has met with some success. Citrus pulp is indicated as a possibility. The plant breeders may even find a corn, sorghum, or other feed plant that will flourish in the area. Sweet potatoes, now looked upon as a successful feed in Louisiana, might come into the picture. The ultimate feeding practice certainly has not yet been determined, but there is reason to hope it will appear in the not too distant future.

Dairying for local consumption could be a big business, but the feed limitation is also a hindrance in this industry. Yet when the problem is solved for beef cattle, it no doubt will have significant implications for dairying.

In recent years, almost every season has brought the news of some new crop successfully grown in Florida that was promised a brilliant future. Unfortunately, months or a year or so later, the original announcement and accompanying fanfare have sounded fairly tinny, as subsequent work with the crop has destroyed the bright hopes and brought out difficulties or insurmountable obstacles in processing if not in growing.

At this point, even though tremendous strides have been made in studying and learning how to practice agriculture successfully in Florida, it cannot be said honestly that an optimistic future is clearly limned. Florida boosters get violently angry when such statements are made. Yet they argue from incomplete or slightly out-of-focus statistics. The hard fact remains—despite the population growth of the state, despite the hordes of northern consumers who descend on it each winter, making a brisk local market, despite success in combating soil and climate drawbacks—that the tourist crop still appears to be a better bet than any of the agricultural crops. In the case of any national economic calamity, Florida, so far as agriculture is concerned, seems to be about the most vulnerable of any area in the nation.

CHAPTER 7

The Corn-Soy Belt: Feedbag of Democracy

(Ohio, Indiana, Illinois, Iowa, Missouri)[1]

It is no chauvinism, no misplaced chamber of commerce boasting, no exaggeration to call this area the richest farm on earth. Other, smaller areas have a higher gross production and income per acre. Others can show greater unit tonnage. Others can produce greater variety. But in no place in the world is the production of food per man hour so high. Nor can any place else make the impact on world agricultural-political economy that this region does. Probably no other combination of areas could so nearly implement a Marshall Plan, even with the aid of the United States Treasury, as this vast triangle. It is hog and cattle rich. Iowa generally ranks from first to third among the states in total farm income. In both 1950 and 1951, when cash receipts from farm marketings were $2,120,266,000 and $2,360,995,000, it fell behind only California. Illinois usually ranks fourth in farm income.

Although all forty-eight states and the offshore territories made their valued contributions to World War II, it was the Corn-Soy Belt that proved to be the real backbone of food defense. Without

[1] Southern Minnesota and eastern Nebraska also make up a vital part of the Corn-Soy Belt. Both Minnesota and Nebraska produce more corn than Ohio or Missouri, although generally not as many soybeans.

GENERAL PATTERN OF GREAT SOIL GROUPS

The Corn-Soy Belt

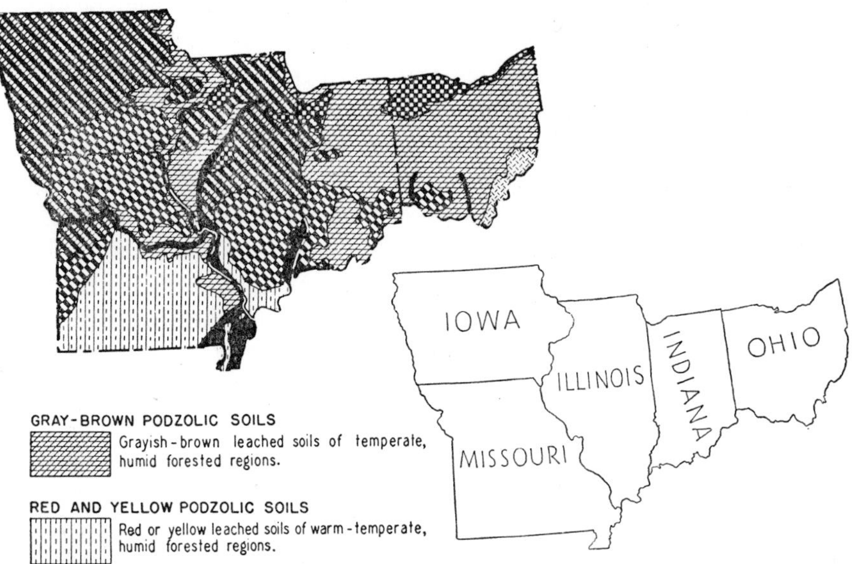

GRAY-BROWN PODZOLIC SOILS

Grayish-brown leached soils of temperate, humid forested regions.

RED AND YELLOW PODZOLIC SOILS

Red or yellow leached soils of warm-temperate, humid forested regions.

PRAIRIE SOILS

Very dark brown soils of cool and temperate, relatively humid grasslands.

PLANOSOLS

Soils with strongly leached surface horizons over claypans on nearly flat land in cool to warm, humid to subhumid regions, under grass or forest vegetation.

WIESENBÖDEN (1), GROUND WATER PODZOL (2), AND HALF-BOG SOILS (3)

(1) Dark-brown to black soils developed with poor drainage under grasses in humid and subhumid regions.

(2) Gray sandy soils with brown cemented sandy subsoils developed under forests from nearly level imperfectly drained sand in humid regions.

(3) Poorly drained, shallow, dark peaty or mucky soils underlain by gray mineral soil, in humid regions, under swamp-forests.

LITHOSOLS AND SHALLOW SOILS (HUMID)

Shallow soils consisting largely of an imperfectly weathered mass of rock fragments, largely but not exclusively on steep slopes.

ALLUVIAL SOILS

Soils developing from recently deposited alluvium that have had little or no modification by processes of soil formation.

it, we would surely have had a more difficult time gaining victory. It was not merely food for soldiers, for allies, but, most important, a powerful diet high in human TDN (total digestible nutrients), strong in animal proteins, for our industrial workers that gave us a sure edge over our enemies. Even though Hitler's forced labor groups had calories, their efficiency was lower because they lacked the diet essentials that our workers had in profusion. And the bulk of these essentials came from this north temperate, upper valley region, where soils are highly productive a century and more after settlement, growing season beneficent, and the topography ideally suited to mechanization.

An appreciation of the riches of this area is hard to come by if the student has never been outside his own country, or even if he has seen some but not the majority of American farm lands. To one who has traveled abroad to study, the greater the area covered, the more of the rest of the world he has seen, the more fabulous this region becomes in comparison.

The Ukraine rightly deserves admiration, but it is limited in the number and quality of its crops. It has inconvenient climatic restrictions. Its best use is for wheat—a crop that cannot compare to corn in optimum land use. Denmark and the Lowlands can and

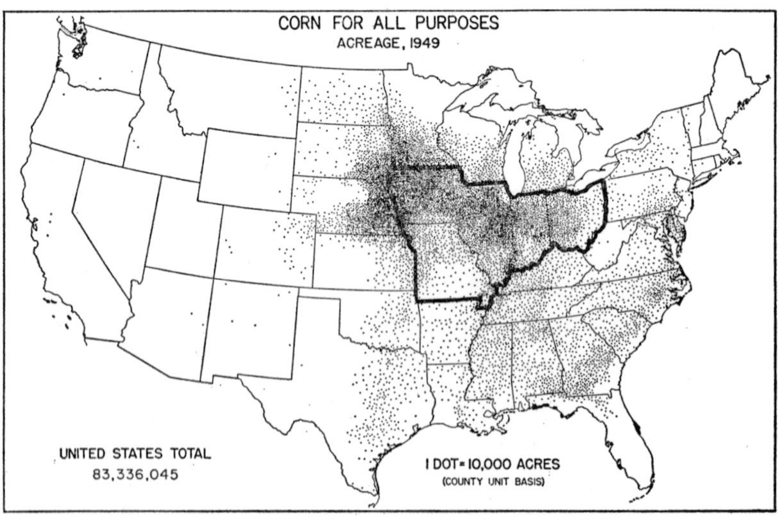

do produce more per acre, both in crop tonnage and in number of livestock, but at a huge cost in human labor. Moreover, they are dependent on the importation of feeds. By themselves they are not self-sufficient. Australia's very small eastern coastal strip of arable lands is not comparable. Argentina, great though its possible output of grains may be, again does not have comparable virtues. In 1950, Iowa alone produced over five times as much corn as Argentina, 579,000,000 bushels to 103,000,000, although Iowa's acreage was only about twice as large.

In the Corn-Soy Belt, almost every crop, except the sub-tropical, that has any importance in our agricultural economy can be grown. There is a huge vegetable industry around the Great Lakes, and vegetables will grow and are grown commercially in small lots in almost every part of this area. It may surprise many to know that only California produces more tomatoes than Indiana, which grew 331,000 tons in 1950, while Ohio usually ranks from fourth to sixth in tomato production. Ohio, Indiana, Illinois, and Missouri all produce potatoes in commercial quantities. Fruits and nuts likewise flourish. Ohio and Illinois are fairly heavy apple-producers. Grape culture is old and well established in the Ohio Valley, as well as along the lower Missouri River. All grains are grown to some extent. Oats is the second-ranking crop on the basis of acreage over practically all of Iowa and most of northern Illinois. Wheat is widely grown in some areas of these states and is especially important in Ohio, which ranked tenth in production in 1949. Forage crops abound, and hay is the leading crop acreage-wise in most of the Ozark Uplands of southern Missouri, and in the rolling area of eastern Ohio. Even hemp is grown on a very limited scale. Dairying, poultry production, beef cattle, hogs, sheep, and even fur farms are everywhere. About the only American crops not found are the southern crops of citrus and rice, for even tobacco and cotton have some culture in this region.

Yet this ability to grow such a variety of crops and animals is not the unique richness of this region, for it is here, as probably no place else, that the premier feed crop of modern times is most at home. This, of course, is corn. In 1950 these five states alone produced 1,461,024,000 bushels of corn, or nearly one-half of the nation's total production. Even more striking is the fact that this output represented more than one-fourth of the estimated world production. And, as if this were not enough, that old-new crop, soybeans, an ideal complement to corn, has also found its warmest welcome and one of its best productive situations here.

The importance of corn in this region is most clearly seen in the land-use patterns. In 1949 corn was the ranking crop in *every* Iowa county. Indiana ranked a close second; corn was the major crop in all except three counties. And in most of Illinois, the western two-thirds of Ohio, and a large part of northern Missouri, corn is of first importance. In 1949 corn occupied 50.2 per cent of the cropland harvested in Iowa, 42.1 per cent in Indiana, and 44.7 per cent in Illinois. The percentage was somewhat less in Ohio and Missouri, being 33.6 and 31.7 per cent, respectively. In Fremont County, in the extreme southwest corner of Iowa, corn occupied 68.9 per cent of the cropland harvested. The predominance of corn in the largest part of these states can also be observed in its relative value. Iowa's corn crop accounted for 65.5 per cent of the value of all crops in 1949; it was 55.8 and 51.9 per cent, respectively, in Illinois and Indiana. McLean County (Bloomington), Illinois, was the country's ranking county in corn acreage and production in

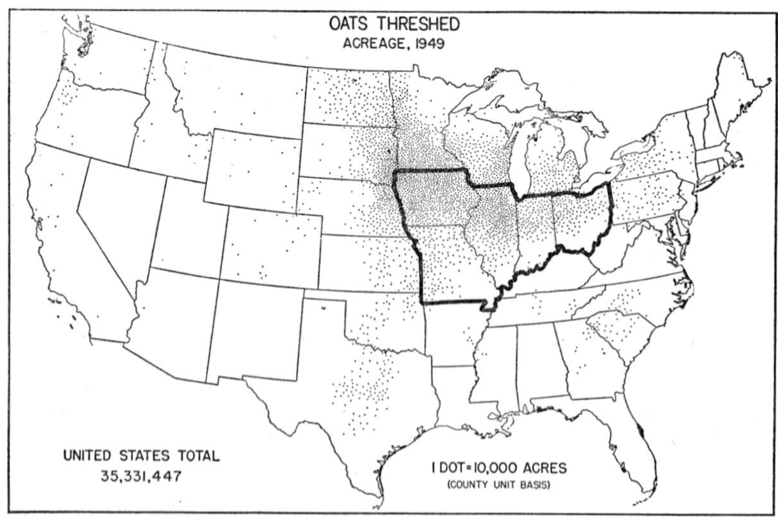

TABLE 48.—*Number of acres of corn harvested for grain, and number of bushels of corn produced in the Corn-Soy Belt, 1899–1949.*

	1949	1939	1929	1919	1899
			Ohio		
Acres	3,246,781	3,167,915	2,911,424	3,563,352	3,826,013
Bushels	168,046,185	156,303,520	102,177,194	149,844,626	152,055,390
			Indiana		
Acres	4,469,717	3,901,080	3,675,946	4,457,400	4,499,249
Bushels	219,032,305	187,635,164	114,871,320	158,603,938	178,967,070
			Illinois		
Acres	8,815,740	7,510,683	7,774,070	7,908,385	10,266,335
Bushels	457,731,394	382,457,687	275,850,367	285,346,031	398,149,140
			Iowa		
Acres	10,847,806	8,899,701	9,683,592	9,006,733	9,804,076
Bushels	503,589,858	469,786,611	389,000,414	371,362,393	383,453,190
			Missouri		
Acres	3,743,435	4,096,205	4,837,812	5,567,079	7,423,683
Bushels	129,968,135	124,058,341	112,348,071	146,342,036	208,844,870

Source: *United States Census of Agriculture, 1950,* II, 538–40.

both 1944 and 1949. Kossuth County (Algona) is the leader in Iowa, and ranked ninth among the nation's counties in production.

The peculiar soil and climatic assets that have proved so hospitable to this great feed crop might easily by themselves have made a great agricultural economy, because swine and dairy cattle can utilize corn so efficiently. But nature, in addition, placed this region in juxtaposition with one of the world's greatest grazing regions, a made-to-order home for beef cattle and sheep. Out of this fortuitous grouping grew up the peculiarly American device of processing feeds through animals. In 1951, for example, 1,351,940 stocker and feeder cattle and calves were shipped into Iowa alone. Thousands more were sent to Illinois and Indiana for finishing. Thus by processing the abundant feed, principally corn, through livestock, we have gained more efficient, more delectable, and more nutritious dietary complexes.

Here we must come to grips with the problem which emerged clearly during World War II—the problem of animal products versus direct-use cereals. It was argued with considerable logic that, in view of the world's great need for calories, it was wasteful—almost sinful—to process feeds through animals. It is still argued that, from a biochemical point of view, there is no reason to rate animal products so highly. The claim is made that bananas and milk, for instance, give all the vitamins, proteins, and calories needed for an ideal diet. The vegetarians admittedly have their point. Food faddists add to but confuse the picture with their theories. This great man or that confesses proudly that he has not eaten any animal products in years and enjoys vigorous health. And so it goes, with various authorities agreeing here and disagreeing there, until nobody is quite sure what the truth is.

However, there can be no doubt that if the entire Corn-Soy Belt were turned to the raising of food grains only for direct human consumption, rather than specializing primarily on feeds to be processed through animals, enormously greater numbers of people could be fed than is now the case. Yet people who enjoy a meat diet seem to possess greater energy. Their "tone" seems better. Their aggressiveness certainly goes up. For whatever it is worth, most animal husbandmen, given a free choice, prefer an animal source for some of their protein requirements. And while cattlemen have no laboratory-proved truths, they find from practical results that tankage and cake, rather than cake alone, seem to do a better job on livestock thrift, gains, output, and finish.

Quite apart from the arguments, a hard practicality that often is labeled "national selfishness" by those who do not enjoy meat is, and probably will remain, the compelling reason the Corn-Soy Belt will stay in feeds and animals. This practicality is the fact that, in the United States and in any other country that has ever had animal products as a part of its diet, people desire their proteins in this form more than any other. When the American laboring man is prosperous, his desires for a new automobile, a home of his own, or education for his children—all high-priority desires for the average American—hardly begin to operate until his No. 1 desire, for meat and animal products, is met. Notice our national slogans: "The Full Dinner Pail," "Two Chickens in Every Pot," "Ham 'n' Eggs." Note also the widest used of all symbols of success—a thick steak smothered in onions or mushrooms.

These secular hints are not just surface observations or manifestations. When national income rises, milk consumption goes up. Beef consumption can be tied loosely to the employment curve, moving up and down with it. Some relative idea of the per capita income of the average American could be figured, if we lacked other means, by the individual consumption of eggs, poultry, and meat. During the depression years of 1930–32, for instance, average individual beef consumption in the United States was only forty-nine pounds; from 1948 to 1950 it was about sixty-three pounds.

When the individual is experiencing poor days, his diet generally favors the farinaceous, or starchy, foods. When the standard of living of the nation was much lower than it is now, potatoes and wheat products enjoyed a much greater popularity than they do in better-fed times. Both individuals and nations, in other words, are constantly trying to upgrade their diets. And this means that, for the long term, the desire will be for animal products. The Corn-Soy Belt can go a long way in fulfilling this desire.

At this point, theorists and realists collide. Direct-use foods are usually land robbers. For that matter, so are most row-crop feedstuffs. But when animal waste, manure, is returned to the land, a part, at least, of the necessary nutrients also go back. If we were to turn all our land to direct-use foods, in a very short time we, too, would be a have-not nation. Complete emphasis upon the production of grains, cereals, and vegetables, as the direct-use people advocate, would mean robbing our land at a more rapid pace. But when animals are introduced to the situation, the process of soil depletion is either slowed down or, under proper management, stopped.

Add to this vital circumstance the fact that the largest part of our agricultural lands now in cultivation will not efficiently grow anything but forage crops, and a most compelling joint argument is made for continuing our traditional livestock-economy pattern. If we used our range lands and grasslands for grazing and did not use grain for finishing, we would not have enough quality meat for our desires. Furthermore, only the ruminants could exist at all, for swine and poultry utilize very little grass. But most mandatory of

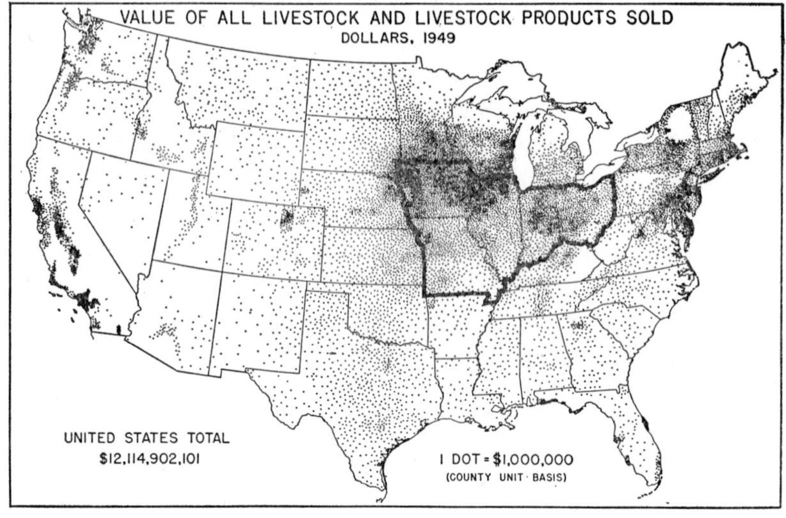

all items is the fact that even now we must turn more and more of our depleted lands into grass, even in the Corn-Soy Belt, to save them from ruin. More grass means more livestock unless the land is to go out of economic production.

Thus the future of this region seems to be clearly marked as a continuation of the past. Corn, soybeans, small grains, and grass will enter into the rotations, no matter what succession or fraction is individually selected.[2] Corn will remain the big money crop and the determining factor in practically all farm plans, except in southern Missouri and eastern Ohio. The bulk of the corn will be fed to livestock, principally swine, with dairy and beef cattle close behind. In 1949, 2,340,406,000 of the 3,131,000,000 bushels of corn raised in the United States were used for feed and seed on the farm. In the five states under consideration, total corn production in 1949 was 1,459,417,000 bushels, of which 1,005,996,000 were used on the farm. Only a small part of the corn and small grains will go into direct human consumption. In 1949 only 242,000,000 bushels of United States corn went into dry- and wet-processed products and alcohol.

[2] For the best appraisal of this problem, see John C. Weaver, "Crop-Combination Regions in the Middle-West," *Economic Geography,* Vol. XLIV (April, 1954), 175–200.

Because of the predominance of corn as a great feed crop, farm income in this region is, and probably will be, derived mostly from livestock and livestock products. In 1949 a little over 80 per cent of the value of farm products sold in Iowa came from livestock and livestock products. The fabulous livestock industry in that state accounted for a staggering 10.9 per cent of the total national value of livestock and livestock products sold. For example, Iowa marketed 16,665,000 hogs in 1950, which brought the state's farmers a gross income of $775,894,000. Receipts from this single source were greater in Iowa than the total farm income in each of thirty-five other states! Gross income from cattle and calf sales was nearly as large as that from hogs, totaling $623,000,000. In Missouri, Indiana, Ohio, and Illinois, about 72, 68, 66, and 57 per cent, respectively, of the value of farm products sold came from livestock and livestock products in 1949.

During World War II, soybean production reached a record development, giving the region an additional important cash crop. Over 14,000,000 acres were planted in 1944. In the immediate postwar period, the acreage declined, but it jumped sharply to about 15,700,000 acres in 1950. In 1954 there was a large increase

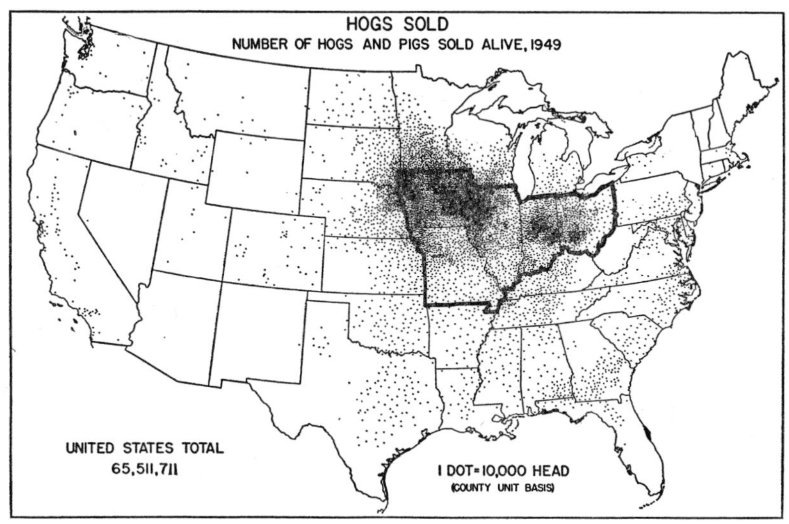

TABLE 49.—*Value of crops and livestock and livestock products sold in the Corn-Soy Belt, 1939–49, and the percentage of each.*

Value of farm products sold

	1949		1939	
	Crops	*Livestock*	*Crops*	*Livestock*
Ohio	$239,837,738	$ 469,333,000	$ 89,484,736	$163,487,817
Ind.	231,484,286	498,809,994	75,246,673	141,140,719
Ill.	588,488,181	772,184,894	208,658,076	205,897,178
Iowa	320,308,808	1,314,601,371	166,474,076	345,709,468
Mo.	199,299,731	518,005,484	71,955,398	141,843,490

Per cent of farm products sold

	1949		1939	
	Crops	*Livestock*	*Crops*	*Livestock*
Ohio	33.7	65.9	35.2	64.4
Ind.	31.6	68.2	34.7	65.0
Ill.	43.2	56.7	50.3	49.6
Iowa	19.6	80.4	32.5	67.5
Mo.	27.7	72.0	33.5	66.1

Source: *United States Census of Agriculture, 1950,* II 752–54.

in soybean plantings because of the government program of cutting back corn acreage.

Until 1919 most soybean production was in the South, with North Carolina, Tennessee, and Virginia leading. Michigan was the only northern state which had any significant production in 1919, when 6,257 acres were planted there. But by the late nineteen thirties, and during the years of World War II, soybeans found their real home in the states of Ohio, Indiana, Illinois, Iowa, and Missouri. Southern Minnesota also became a heavy producer. Of the 299,279,000 bushels of soybeans produced in the United States in 1950, the five states in the Corn-Soy Belt had an output of 227,-698,000 bushels. By 1950 Illinois' production was greater than that of the entire United States eleven years before. Soybeans held first rank in cropland harvested in five counties in the claypan area of southeastern Illinois. Of the one hundred ranking soybean counties in 1949, all but fifteen were in the five states under consideration.

TABLE 50.—*Per cent of value of all livestock and livestock products sold as represented by dairy products, poultry and poultry products, and livestock and livestock products other than dairy and poultry, 1939–49.*

	Dairy products		*Poultry & poultry products*		*Livestock & livestock prod. other than dairy & poultry*	
	1949	1939	1949	1939	1949	1939
Ohio	30.3	31.8	15.7	18.0	54.0	50.2
Ind.	18.8	23.3	14.1	14.4	67.1	62.3
Ill.	16.5	23.5	8.4	11.2	75.1	65.3
Iowa	8.9	14.6	9.2	9.8	82.0	75.6
Mo.	15.3	17.2	11.6	15.7	73.1	67.1

Source: *United States Census of Agriculture, 1950,* II 760.

In contrast to corn, relatively few soybeans are used on the farm. In 1950 only 2,530,000 bushels out of the total production were fed to livestock. Most soybeans go into cash sales. In 1950, of the 95,736,000 bushels produced in Illinois, 92,181,000 were sold; only 191,000 bushels were fed to livestock on the farm.

Increased soybean acreage in the Corn Belt came as a result of this crop's displacing small grains, hay, and rotation pasture. Gen-

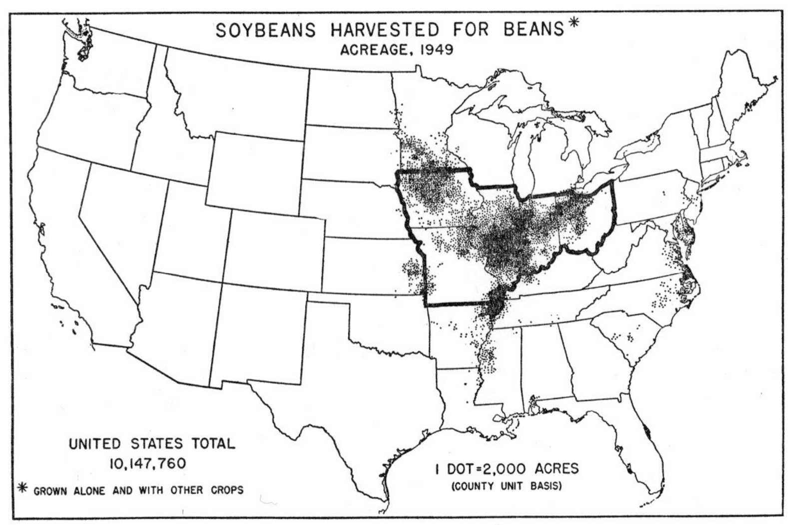

TABLE 51.—*Soybean acreage, production, and farm value in the United States, 1909–50.*

	Acreage grown[1]	*Prod. (in bu.)*	*Farm value*
1909[2]	1,629	16,835	$ 20,577
1919[2]	112,826	1,084,813	4,592,000
1929[3]	2,736,000	9,398,000	17,736,000
1939[3]	9,565,000	90,141,000	73,049,000
1944[4]	13,118,000	192,121,000	393,893,000
1950[4]	15,129,000	299,279,000	738,822,000

[1] Until about 1941, the total acreage harvested for soybeans was usually less than half of the total grown (*Agricultural Statistics, 1953,* 134).

[2] *Fourteenth Census of the United States, 1920,* V, (Agriculture), 777.

[3] *Agricultural Statistics, 1940,* 306.

[4] *Agricultural Statistics, 1953,* 134.

erally speaking, with the exception of where they have been substituted for corn because of the federal acreage-control program, soybeans have replaced crops which have a smaller output value per acre. Thus soybeans have added materially to total production in the Corn-Soy Belt.

No doubt the concerted effort to get more soybeans, ideal food that they are, directly into the diet will continue. And the effort may meet with even more success than it has had to date. True, soybeans are now used in soup, bread, pastry products, candy, frozen dessert, and many other supplementary foods. No doubt, once the inequity of the remaining state margarine laws is corrected, even further food usage will eventuate.

Production of soybeans was encouraged during the nineteen forties, when the world-wide shortage of fats and oils was hardly less than catastrophic. But even with wartime demands over, soybeans remain a favored crop. Sherman E. Johnson of the Department of Agriculture has said on this point: "The levels of wartime acreage are not likely to be maintained as other sources of oil become more readily available, but it seems probable that both acreage and production will remain at much higher levels than they reached before the war. Soybeans in the Corn Belt have a near-by market for meal, which usually equals or exceeds the value of the oil, so the oil may become the by-product from soybeans grown chiefly to supply high-protein concentrates. On this basis they can compete more readily with other sources of edible oil."

The future of this crop seems assured for other reasons. It is a plant nicely adapted to this area, and it fits well into the rotation program. It can be a soil builder, as well as a soil depleter, depending upon the growing and harvesting practice. Its cake, after the oil has been extracted, is of high value in livestock feeding, and this is the greatest feeding area in the world. In addition, the oil is so amenable to the chemist's manipulation that we may assume that industry will find additional demands for the crop so that production will be kept high. Probably the greatest influence on soybean output, however, will be the acreage-restriction programs for corn and, to a much lesser extent, wheat. If corn acreage is restricted severely enough, soybean acreage will likely grow beyond anything ever seen in this country, unless that acreage, too, should be controlled.

The very fact that the climate, the soil, and the largely flat topography make this region so ideal for a great feed crop and a top industrial crop, plus the small grains, also gives an indication of what other items will appear in the picture of the future. Almost from the time when the farm size was set at 80 or 120 or 160 acres, the pattern has been expanding. The land itself, as well as the crops, begged for mechanization. The area is ideally suited to originate and develop tools to take the backache and low production of the man-and-horsepower method out of agriculture.

Tractors, grain combines, corn pickers, plows, discs, planters, cultivators, elevators, haying equipment, feed grinders, trucks, and other equipment have all been eagerly adopted here. Four-row planting and harvesting equipment is becoming increasingly common in parts of this region, and recently a corn combine—a machine which picks and shells corn in a single field operation—has proved practical. As a result of increased mechanization, the number of man-hours necessary to grow and harvest corn and small grains has been cut drastically. Under favorable conditions and advanced mechanical practices, it took only 3.85 man-hours to produce an acre of corn in Iowa in 1939. On the basis of eighty-five bushels per acre, that meant a time expenditure of only 2.7 minutes

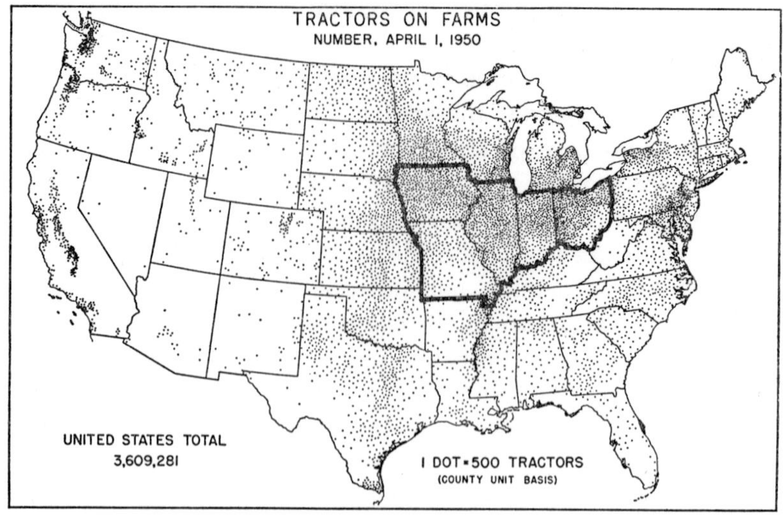

per bushel. By the early nineteen fifties, with higher yields and even better machines, only one to one and one-half minutes were required to produce a bushel of corn by some of Iowa's most efficient farmers. But these machines are expensive—very expensive. It is not uncommon for an Iowa or Illinois farmer who operates around 400 acres to have $20,000, or more, invested in machinery and equipment. This means an investment of some $50 an acre just for machinery.

TABLE 52.—*Number of tractors on Corn-Soy Belt farms, and the per cent of farms reporting tractors, 1920–50.*

	1950	1945	1940	1930	1925	1920
Ohio	182,481	130,486	89,999	52,974	30,905	10,469
	63.9	50.2	35.6	23.1	12.2	3.9
Ind.	153,980	105,263	73,221	41,979	23,567	9,230
	63.6	50.8	37.1	22.3	11.7	4.3
Ill.	234,789	174,270	126,069	69,628	43,325	23,102
	72.7	64.6	51.8	30.8	18.4	9.2
Iowa	240,941	181,049	128,516	66,258	37,230	20,270
	79.4	72.3	55.3	29.4	16.7	9.1
Mo.	125,536	76,110	45,155	24,999	12,745	7,889
	43.6	27.8	16.4	9.2	4.6	2.8

Source: *United States Census of Agriculture, 1950,* II, 226.

As machines have multiplied the work output of man, it was only natural that he should seek fuller employment by increasing the size of his job. Hence, farm sizes have steadily grown. Also important in this connection is the fact that a much higher percentage of the farm acreage in the Corn-Soy Belt is in harvested cropland than in most other sections of the country. Iowa and Illinois, with 68.8 and 68.7 per cent, respectively, had the highest percentage of their farm lands in harvested cropland of any states in the Union in 1949. And the cropland acreage, like the total acreage per farm, is becoming increasingly large. In Illinois 34 per cent of the farms harvested between 100 and 199 acres of cropland in 1949, and 15 per cent harvested over 200 acres; in Iowa 43 per cent of the farms harvested 100 to 199 acres, and 12 per cent harvested over 200.

The capital investment necessary to do an all-out mechanized job is so large today that few could afford it on yesterday's acres. Undoubtedly, the trend toward more land per unit will continue. Where once a "family farm" consisted of 160 acres in much of this region, today it consists of 240 or 320 acres; and many of even this

TABLE 53.—*Number of farms in the Corn-Soy Belt, 1850–1950.*

	1950	1940	1930	1920	1910	1900	1880	1850
Ohio	199,359	233,783	219,296	256,695	272,045	276,719	247,189	143,807
Ind.	166,627	184,549	181,570	205,126	215,485	221,897	194,013	93,896
Ill.	195,268	213,439	214,497	237,181	251,872	264,151	255,741	76,208
Iowa	203,159	213,318	214,928	213,439	217,044	228,622	185,351	14,805
Mo.	230,045	256,100	255,940	263,004	277,244	284,886	215,575	54,458

Source: *United States Census of Agriculture, 1950,* II, 51–52.

TABLE 54.—*Average number of acres per farm in the Corn-Soy Belt, 1850–1950.*

	1950	1940	1930	1920	1910	1900	1880	1850
Ohio	105.2	93.7	98.1	91.6	88.6	88.5	99.2	125.2
Ind.	118.0	107.3	108.4	102.7	98.8	97.4	105.3	136.2
Ill.	158.6	145.4	143.1	134.8	129.1	124.2	123.8	158.0
Iowa	168.7	160.1	158.3	156.8	156.3	151.2	133.5	184.8
Mo.	152.7	135.6	131.8	132.2	124.8	119.3	129.3	178.7

Source: *United States Census of Agriculture, 1950,* II, 799.

size are rapidly expanding into the 500-acre class, while still larger farms up to 1,000 acres are no longer curiosities of grandeur. There were over 400 such farms in Illinois alone in 1950. In order to enlarge their operating units, farmers have tended to try to rent or buy another 40, another 80, possibly another 160 acres, or more. This pressure for land was so great in the early nineteen fifties that very little good farm land was for sale at all in many parts of the Corn-Soy Belt. Scarcity of available high-quality land has been caused not only by farmers trying to get more, but also by the purchases of businessmen, doctors, lawyers, and other town and city investors who had surplus cash.

TABLE 55.—*Value of land and buildings per acre in the Corn-Soy Belt, 1850–1950.**

	1950	1940	1930	1920	1910	1900	1880	1850
Ohio	$136.34	$ 65.91	$ 78.65	$113.18	$ 68.62	$ 42.31	$ 45.97	$ 19.93
Ind.	136.90	63.20	71.90	125.98	74.85	38.93	31.11	10.66
Ill.	174.15	81.76	108.68	187.59	108.32	53.84	31.87	7.99
Iowa	160.71	78.79	124.18	227.09	96.00	43.31	22.92	6.09
Mo.	63.66	31.87	53.23	88.08	49.61	24.82	13.47	6.50

Source: *United States Census of Agriculture, 1950,* II, 50–52.

* By 1952 the Bureau of Agricultural Economics estimated that the average value of land and buildings per acre was: Ohio, $181; Ind., $178; Ill., $222; Iowa, $197; Mo., $82.

High capitalization in the Corn-Soy Belt is likely to remain a permanent feature of agriculture in this region. A recession might drive back acreage prices, but it is doubtful if such a calamity would make a corresponding reduction in other costs. That is, machinery and equipment are likely to stay at about the same prices even in a recession. History shows this rather clearly: in depression periods industry maintains prices by curtailing output, while farm production continues heavy and prices fall to ruinous levels, unless there is a government price-support program of some kind. Perhaps the best example of this trend is found in the period from 1929 to the spring of 1933. The statistics were revealed by a Senate committee and appear in the following chart:

Courtesy Standard Oil Company of New Jersey

On a Delta plantation in Mississippi, this cotton is being dusted with benzene hexachloride to kill weevils.

A one-row cotton picker at work in the Mississippi Delta country.

Courtesy National Cotton Council

Courtesy United States Department of Agriculture

Picking oranges near Orlando, Florida.

A multiple-nozzle power duster in operation in a Florida citrus grove.

Courtesy United States Department of Agriculture

Courtesy United States
Department of Agriculture

This hybrid corn, which attained considerable growth despite severe drought, was planted in a three-year rotation plan with wheat and red clover on land which had been heavily fertilized.

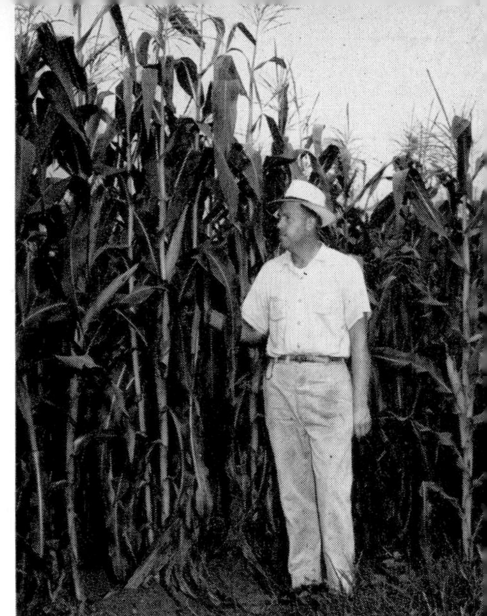

Three Hampshire sows and their litters.

Courtesy United States Department of Agriculture

Courtesy United States Department of Agriculture

A field of soybeans in Saline County, Missouri.

Soybeans, an annual summer legume, are grown extensively in parts of the Middle West.

Courtesy United States Department of Agriculture

Courtesy United States Department of Agriculture

Holstein cattle in an alfalfa-ladino improved pasture, Green County, Wisconsin.

Milking machines, now highly perfected, are labor-savers on many American dairy farms.

Courtesy United States Department of Agriculture

A forage harvester of the sickle-bar type.

A modern baler in a field of alfalfa.

Courtesy Extension Division, Oklahoma A. and M. College

The prairie is an ocean of wheat in this Oklahoma farm scene.

Combining grain near Cut Bank, Montana.

Courtesy Standard Oil Company of New Jersey

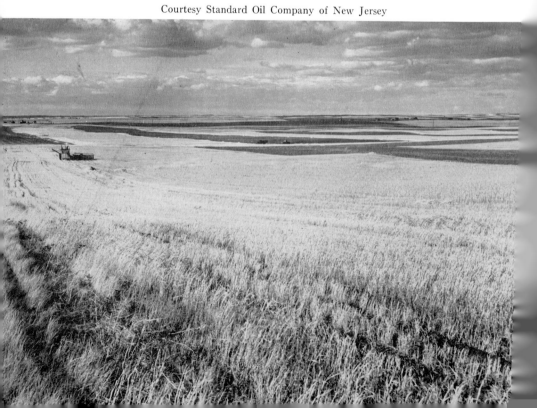

	Per cent drop in prices	*Per cent drop in production*
Agricultural implements	6	80
Motor vehicles	16	80
Cement	18	65
Iron and steel	20	83
Auto tires	33	70
Petroleum	56	20
Agricultural commodities	63	6

In the Corn-Soy Belt, even before World War II, the cost of setting up a farm operation ran anywhere from $15,000 to $50,000. This put the farmer in the class of the small manufacturer, a far cry from the hallowed tradition of American farming which proclaimed that any hired hand could one day own his own place. By mid-century, a lower minimum would put a small but fairly good farm of one-family capacity somewhere in the $25,000 to $35,000 class, and the upper "average," but not the peak, at around $80,000 to $100,000. The little good farm land that was selling in Iowa and Illinois was bringing from $200 an acre, and upward (mostly considerably above this figure), in the early nineteen fifties. The 1950 census showed 27,534 farms in Illinois in the 260-499-acre class out of a total of 195,212. The average value of land and buildings on these 27,534 farms was $59,347. When the cost of machinery and equipment is added in, one readily sees that an operation on a farm this size runs to around $75,000 to $80,000. Indeed, the cost of farming in much of this area is becoming so high that young men find it extremely difficult, if not impossible, to begin operations unless they inherit part of the land or have unusual financial backing.

Part of this large figure admittedly derives from inflated land values, but only part. It is possible that real-estate values might decline somewhat, but on the whole, the financial condition of owners, renters, and lenders indicates that a depression as bad as, or worse than, the last would have to occur to produce a drastic reduction in them. Moreover, as has been noted before, the other capital items do not recede proportionately. Industry simply stops producing, but does not noticeably cut prices. Inasmuch as other-than-real-estate items today constitute much of the mechanized farm's total capitalization, it may be seen that nothing short of a major disaster will affect their value, as was once the case. We must also take into consideration the likelihood that some kind of government price-support program for farm commodities will be a permanent part of national policy. Besides, even in a recession, the progressive demand-supply position, because of population growth and continued depletion of soil resources elsewhere, favors this region more than it did in the mid-thirties, when milk was poured into the roadside ditches.

TABLE 56.—*Per cent of commercial farms in the Corn-Soy Belt by economic class.**

	Per cent of total farms considered commercial	*Economic class* I	*II*	*III*	*IV*	*V*	*VI*
Ohio	67.6	1.3	8.9	24.7	29.6	22.9	12.6
Ind.	73.9	1.8	12.9	25.3	26.8	21.3	11.9
Ill.	82.4	4.1	23.0	30.1	20.8	13.5	8.5
Iowa	92.4	3.9	23.2	36.1	21.8	10.3	4.7
Mo.	71.6	1.3	6.0	16.1	27.0	28.9	20.6

Source: *United States Census of Agriculture, 1950,* II, 1133.

* See Table 5 for basis of classification.

When so much that is optimistic, even laudatory, can be said about this American Garden of Eden, it is discouraging to have to report that, although the lands as a whole are not subject to serious water erosion, the fertility quotient, nevertheless, is going down. It has not yet reached the disaster point, but it is far closer to it than it should ever have been allowed to be.

In some areas of Ohio, Indiana, Illinois, southern Iowa, and Missouri, actual stream and water erosion are almost as terrible as in the South. One need only drive southward from Des Moines toward the Missouri border to see deep gullies washed out by the heavy rains. In other areas, sheet erosion has taken its toll. In still others, notably the rich loess area at the western side of the belt, winds have swept away millions of dollars of value. These things are bad, but not unnoticed. Soil conservation districts are increasing. Defense measures are being put to work. There is good hope that a change can be effected before it is too late.

TABLE 57.—*Soil conservation districts in the Corn-Soy Belt as of 1951.*

	Number of districts organized	*Farm acres included in organized districts*
Ohio	82	20,603,517
Ind.	54	11,562,001
Ill.	95	30,224,684
Iowa	99	34,170,206
Mo.	26	7,922,747

Source: *Agricultural Statistics, 1952,* 774.

Elsewhere, all over the area, however, there is a more insidious disease. Farmers in the whole region have always laughed at the red soils of the Southeast. They have bragged that their black soils were eternal. Even when they skimmed off the cream and moved westward, others behind them came on to find better second-owner lands than original-owner lands in less favored districts. Still, bit by bit, crop by crop, rain by leaching rain, those never-eternal nutrients were being used up or carried away, particularly where corn had been planted year after year for generations.

Then came the huge demands of World War II. To get even greater production, the farmers used fertilizer in quantity for the first time. When the war was over, it was found to the dismay of many a man who thought his soil eternal that he had to keep on using fertilizer, not for greater yields, but to maintain prewar yields. Hybrid corn was a billion-dollar boon to the region, but high yielders need more plant food than low yielders, and this had had its negative effect too, in an area virtually 100 per cent hybrid.

For the future, then, not only will capital costs remain high, but so will operating costs. In 1940 Iowa used only 16,000 tons of commercial fertilizer. In 1950 the state's farmers bought 386,050 tons. Even that was not all they needed or wanted, and it is likely that Iowa's fertilizer need will hit the 500,000-ton mark, or more. One of the most recent developments in fertilization has been the use of anhydrous ammonia, which has produced remarkable results in boosting corn production. But the cost is high. For example, farmers around Algona, Iowa, in the state's biggest corn county, were spending as much as $12 to $14 an acre to apply this type of fertilizer to their land in 1954.

TABLE 58.—*Amount of commercial fertilizers used annually in the Corn-Soy Belt.*

	1950	*Average* 1940–44	*Average* 1935–39
Ohio	951,728 tons	456,750 tons	335,316 tons
Ind.	934,649 tons	344,977 tons	217,020 tons
Ill.	1,176,908 tons	198,298 tons	43,835 tons
Iowa	386,050 tons	45,087 tons	9,039 tons
Mo.	637,329 tons	117,830 tons	74,832 tons

Source: *Agricultural Statistics, 1952,* 706–707.

Not only must more fertilization be practiced—along with more contouring, more strip cropping, and more drainage—but rotations must be longer. At the present time, perhaps the most common rotation schedule is corn, corn or soybeans, oats, and hay or grass. Tomorrow, it may have to be corn, soybeans, oats, hay, and hay, or even a five-year plan that will cut the annual row-crop acreage severely. However, here, as wherever else that grass will grow—and it should be remembered that grass is the climax growth for most of this land, including even parts of the once-forested eastern side of the Mississippi—new grasses with higher feed and protein values may aid greatly in maintaining farm value and livestock output. As mentioned elsewhere, there is considerable question on the part of livestockmen if putting eighty to ninety bushels of corn into an animal is ever justified, even in times of very weak corn prices. If corn production is cut back because of better land-use practices, or because of government acreage controls, feeding to high finishes may become less common. Lorin Clark, a prosperous farmer in Champaign County, Illinois, was quoted in 1954 as saying that "grass is the most underrated crop in America today." Even though his land was worth some $500 an acre, he considered good grass one of his most profitable crops, processing it through steers.

If these lines had been written a few years ago, the threat of such pests as the European and Mexican corn borers would have had of necessity to be given extended treatment. At that fairly recent time, it seemed as if the glamorously rich Corn Belt might be facing partial destruction by entomological pests. That possibility is not gone, but it seems more remote because of the development of the whole pharmacopoeia of new mists and sprays, plus airplane and fog-machine distribution. For the moment, at least, the outlook is good for control of such pests. And some researchers are predicting that possibly by 1960 a corn plant can be developed which will be resistant to the corn borer.

Despite the apparent clouds of fertility loss, insect depredation, and possible decline in consumers' buying power that mar the clear horizon of this area's future, it is probable that not in the lifetime of any living man will there ever be another place in the world so blessed by the gods as the Corn-Soy Belt. It is the top index by which most other areas may be judged. It is the most important region in the agricultural geography of this country. It is the one area every farmer should plan to visit someday, even though it is without doubt the least scenic region in America.

CHAPTER 8

The North North-Central Region: Dairyland

(Michigan, Wisconsin, Minnesota)

THE student is familiar with usual USDA regional breakdowns of East North-Central and West North-Central. For our purpose we are changing these traditional labels and creating a new one of North North-Central, because one type of farming, dairying, is most typical of all three states in this region—and we have borrowed from the Wisconsin auto license plates the descriptive word "Dairyland."

It should be noted, however, that there is great diversity in the region's farm production. Minnesota is the center of the flax industry and also has rich wheatlands, much corn and general farming. Indeed, southern Minnesota is a vital part of the Corn Belt. Wisconsin, the prime dairy state, additionally grows such diverse crops as fruit, vegetables, grains, tobacco, and all livestock. Michigan has a little bit of everything from peppermint to tree farms to tulips, raises pregnant mares for urine (valuable because of its estrogenic content), supports fur farms, is a big fruit-producer, and has some of the heaviest-producing vegetable lands in the country. But in all three states, dairying has nearly the prominence that corn does a bit farther south. In Wisconsin especially, agricultural activities have come to center more and more around the dairy industry.

GENERAL PATTERN OF GREAT SOIL GROUPS

Dairyland

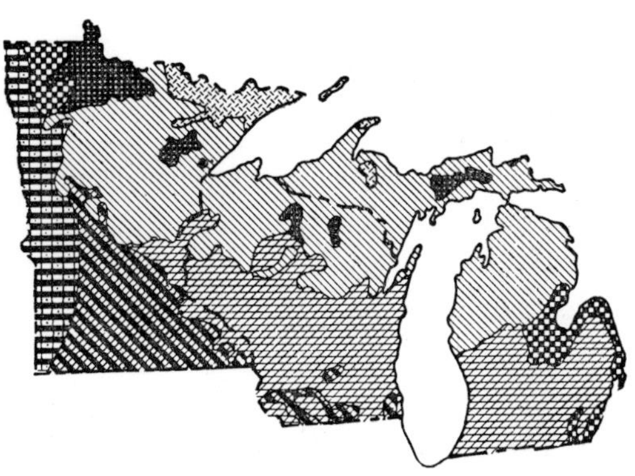

PODZOL SOILS

Light-colored leached soils of cool, humid forested regions.

GRAY-BROWN PODZOLIC SOILS

Grayish-brown leached soils of temperate, humid forested regions.

PRAIRIE SOILS

Very dark brown soils of cool and temperate, relatively humid grasslands.

CHERNOZEM SOILS

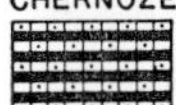

Dark-brown to nearly black soils of cool and temperate, subhumid grasslands.

WIESENBÖDEN (1), GROUND WATER PODZOL (2), AND HALF-BOG SOILS (3)

(1) Dark-brown to black soils developed with poor drainage under grasses in humid and subhumid regions.

(2) Gray sandy soils with brown cemented sandy subsoils developed under forests from nearly level imperfectly drained sand in humid regions.

(3) Poorly drained, shallow, dark peaty or mucky soils underlain by gray mineral soil, in humid regions, under swamp-forests.

BOG SOILS

Poorly drained dark peat or muck soils underlain by peat, mostly in humid regions, under swamp or marsh types of vegetation.

LITHOSOLS AND SHALLOW SOILS (HUMID)

Shallow soils consisting largely of an imperfectly weathered mass of rock fragments, largely but not exclusively on steep slopes.

MINN.
WISCONSIN
MICHIGAN

TABLE 59.—*Number of farms in Michigan, Wisconsin and Minnesota, 1850–1950.*

	1950	1940	1930	1920	1910	1900	1880	1850
Mich.	155,589	187,589	169,372	196,447	206,960	203,261	154,008	34,089
Wis.	168,561	186,735	181,767	189,295	177,127	169,795	134,322	20,177
Minn.	179,101	197,351	185,255	178,478	156,137	154,659	92,386	157

Source: *United States Census of Agriculture, 1950,* II, 51.

TABLE 60.—*Average size (in acres) of farms in Michigan, Wisconsin, and Minnesota, 1850–1950.*

	1950	1940	1930	1920	1910	1900	1880	1850
Mich.	111.0	96.2	101.1	96.9	91.5	86.4	89.7	128.6
Wis.	137.8	122.5	120.3	117.0	118.9	117.0	114.3	147.5
Minn.	183.6	165.2	166.9	169.3	177.3	169.7	145.1	183.9

Source: *United States Census of Agriculture, 1950,* II, 799.

The reason for this is largely ecological. The area is a little far north for the best corn culture, with growing season too short, and sunny and rainy days plus hot nights not quite in the sequence or intensity they should be to make the best corn. On the other hand, grass and forage crops thrive. Where the land is too hilly for row cropping, cows can do an excellent job of converting nonfood plants into human comestibles. About nine-tenths of Wisconsin's cropland has been used for feed production in recent years.

From almost every angle, dairying dominates the agricultural industry of this region. This can be seen in the number of milk cows, value of dairy products sold, type of farm, and crop combinations. Looking at the nation as a whole, we find that in 1951 there were 23,722,000 milk cows and heifers two years old and over kept for

TABLE 61.—*Average value of land and buildings per acre in farms in Michigan, Wisconsin, and Minnesota, 1850–1950.*

	1950	1940	1930	1920	1910	1900	1880	1850
Mich.	$ 98.52	$ 50.59	$ 67.80	$ 75.48	$ 47.58	$ 33.17	$ 36.15	$ 11.83
Wis.	88.58	51.96	79.16	98.78	57.06	34.54	23.30	9.58
Minn.	84.46	44.26	68.74	109.23	45.62	25.51	14.45	5.61

Source: *United States Census of Agriculture, 1950,* II, 51.

milk. Iowa, Texas, Ohio, and New York all reported over 1,000,000 head, but the three states under consideration had 4,766,000, or about 20 per cent of all such animals in the country. Wisconsin alone had 2,380,000 milk cows.

TABLE 62.—*Number of milk cows in Michigan, Wisconsin, and Minnesota, 1900–50.*

	1950	1940	1930	1920	1910	1900
Mich.	794,341	923,779	715,105	802,095	635,966	563,905
Wis.	2,075,571	2,189,235	1,814,995	1,795,122	1,213,461	998,397
Minn.	1,354,386	1,699,849	1,442,031	1,229,179	870,590	753,632

Source: *United States Census of Agriculture, 1950,* II, 403–404.

By far the largest number of commercial farms in this region are classified as dairy farms. In 1949 the figure was 31.9 and 42.9 per cent in Minnesota and Michigan, respectively, and a predominant 79.9 per cent in Wisconsin. About 33 per cent of the total farm income was derived from dairy products alone. In 1949 the value of dairy products sold amounted to $729,260,343 out of a national total of $3,079,131,579. The average-size dairy farm was 145, 146, and 164 acres, respectively, for Michigan, Wisconsin,

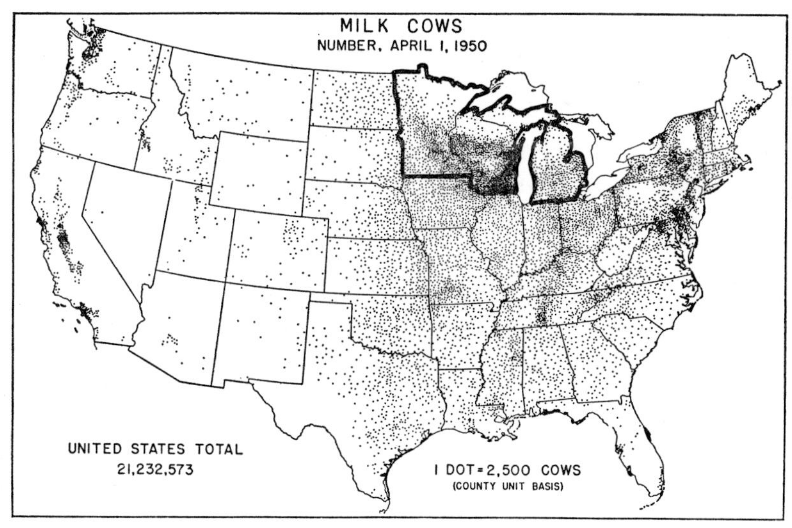

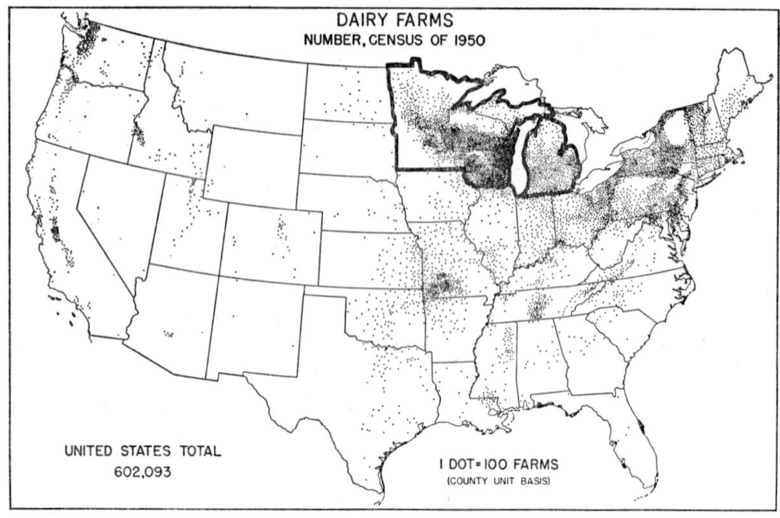

and Minnesota. The average value of products sold on these farms in 1949 was $3,905 in Michigan, $4,866 in Wisconsin, and $4,147 in Minnesota. There is a high percentage of what might be considered middle-class farms. The 1950 census showed that 62 and 66 per cent of the commercial farms in Minnesota and Wisconsin, respectively, sold between $2,500 and $10,000 worth of products. The most common size herd on the commercial dairy farms in Michigan and Minnesota is five to fourteen cows; in Wisconsin it is ten to thirty cows. On many dairy farms, operations are highly mechanized; for example, in 1949, 70.1 per cent of the commercial dairy farms reporting in Wisconsin had milking machines.

The major crop patterns in this region are fitted closely to the dairy and livestock industries. In Wisconsin, for example, over 90

TABLE 63.—*Pounds of whole milk sold in Michigan, Wisconsin, and Minnesota, 1909–49.*

	1949	1939	1929	1919	1909
Mich.	3,432,348,882	2,404,856,459	1,904,130,635	1,125,433,548	636,621,613
Wis.	12,661,443,632	8,706,039,453	7,253,474,728	4,074,824,755	2,556,366,933
Minn.	3,844,358,864	1,091,889,867	823,510,699	371,106,306	457,363,351

Source: *United States Census of Agriculture, 1950,* II, 410.

TABLE 64.—*Value of dairy products sold in Michigan, Wisconsin, and Minnesota, 1939–49.*

	1949	1939
Mich.	$143,115,068	$ 51,571,122
Wis.	397,704,803	127,074,592
Minn.	188,440,472	72,838,147

Source: *United States Census of Agriculture, 1950,* II, 758.

per cent of the cropland harvested in 1949 was devoted to the production of the major feed crops: hay, oats, and corn. The same feed crops occupied most of the cropland in Michigan and Minnesota, but not in quite the same heavy proportion. The dairy and livestock industry processes these crops into animal products such as

TABLE 65.—*Total acres of cropland harvested and major cropland uses in Michigan, Wisconsin, and Minnesota in 1949.*

Total acres of cropland harvested in 1949

Michigan	7,797,346
Wisconsin	10,112,027
Minnesota	19,709,121

Major cropland uses

	Number of Acres	*Per cent of total harvested cropland*
Michigan		
Hay*	2,192,375	28.1
Corn	1,599,149	20.5
Oats	1,355,848	17.4
Wisconsin		
Hay*	3,733,744	36.9
Corn	2,664,680	26.4
Oats	2,798,817	27.7
Minnesota		
Hay*	3,689,395	18.7
Corn	5,762,384	29.2
Oats	4,699,124	23.8

Source: *United States Census of Agriculture, 1950,* II, 532 ff.

*Excludes soybeans, cowpeas, and peanut vines cut for hay.

eggs, milk, and meat, contributing greatly to the nutritious high protein diet which is so desired by most Americans.

Although 33 per cent of the farm income in Michigan, Minnesota, and Wisconsin is from dairying (it is over 50 per cent in Wisconsin), the value of all livestock and livestock products sold in 1949 was 60.4, 70.9, and 88.8 per cent, respectively, of total sales. There was practically no change in the ratio of income from crops and livestock in Michigan between 1939 and 1949, but in the other two states there was a slight increase in the percentage of total income represented by livestock and livestock products.

Unlike the Middle Atlantic States, where most milk goes into daily consumption, the bulk of Dairyland's milk goes into manufactured products. Among other uses, it is converted into cheese, powdered and evaporated milk, and butter. In 1946 it was found that the major single outlet for Wisconsin milk was the manufacture of cheese. This took about 35 per cent of the total production. The amount of milk going into butter has been declining, especially in Wisconsin, but Minnesota is a very important producer of butter and continues to lead all other states in this industry.

Although dairying is the leading agricultural enterprise in this region, many crops are grown in various combinations. As men-

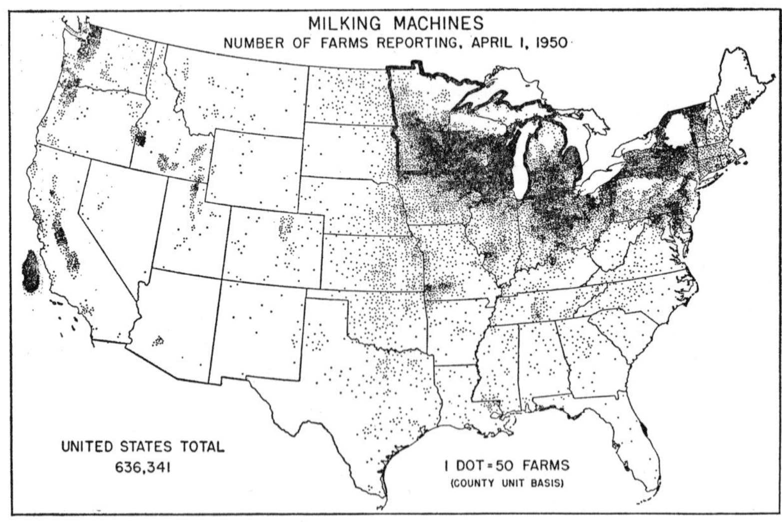

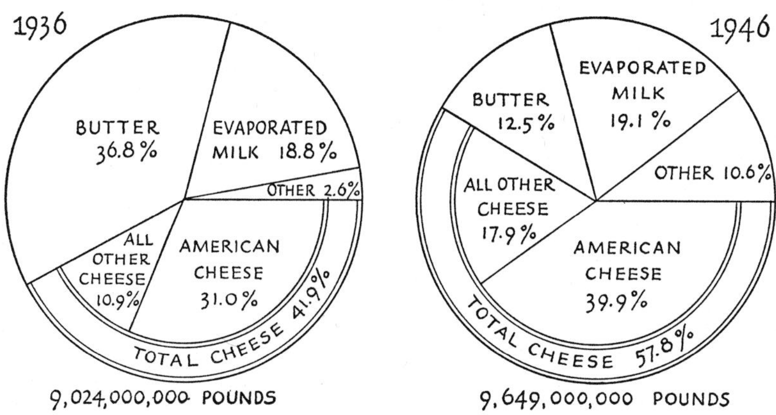

Utilization of Milk by Wisconsin Dairy Plants

From *A Century of Wisconsin Agriculture* (Wisconsin Crop and Livestock Reporting Service *Bulletin No. 290*), 69, Figure 85.

tioned earlier, this wide variation of land use and crop production, even within a fairly small geographical area, makes most generalizations about a larger region not only dangerous, but often erroneous. For example, while we speak of the Dairy Belt, there are sections within the area where dairying is of only minor or supplementary importance. The greatest amount of dairying in Minnesota is in the eastern half of the state. In the south and southwestern parts of the state there is a distinct corn-hog economy. Minnesota farmers sold over $188,000,000 worth of hogs and pigs in 1949, which was equal to the value of dairy products sold. In the northwest corner of the state wheat and flax are major crops. Minnesota, with 1,638,870 acres, ranked second only to North Dakota in flax acreage in 1949 and was first in production. Wheat brought a little over 5 per cent of the value of all crops sold. Minnesota also produces a large amount of barley, ranking third among all states in 1949. Potatoes are an important crop in the east central region and in the Red River Valley. In 1949 the state ranked sixth in acreage.

Moving eastward into Wisconsin, a similar pattern of diversity is present. Potatoes are important in the economy of central Wisconsin farmers, especially in Portage County. The state followed

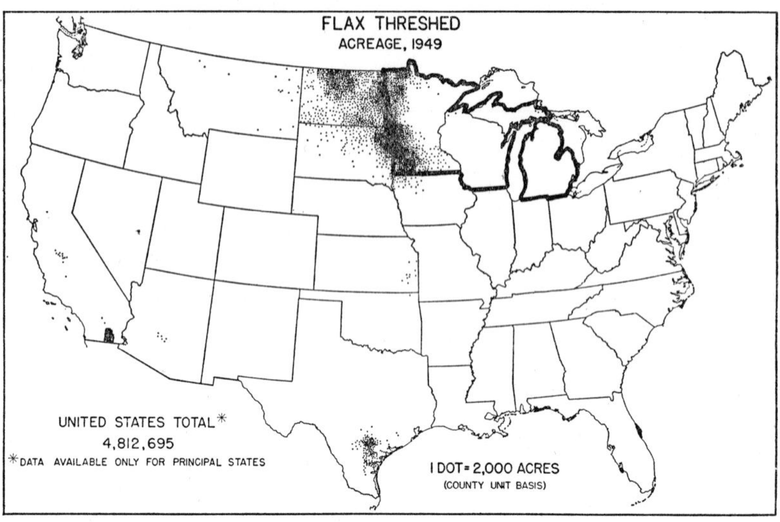

Minnesota in 1949 and was in seventh place in acreage, although it rated only eleventh in production. Tobacco is an old and significant crop in Dane and Vernon counties. Barley is grown in eastern Wisconsin, and is used mostly for malting. Other crops that play important roles in the agriculture of certain localities are sugar beets, soybeans, and buckwheat.

In the late nineteen forties, Wisconsin was the leading state in the nation in the production of vegetables for canning and processing. The most important vegetables grown for commercial purposes are sweet corn, green peas, tomatoes, lima beans, red beets, cucumbers, and snap beans. Wisconsin was by far the leading sweet corn state in 1949 with 93,788 acres. Minnesota was second with 64,113 acres. The main commercial fruit crops in Wisconsin are cranberries, cherries, strawberries and apples. Considering total farm income, fruit plays only a small part, but in some localities it accounts for a sizable part of the farm take.

Michigan agriculture is less dominated by the dairy and livestock industry than either Minnesota or Wisconsin. Cash crops make up a larger percentage of farm income, accounting for about 40 per cent of the value of all farm products sold. Hay, corn, and oats, in that order, occupy about 65 per cent of the cropland harvested. On the rest of Michigan farm land, a wide variety of crops are grown which contribute significantly to total farm income. The growing industrialization in Michigan since World War I has in-

TABLE 66.—*Value of all crops and livestock and livestock products sold, and per cent of all farm products sold represented by crops and by livestock and livestock products in Michigan, Wisconsin, and Minnesota, 1939–49.*

	Value of all crops sold		*Value of all livestock & livestock products sold*	
	1949	1939	1949	1939
Mich.	$184,669,069	$ 69,602,436	$285,911,779	$107,179,458
Wis.	80,678,121	31,202,200	679,287,651	205,944,897
Minn.	277,000,558	105,750,808	681,394,415	194,279,003

	Per cent of all farm products sold represented by sales of			
	Crops		*Livestock and livestock products*	
Mich.	39.0	39.2	60.4	60.3
Wis.	10.6	13.1	88.8	86.2
Minn.	28.8	35.1	70.9	64.5

Source: *United States Census of Agriculture, 1950,* II, 753.

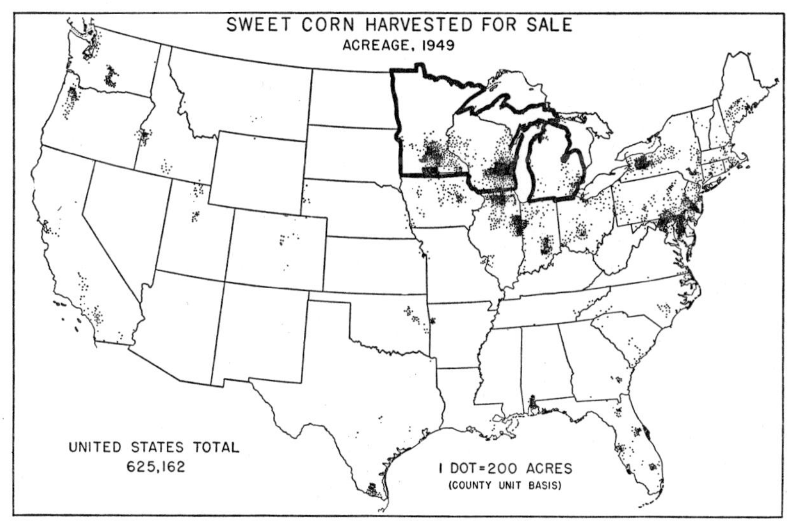

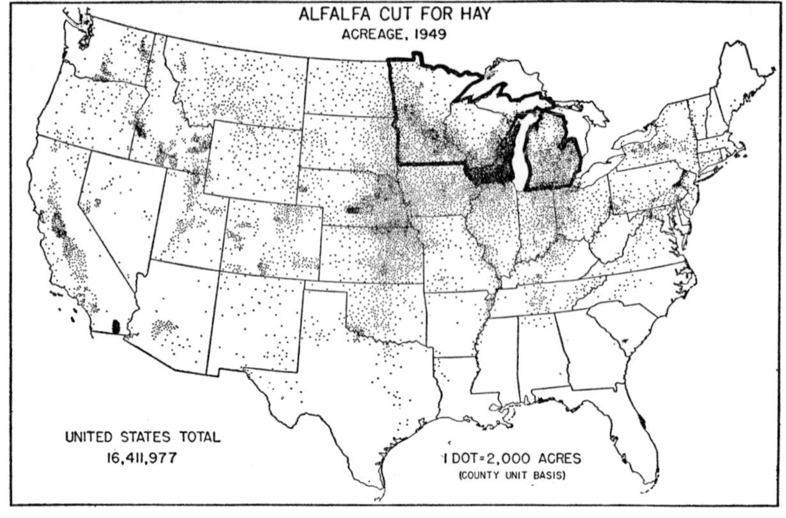

creased the markets not only for dairy products, but for meats, fruits, vegetables, eggs, and milk.

In 1949 Michigan had 16 per cent of her cropland in wheat and ranked thirteenth in production with over 31,000,000 bushels. Soybeans have become a major cash crop in some southern counties, and field beans are a very important crop in east central Michigan, especially in the vicinity of Huron County. In the Saginaw and Bay City area, sugar beets rank high and brought growers over $8,000,000 in 1949. Several sections of the state grow potatoes, with Montcalm County in the west central section an important center of production.

Along Lake Michigan, in the western part of the state, fruit crops are a prominent money-maker. The value of fruits, berries, and nuts sold in 1949 was over $30,000,000, or 16.6 per cent of all crops sold. In Berrien County, in the extreme southwest corner of the state, fruits and berries occupied more cropland in 1949 than any other crop. Apples are grown in that county and in Van Buren and Allegan counties, along Lake Michigan to the north. Farther north, in Oceana, Mason, and Grand Traverse counties, cherries are produced in large quantities. The 110,000,000 pounds harvested in 1949 far exceeded California's output. Southwestern

Michigan also has a strong strawberry and grape industry. The 1950 census showed that Michigan ranked seventh in strawberry acreage, and only New York and California had more grapevines. Vegetables, including tomatoes and sweet corn, are important in the Michigan farm economy, but they brought only $17,000,000 in 1949, little more than half as much as the fruit crop. Agriculture, on the whole, presents an unusually well-balanced picture in Michigan.

TABLE 67.—*Percentage of commercial farms by economic class in Michigan, Wisconsin, and Minnesota, 1949.**

	Per cent of farms considered commercial	*Economic class* I	*II*	*III*	*IV*	*V*	*VI*
Mich.	68.7	0.9	5.7	19.6	30.8	28.7	14.3
Wis.	86.5	0.7	7.8	30.3	35.7	18.8	6.6
Minn.	87.8	1.4	13.1	33.2	28.9	16.3	7.1

Source: *United States Census of Agriculture, 1950,* II, 1133.

* See Table 5 for basis of classification.

So far we have said nothing about poultry, but any consideration of the Dairy Belt cannot ignore this very important source of income. In 1949 Minnesota farmers sold 230,323,712 dozen eggs, and sales of poultry and poultry products totaled $122,338,-260. Only Iowa sold more eggs than Minnesota. Wisconsin and Michigan farmers realized $54,496,142 and $41,120,072 respectively, from their poultry and poultry products.

Dominant though dairying is and immense though its contribution to the national product, still it can be argued that this region needs even more of the same. Outside of the muck lands around the lakes, most of the soils in this glaciated region are thin, not too rich, and subject to erosion. Many an acre now put into row crops would be more resistant to erosion and offer a greater long-term return if it were in grass or forage.

Curiously enough, some of the land now used for dairying could better be utilized for another purpose. The Upper Peninsula of Michigan and the cutover areas of Wisconsin and Minnesota were ordained to be tree lands and should be put back into this use as rapidly as possible. Happily, it can now be reported, when it could not have been several years ago, that a large acreage has already been reforested, and more land is being replanted in trees each year. It is to be hoped that individual or community selfishness will not hold up this movement, for, while a good start has been made, there are still thousands of acres which should be taken out of starve-to-death stump farms and put into trees.

During and since World War II, there has been a marked change everywhere in the use of dairy products that has also affected the subject area. Indeed, this region, like most of American agriculture, is faced with pressing problems. In prewar years, large sums of money were expended to find uses, other than fluid consumption, for milk. The success of such organizations as Kraft in creating a market for cheese spreads, the promotion of American-made European types of cheeses, the coming of powdered skim milk, ice cream mixes, pastry mixes, and similar products were hailed with satisfaction by dairymen. But surpluses and nervous markets were still the rule rather than the exception. When an Italian company announced it could make fabrics from milk, great was the interest. Milk into plastics was another hopeful sign. The Eastern Regional Research Laboratory devoted the bulk of its attention to finding nonfood uses for milk, extending all the way to its utilization as a constituent of paint and unbreakable bottles.

During World War II, the demand for milk was so heavy that a production goal of over 120,000,000,000 pounds was set, when 105,000,000,000 pounds was about the top we could hope to use in prewar days. Dairymen everywhere shuddered when they looked ahead to the postwar years with a supposed 15,000,000,000 pound surplus hanging over their market. Those years came, and for a while demand kept up with supply. And the backbone of that demand was for fluid milk, the form in which the producer gets the greatest money return.

This phenomenon has considerably changed the thinking of the dairy industry, and for a time it allayed the worst fears of the milk producers. Part of the new demand, of course, came from the huge wartime crop of babies. We have something over 12,000,000 more mouths to feed, and the bulk of the increase is in the younger years where milk consumption is highest. But how long will the baby boom last? Will the birth rate again tumble and the trend to an average older-aged population take precedence? As of now, the baby crop seems fairly stable at better than 2,000,000 a year.

Dairymen hope that, should the baby crop ever thin out, a nutritionally wiser people will keep milk and dairy products high on their diet priority list. It would seem that as long as employment remains up this preference will obtain. However, in the past, when national income went down, milk consumption followed. Nutrition did not figure in the choice. Comparative prices for foodstuffs did. And dairy prices have seemed higher to the housewife than other foods on a bulk basis, despite the educational efforts of the nutritionists.

An example of how price instead of nutrition affects the buying decision was seen after World War II. A dozen eggs will provide approximately 15 per cent more protein, significantly more calcium, phosphorus, and iron, and a higher content of riboflavin than a pound of sirloin, yet when beefsteak was a dollar a pound and eggs were around a dollar a dozen retail, we again saw the operation of an old phenomenon. Housewives bought fewer eggs when the price passed the dollar mark, yet enough of them kept buying steak to support an even better price than a dollar a pound.

In a time of declining national income, at what point in the price scale will the housewife decide she can no longer afford fluid milk? In prewar days, a rise of a cent a quart in the retail price of milk in New York City was almost certain to bring a drop in consumption just about equal to the price rise. After World War II, however, milk went to an all-time high of twenty-five cents a quart, and sometimes slightly more, and there have been no significant changes in total consumption as the price climbed. Farmers with long memories, however, were uneasy, even though consumption figures were reassuring. By the mid-nineteen fifties, is was evident that consumption was not keeping up with production. Surpluses of dairy products plagued both farmers and the federal government.

Butter is the key to the price structure of dairy products, and butter today has only about 50 per cent of the per capita acceptance it had in the nineteen twenties. In 1926 the average per capita consumption of butter among civilians was 18.4 pounds; by 1951 it had declined to only 9.7 pounds. At the same time that butter was pricing itself out of a market, the soybean and cottonseed growers were putting on their biggest drive to remove the color ban on margarine. Not only has this drive been quite successful, but people's tastes have become increasingly educated to margarine instead of butter. For example, when the price of butter was lowered considerably in the spring of 1954, a reporter in Oklahoma City interviewed a number of housewives in a supermarket. He asked several women if, because of lower butter prices, they would buy more butter. It was especially significant to observe that some of the younger housewives said they would not buy butter even if it were fully as cheap as margarine. They said they did not "like" the taste of creamery butter.

One encouraging trend for dairymen, however, is the increased consumption of other dairy products. And, as previously shown, more and more of Dairyland's milk is being diverted to manufactured products other than butter. Consumption of cheese, condensed and evaporated milk, and ice cream has been climbing steadily upward. Cheese consumption averaged only 4.6 pounds per person in 1926; it was 7.2 pounds in 1951. Ice cream consumption grew from 9.1 pounds to 16.1 pounds between 1926 and 1951; for condensed and evaporated milk the rise was from 11.7 pounds to 18.1 pounds per person. But even with these increases, consumption is not keeping up with current and potential production. Undoubtedly, the government price-support program has saved many dairymen from hard times and possible bankruptcy.

Producer understanding of the marketing situation is probably back of the strange situation that, with an all-time high in current demand, the number of dairy cows is decreasing. Yet production is holding up. This made 1948 the first year in which the national average of per cow production passed the 5,000-pound mark, and by 1950 the average had grown to 5,314 pounds. Obviously, stricter culling, artificial insemination, and better feeding practices are raising milk-cow efficiency. Wisconsin milk cows averaged 6,850 pounds of milk in 1950.

This rise in efficiency can be translated as a cut in costs. But as feed costs are also in the stratosphere, it is probable that the dairyman is no more than holding his own. If a drop in the wholesale price of milk were not at once joined with a drop in feed prices, dairying would be facing bankruptcy if present practices were maintained.

In this qualifier may lie the future of Dairyland and the biggest reason that this area will not see a major shift in enterprise. As long ago as the early nineteen twenties, a dairyman here and there, particularly in Wisconsin, began to experiment with an all-forage feeding program. Now the farm magazines are showing ever more attention to such examples.

The January, 1948, issue of *Capper's Farmer,* for example, tells the story of a Buffalo County, Wisconsin, farmer who has maintained an all-forage program since 1932. His 546-acre farm made $13,000 in milk and $4,000 in livestock sales in 1946. For a farm of this size in that area, the figures, as gross income, are not impressive. But when the information is added that not a dollar was spent for corn or protein and only twenty-seven man-days of help were hired, then the picture is entirely different.

The farm is entirely grassed down. At first, native grasses and bluegrass were the crops. With time and experience, however, the owner changed slowly to taller grasses. Now, brome, alfalfa, and ladino dominate the fields. If weather is right for haying, the crop goes in the mow. When another cutting is ready and the weather is not right, the crop goes in the silo. The cattle are grazed on rotation pastures as much of the year as is suitable. The ensilage from high-protein grasses keeps up the winter milk production, while clean, bright hay stops any tendency to scour. The owner claims mastitis is much less of a problem with him now than when he was feeding corn, and credits a higher calf crop and thriftier calves to his grass program.

It will be a long time before the arguments that you cannot make milk economically and efficiently without concentrates are beaten down. A grass-feeding program flies in the face of everything the land grant colleges have been teaching for a generation. It is against every bit of propaganda the feed industry can muster. It violates the precepts in almost all the livestock books. Yet a cow is naturally a grass-feeding animal. Concentrates are something that man introduced, and even when they are fed, 70 per cent of a cow's output comes from forage.

Quite apart from theories on feeding, or mountains of statistics, a drop in milk prices may find this all-grass economy the one thing that can keep dairying a going concern. It is evident that distribution costs have gone up, probably never to come down. Today such costs are taking a larger share of the milk dollar than ever before in history. Labor constitutes the large part of distribution costs, and milk-distributing labor is highly organized. Even in a depression, it is not likely there will be an important change downward. That leaves only one thing for the producer to do—cut costs drastically.

A drastic cut means hired labor must go. It means fewer acres in row crops, and, in turn, fewer cows. It means bought feed must be curtailed sharply. But, as the example above shows, if the cows graze the fields, the number of man-days needed drops significantly. The new hay machinery, the forage chopper-harvester, elevators, and self-feeders suggest further savings in labor. It is not at all improbable, therefore, that at least part of Dairyland will show a trend toward an all-grass economy in the future when, and if, full national prosperity should languish somewhat.

From the standpoint of conservation and safeguarding the national soil heritage, such a change is all to the good. Grasslanding is as near perfection in conservation as can be hoped for, providing the grasslands are managed properly. This means mowing, planting proper varieties, draining, rotating pastures, and not overgrazing. Manure distribution and plant feeding are necessities.

This area of the nation should probably be given credit for sticking closest to the principles of ecology. Here we have the proper setting for the chosen animals, and much of the land planted in the proper crop. Dairyland should survive any untoward economic blow better than many of the other more vulnerable sections of the country. As debt is low, savings high, and land inflation not too far out of line, the future looks moderately fair, the pattern stable as it is.

CHAPTER 9

The Western Prairies and High Plains: American Granary

(Northwest Texas, Western Oklahoma, Kansas, Nebraska, South and North Dakota, and Eastern Montana)

In many ways, this is one of the most fabulous farming regions in the world. "American Granary" is a good description of the vast expanse of country from the Canadian border southward to the Texas Panhandle and western Oklahoma. It has been commonly called the Wheat Belt, and well it might be. The states under consideration produced over half of the wheat grown in the entire United States in 1949. Kansas and North Dakota alone usually grow between a third and a fourth of the total crop. Responding magnificently in wartime, this area has produced wheat for both domestic and foreign needs. In peacetime the vast output has swelled elevators and terminals and created surplus problems which have plagued economists and politicians alike. People who have never actually seen the miles after miles of waving grain cannot truly feel or understand the role which this great crop plays in the agricultural economy of the region.

At one time or another, many kinds of farming have been tried in this region of low rainfall and easily wind-blown soil. When the

GENERAL PATTERN OF GREAT SOIL GROUPS

The Wheat Belt

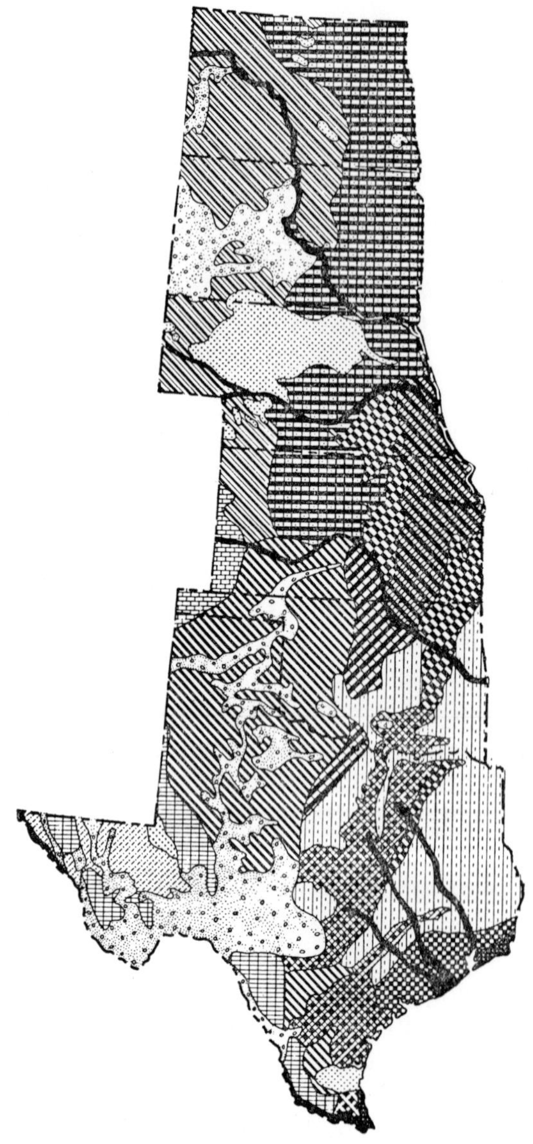

PODZOL SOILS

Light-colored leached soils of cool, hu
forested regions.

RED AND YELLOW PODZOLIC SOILS

Red or yellow leached soils of warm-tempe
humid forested regions.

PRAIRIE SOILS

Very dark brown soils of cool and tempe
relatively humid grasslands.

REDDISH PRAIRIE SOILS

Dark reddish-brown soils of warm-temp
relatively humid grasslands.

land was first settled after the Civil War, a few unnaturally wet years gave hope that a type of farming similar to that in the humid areas farther east could be practiced. Then came years of more normal precipitation (generally less than twenty-two inches west of the 98th meridian) which showed the error of this judgment. Indeed, a major handicap to agriculture in the Great Plains part of this area, roughly between the 100th meridian and the Rocky Mountains, is its semiaridity. The Great Plains is not a desert or even a subhumid region. It is semiarid, meaning that in some years there may be plenty of rain to make a crop, while in others drought may destroy all efforts at farming. It is the uncertainty of the rainfall which plays havoc with farmers in so much of the Wheat Belt.

Eventually it was found that, in the Great Plains part of the Wheat Belt, farming, to be successful, must take advantage of the meager rainfall which falls mostly from April to June. This meant that drought-resistant crops which matured early and quickly were necessary. Fresh hope was engendered by a supposedly new technique of "dry farming" which was successful mostly for grains. Before long, the best agricultural use of these lands, outside of grass, was found in grain, principally in wheat. Although they

RNOZEM SOILS
Dark-brown to nearly black soils of cool and temperate, subhumid grasslands.

STNUT SOILS
Dark-brown soils of cool and temperate, subhumid to semiarid grasslands.

DISH CHESTNUT SOILS
Dark reddish-brown soils of warm-temperate, semiarid regions under mixed shrub and grass vegetation.

WN SOILS
Brown soils of cool and temperate, semiarid grasslands.

DISH BROWN SOILS
Reddish-brown soils of warm-temperate to hot, semiarid to arid regions, under mixed shrub and grass vegetation.

DESERT SOILS
Light reddish-brown soils of warm-temperate to hot, arid regions, under shrub vegetation.

IOSOLS
Soils with strongly leached surface horizons over claypans on nearly flat land in cool to warm, humid to subhumid regions, under grass or forest vegetation.

RENDZINA SOILS

Dark grayish-brown to black soils developed from soft limy materials in cool to warm, humid to subhumid regions, mostly under grass vegetation.

WIESENBÖDEN (1), GROUND WATER PODZOL (2), AND HALF-BOG SOILS (3)
(1) Dark-brown to black soils developed with poor drainage under grasses in humid and subhumid regions.
(2) Gray sandy soils with brown cemented sandy subsoils developed under forests from nearly level imperfectly drained sand in humid regions.
(3) Poorly drained, shallow, dark peaty or mucky soils underlain by gray mineral soil, in humid regions, under swamp-forests.

BOG SOILS

Poorly drained dark peat or muck soils underlain by peat, mostly in humid regions, under swamp or marsh types of vegetation.

SANDS (DRY)
Very sandy soils.

LITHOSOLS AND SHALLOW SOILS (ARID-SUBHUMID)
Shallow soils consisting largely of an imperfectly weathered mass of rock fragments, largely but not exclusively on steep slopes.

ALLUVIAL SOILS

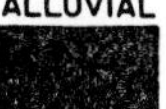

Soils developing from recently deposited alluvium that have had little or no modification by processes of soil formation.

TABLE 68.—*Number of farms in the Wheat Belt, 1880–1950.*

	1950	1940	1930	1920	1910	1900	1880
Mont.	35,085	41,823	47,495	57,677	26,214	13,370	1,519
N. D.	65,401	73,962	77,975	77,690	74,360	45,332	3,790
S. D.	66,452	72,454	83,157	74,637	77,644	52,622	13,645
Nebr.	107,183	121,062	129,458	124,417	129,678	121,525	63,387
Kans.	131,394	156,327	166,042	165,286	177,841	173,098	138,561
Okla.	142,246	179,687	203,866	191,988	190,192	108,000*	——
Tex.	331,567	418,002	495,489	436,033	417,770	352,190	174,184

Source: *United States Census of Agriculture, 1950,* II, 52–55.

* Oklahoma and Indian territories.

helped, the dry-farming techniques and the introduction of more drought-resistant varieties of wheat did not create a very stable agriculture. There were more heartaches, more bankruptcies, more droughts, and more windstorms, until the system of summer fallowing was evolved that finally fixed wheat as the major crop in this area and made biennial cropping almost mandatory in many parts of it.

Before World War II this system was in wide use. Only one half of the cropland was planted in any one year. The other half was worked, usually with discs and a rodweeder, to keep down the weed population, but no crop was planted. Thus part of the moisture of that year was stored for next year's crop. In the Great Plains it has been possible to store from 20 to 25 per cent of the precipitation in this manner. North Dakota had 4,581,209 acres, Montana 4,224,669, and Kansas 3,995,639 acres of cultivated summer fallow in 1949.

After the tragedy of the Dust Bowl in the nineteen thirties, a technique called trash or stubble mulching came into use. After the crop is harvested the straw is worked into the land, but not covered. A portion is left sticking from the ground or on top of it to act as a wind deterrent and a moisture retainer. Again, the only working this land is given in the fallow year is for the purpose of controlling weeds. The favored tool is a duckfoot, of which there are innumerable variations. The type used is determined by individual preference, but all have one characteristic in common, however, in that they do not turn the soil, but stir it under the surface as they cut the weeds. These fairly modern techniques seem to permit, for the first time, a permanent agriculture in the Great Plains. Droughts will come when even fallowing will not make a very good crop. Wet years will come, however, to make up for the dry ones. Over the longer term, the farmer can expect a fair return if prices are reasonable—and if he holds his land in place. But some of this land cannot be held in place once it is broken.

Despite the natural handicaps of much of the Wheat Belt, it is a fabulous farm. It has made men rich almost overnight. Some of the time, like the periods of World War I and II, the coincidence of sufficient rainfall and high prices prevailed. The result was quick and sudden wealth for many who had enough acres to exploit. It has, of course, also made paupers when these favorable conditions did not exist.

The Wheat Belt extends roughly from Wichita Falls, Texas, in the south to the Canadian border in the north, but, like the Cotton Belt, it is not a contiguous or continuous area. In 1949 the average percentage of cropland acres in wheat for the states under consideration was nearly 37 per cent. However, it varied from a low of 20 per cent in Texas to 62 and 50 per cent, respectively, in Kansas and North Dakota. Most of the wheat is grown in the Texas Panhandle, western and northwestern Oklahoma, the western two-

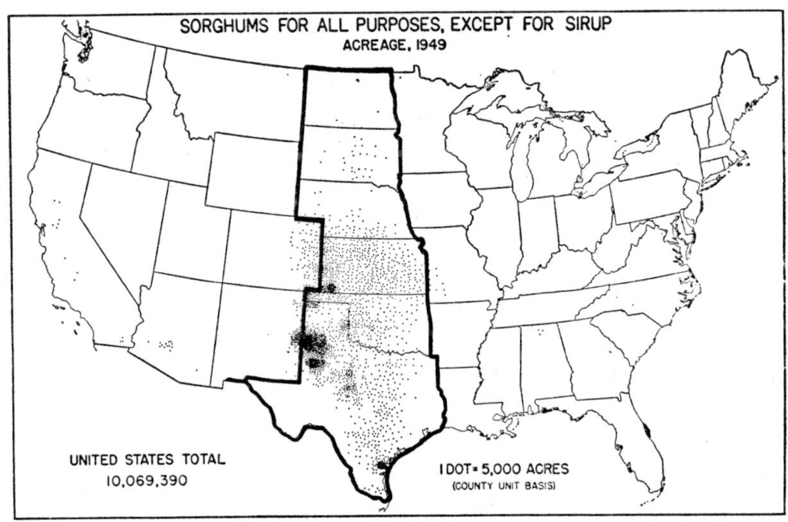

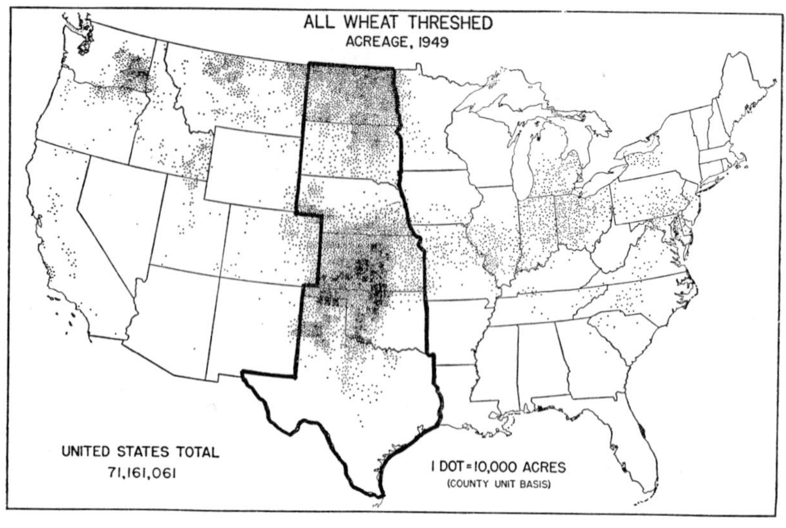

thirds of Kansas, southern and southwestern Nebraska, north central South Dakota, all of North Dakota, and northeastern Montana. There are large areas in these states in which little or no wheat is grown. For example, there is very little wheat in southeastern South Dakota, eastern Nebraska, the Sand Hills area of Nebraska, the Flint Hills of Kansas, and eastern Oklahoma. In Texas most of the wheat is raised north and west of a line from Wichita Falls to Abilene.

Kansas, of course, is the premier wheat state. As one thinks of Iowa and corn, Wisconsin and dairying, Delaware and broilers, Mississippi and cotton, he automatically thinks of Kansas and wheat. As has been noted, Kansas had over 62 per cent of her cropland in wheat in 1949, and this grain ranked as the number one crop acreage-wise in all but twenty-four counties. The state had 13,397,688 acres of wheat and harvested 145,657,700 bushels, which was nearly one-fifth of the acreage and over one-seventh of the nation's entire production. The total value of Kansas' wheat crop in 1949 was $270,387,303, or 54.6 per cent of the value of all crops in the state. Money from wheat brought nearly 75 per cent of the value of all crops sold.

North Dakota ranks second in wheat production, commonly

TABLE 69.—*Number of acres of wheat in the Wheat Belt, 1909–49.*

	1949	1939	1929	1919	1909
Mont.	4,647,789	3,054,876	4,418,588	1,698,531	258,377
N. D.	10,202,747	6,898,799	9,969,370	9,098,042	8,188,782
S. D.	3,927,575	2,098,282	3,539,320	3,891,468	3,217,255
Nebr.	3,902,764	3,144,171	3,699,967	4,294,156	2,662,918
Kans.	13,397,688	9,214,150	12,081,021	11,266,664	5,973,785
Okla.	6,265,789	4,158,230	4,575,558	4,702,280	1,169,420
Tex.	5,625,259	2,744,064	2,969,511	2,414,903	326,176

Source: *United States Census of Agriculture, 1950,* II, 556–57.

producing over 100,000,000 bushels. The average for the state from 1938 to 1948 was 134,000,000 bushels. The dominance of wheat in North Dakota can best be understood by considering that in 1949 this crop held first position in cropland harvested in every county except two. The value of wheat was about 52 per cent of the value of all crops, and over 40 per cent of the value of all farm products sold in the state. Wheat alone in North Dakota brought farmers more money than the sales of all livestock and livestock products.

TABLE 70.—*Number of bushels of wheat produced in the Wheat Belt, 1909–49.*

	1949	1939	1929	1919	1909
Mont.	52,516,438	40,349,690	40,558,049	7,799,647	6,251,945
N. D.	105,579,644	69,261,286	95,574,408	61,540,404	116,781,886
S. D.	30,462,570	17,592,727	34,044,975	31,086,995	47,059,590
Nebr.	52,599,446	34,676,159	53,867,855	57,843,598	47,685,745
Kans.	145,657,700	112,413,657	148,482,595	148,475,729	77,577,115
Okla.	78,682,555	58,492,919	51,184,128	65,761,843	14,008,334
Tex.	75,277,232	28,096,367	44,077,764	36,427,255	2,560,891

Source: *United States Census of Agriculture, 1950,* II, 549, 558.

After Kansas and North Dakota, wheat is of most relative importance in the agricultural economy of Montana. There over 50 per cent of the harvested cropland is usually in wheat, and in 1949 it made up 52.2 per cent of the value of all crops. However, Oklahoma customarily ranks third in production. Then comes Texas or Montana. The golden grain is by far the leading cash crop in Montana, North Dakota, Kansas, and Oklahoma. It is very important in South Dakota, Nebraska, and Texas. The most specialized cash-crop part of the region is North Dakota.

Agriculture in the Wheat Belt is characterized by its extensive nature, especially in the Great Plains. Farms are large and they are rapidly growing larger. The census of 1950 showed that the average acreage varied from 253 acres per farm in Oklahoma to 1,688 acres in Montana. The average size of farms in North and South Dakota was 629 and 674 acres, respectively. The startling thing, however, is the rapidity of the increase in size. The average farm in South Dakota was 130 acres larger in 1950 than ten years earlier, and 117 acres larger in North Dakota. One of the authors has watched this trend closely in east central South Dakota, where he was raised and where he still owns a farm. At first a farm would be sold to a neighbor or distant investor. For a while the buildings would stand vacant as mute testimony to the decreased number of farmers. Then gradually the buildings would be sold and torn down, or possibly moved to town, and the whole community took on a different look as fewer and fewer homesteads dotted the landscape.

The geography of most of this area requires large acreages for successful and profitable farming, and large-scale, highly mechanized operations are the order of the day. No other farming region

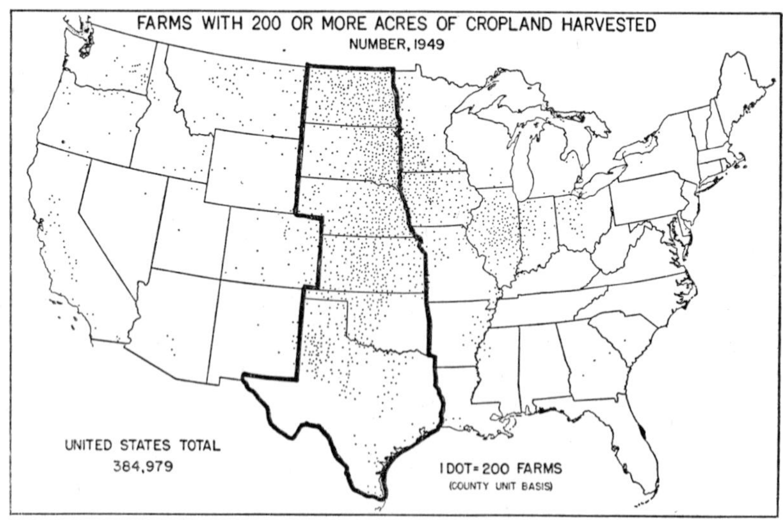

in the United States can boast of so many large farms on the basis of cropland harvested. Over 69 per cent of North Dakota's farms harvested 200 acres or more of cropland in 1949. It was 38.5, 56.3, 33.1, and 31.3 per cent, respectively, in Montana, South Dakota, Nebraska, and Kansas. But state-wide averages do not present the real picture. In the Texas Panhandle, where wheat is the main cash crop, 7,675 farms out of 12,202, or about 62 per cent, reported harvesting over 200 acres in 1949. For the state as a whole, only 13.6 per cent of the farms harvested such large acreages. The average size of the cash-grain farms in the wheat area of the Texas Panhandle was 956 acres in 1950. In Oklahoma the average size farm was 253 acres in 1949, but in the northwestern wheat counties

TABLE 71.—*Average size of farms (acres) in the Wheat Belt, 1880–1950.*

	1950	1940	1930	1920	1910	1900	1880
Mont.	1,688.7	1,110.7	940.3	608.1	516.7	885.9	267.1
N. D.	629.9	512.9	495.8	466.1	382.3	342.9	271.2
S. D.	674.0	544.8	438.6	464.1	335.1	362.4	203.2
Nebr.	442.9	391.1	345.4	339.4	297.8	246.1	156.9
Kans.	370.0	308.2	282.9	274.8	244.0	240.7	154.6
Okla.	253.1	193.7	165.8	166.8	151.7	212.9	——
Tex.	438.5	329.4	251.7	261.5	269.1	357.2	208.4

Source: *United States Census of Agriculture, 1950,* II, 799.

it was 653. Over 85 per cent of Kansas' wheat acreage is on farms of 260 acres or more, and in 1949 over 25 per cent of the wheat farms reporting actually harvested over 200 acres. It is difficult for people outside the region to understand the extensive operations so characteristic of the area.

Every aspect of production is highly mechanized. The horse is rapidly becoming nothing more than a curiosity on most specialized wheat farms. North and South Dakota, respectively, reported in 1950 that 89.3 and 84.8 per cent of their farms had tractors, the highest percentage among all the states. There are areas in Montana where they measure the size of a wheat farm by the number of tractors rather than by the number of acres. In 1950 there were 20,357 tractors on 10,043 farms in the Texas Panhandle, or a little

TABLE 72.—*Per cent of all farms with tractors in the Wheat Belt, 1920–50.*

	1950	1940	1930	1920
Mont.	77.4	47.6	36.0	11.9
N. D.	89.3	59.2	43.8	15.2
S. D.	84.8	55.1	37.2	16.3
Nebr.	81.7	53.4	29.3	8.3
Kans.	75.3	53.6	35.6	9.8
Okla.	50.4	22.9	11.4	3.0
Tex.	49.1	20.6	6.4	1.9

Source: *United States Census of Agriculture, 1950,* II, 226.

more than an average of two per farm. Many wheat farmers have three or four tractors. Over 50 per cent of North Dakota's farms (35,043 out of 64,401) had combines in 1950, and nearly 50 per cent of the farms in Kansas reported them. In addition, the percentage of Wheat Belt farms having motor trucks is high, amounting to 68.4 per cent in North Dakota.

With extensive acreages and a high degree of mechanization, investment per farm is heavy. For example, of 12,202 farms in the Texas Panhandle, 8,726 of which grew wheat in 1949, the average value of land and buildings per farm was $64,468. The average value of land and buildings per farm throughout Oklahoma was $13,010, but in the northwestern and panhandle counties it was $28,209, more than twice the state average. Add to this an invest-

TABLE 73.—*Value of land and buildings per acre for farms in the Wheat Belt, 1880–1950.*

	1950	1940	1930	1920	1910	1900	1880
Mont.	$16.86	$ 7.54	$11.81	$22.15	$18.58	$ 5.24	$ 7.97
N. D.	28.86	12.92	24.61	41.10	28.94	12.79	8.34
S. D.	31.30	12.80	35.24	71.40	38.63	11.54	4.99
Nebr.	57.62	24.03	55.81	87.91	46.95	19.31	10.65
Kans.	65.80	29.51	48.56	62.30	40.05	15.45	10.98
Okla.	51.42	23.88	36.78	42.68	25.60	7.43*	——
Tex.	46.21	18.81	28.85	32.45	16.39	5.50	4.70

Source: *United States Census of Agriculture, 1950,* II, 52–55.

* Oklahoma and Indian territories.

ment of from $10,000 to $30,000 for machinery and equipment and it becomes clear that farming in this region is big business.

Averages, however, do not present as clear a picture as one or two actual farm situations. A friend of one of the authors who farms in north central South Dakota customarily raised around 300 acres of wheat before the acreage restriction programs of 1954 and 1955. He usually had a total of between 600 and 700 acres of cropland, including hay. He owns three tractors, a truck, a self-propelled combine, plus a long list of other machines and implements. His total investment in machinery in 1954 was a little over $20,000. Another friend near St. John, in west central Kansas, usually farms about 285 acres, of which around 170 acres was in wheat before acreage was cut back in 1954. He has about $8,500 invested in machinery. Most operators in this region who farm 300 acres or more will have at least $10,000 tied up in farm equipment.

Because of the heavy investment required and the forced decline in wheat acreage, some farmers are finding it uneconomical to own a combine. Wheat producers in some areas prefer to hire a custom operator. It is not uncommon to see a custom machine in the field beside one owned by the farmer. Some observers believe that when the older combines wear out farmers will not replace them, but will depend even more on custom operators. This will cut down on the heavy investment in machinery, but, in any event, many farms at the present time have a capitalization of from $50,000 to $100,000, or more.

Although wheat gives the region its name, the agricultural economy of many areas within the states under consideration is dominated by other crops or by livestock. In Nebraska corn is the major crop. In both eastern Nebraska and southeastern South Dakota the predominantly corn-hog economy properly places the area within the Corn Belt. Northeastern Kansas also has a large corn acreage. Income from the sale of hogs in Nebraska was over $125,000,000 in 1949, which was about 20 per cent more than the value of the wheat crop. In 1952 hogs brought Nebraska farmers 16 per cent and wheat 14.4 per cent of their cash income. Soybean acreage has been growing significantly in this section, too, but the greatest expansion of soybeans in these states has occurred in eastern Kansas. Farmers there planted only 11,305 acres in 1939, but this had jumped to 703,000 by 1952. Oats are an important feed crop, especially in eastern Nebraska and southeastern South Dakota. North Dakota is a leading flax producer, growing 1,775,884 acres and over 12,000,000 bushels in 1949. In that year it ranked second in production, being exceeded only by Minnesota. South Dakota is also a heavy flax producer, ranking third.

There are areas of irrigated agriculture which cannot be ignored in any discussion of this region. In 1948 over 974,000 acres were irrigated in Nebraska, more than were irrigated in New Mexico or Washington. By 1953 Nebraska farmers were irrigating 1,218,385 acres, an increase of 25 per cent in five years. One of the most startling developments has been the tremendous increase in deep-well irrigation. There were 9,718 irrigation wells in the state at the end of 1953, and more were drilled in 1954. Acreage irrigated by well water increased from 392,980 in 1948 to 587,695 in 1953, or nearly 50 per cent of the total acreage irrigated. The main irrigated crops on an acreage basis are corn, alfalfa, dry beans, sugar beets, and potatoes, in that order. One of the nation's leading sugar beet centers is in Scotts Bluff County and parts of Sioux, Box Butte, and Morrill counties along the Platte River in western Nebraska. Potatoes are also an important crop there. Scotts Bluff County produced 3,828,500 bushels in 1952. McKenzie County in western North Dakota has considerable irrigated agriculture, and South Dakota has a small irrigated area in the western part of the state around Belle Fourche. Irrigation is expanding along the Arkansas River in Kansas. In southwestern Oklahoma, especially in Jackson and Harmon counties, there has been a surprising growth of irrigated farming in the last ten or fifteen years, and by 1954 some 70,000 acres were being irrigated. Harmon County had only 13 irrigated farms in 1949, but by 1954 the total had grown to about 220. Water is supplied mainly from deep wells. In Jackson County, to the east, water comes from the Lugert Dam on the Red River, although a scarcity of water has deterred operations there. On these irrigated acreages fine crops of cotton, wheat, grain sorghums, alfalfa, and potatoes are raised. Of course, the greatest irrigated region in the Southwest is in the High Plains of West Texas around

Lubbock. In 1949 there were about 3,300,000 acres in irrigated farms in that region. The water comes from deep wells and is used heavily in the irrigation of cotton.

Because of the importance of the livestock industry in the Wheat Belt, hay occupies a large percentage of the harvested cropland, especially from Kansas northward. The little town of Yates Center in east central Kansas boasts of being the hay capital of the world. Yet much more hay is harvested in Nebraska, and usually in South Dakota. The four states of Kansas, Nebraska, and North and South Dakota cut 14,453,044 acres of hay in 1949, excluding specified annual legumes and sorghum hay. South Dakota had 25 per cent of her cropland in hay, and Nebraska 24 per cent. The Dakotas and Nebraska are the principal producers of wild hay, and Nebraska was surpassed only by Wisconsin and California in the production of alfalfa. This crop is also rapidly expanding in parts of Kansas.

No discussion of agriculture in the Wheat Belt would be meaningful without considering the tremendous livestock industry. The Great Plains part of this region is one of the greatest grazing areas in the world. North of the Platte River both short grasses and midgrasses abound, including wheat and needle grasses. Between the

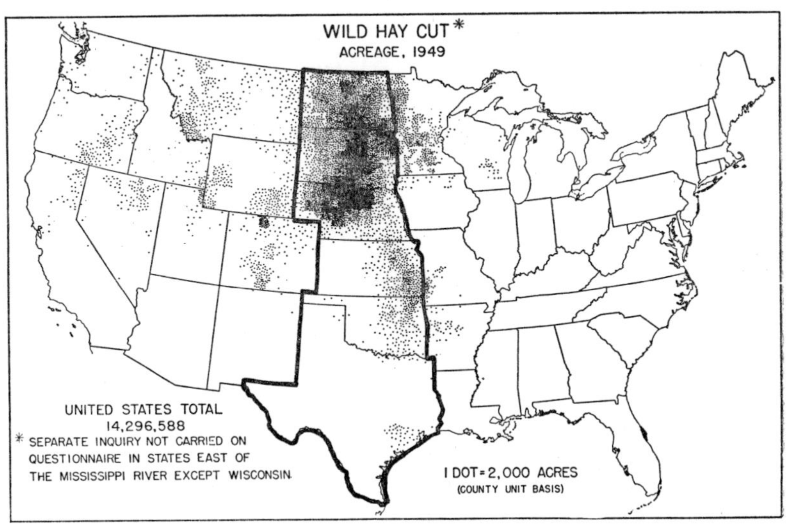

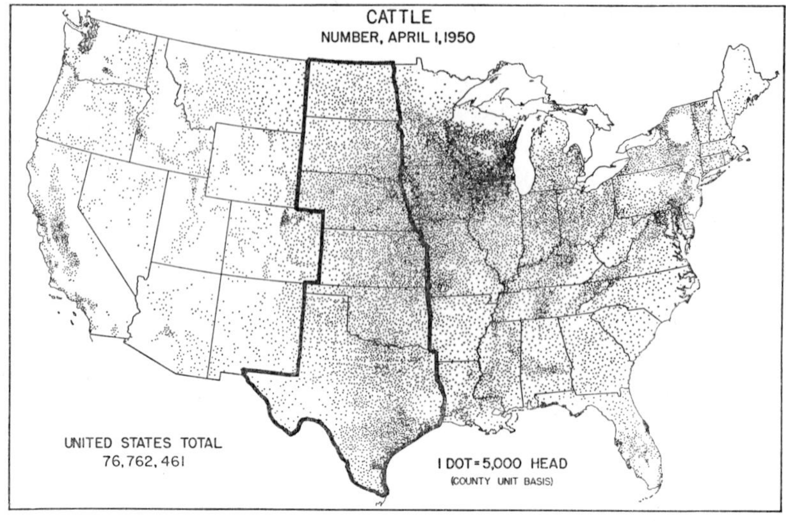

Niobrara and Platte rivers in northwestern Nebraska is the fabulous Sand Hills country, a cattlemen's paradise, a sort of biological island where tall grasses predominate. Farther south in the Central Plains the short grasses (buffalograss and some of the gramas) are most characteristic. (The vast ranching empire of Central and West Texas is considered in the following chapter.)

If Nebraska cattlemen can boast of their range in the Sand Hills, ranchers in east central Kansas have the wonderful bluestem pastures of the Flint Hills. This area extends southward into northeastern Oklahoma, where the famous Osage ranching country is located. In 1952 Nebraska and Kansas ranked third and fourth in the number of cattle, being exceeded only by Texas and Iowa. Together, Kansas and Nebraska had 8,987,000 head of cattle, a few more than all the states of Montana, Idaho, Wyoming, Colorado, New Mexico, Arizona, Utah, and Nevada combined. Cherry County, Nebraska, reported 291,960 cattle in 1952 and Custer County, in the same area, had 187,180. In Kansas, east and northeast of Wichita, the famous long-grass, bluestem pastures of the Flint Hills make up another great cattle country. A twelve-county area there reported 612,888 head in 1950, more than either Utah or Nevada. Osage County of northeastern Oklahoma, a part of this same bluestem region, reported 113,839 head of cattle in 1950, putting it among the top cattle counties in the nation. The western parts of Oklahoma and Kansas have heavy cattle populations, for most of the wheat farmers in that area also run cattle, and a wonderful ranching area exists in the Arbuckle Mountain region of south central Oklahoma. Despite the predominance of wheat in Kansas, farmers there sold nearly 2,000,000 head of cattle and calves in 1949, which brought a total of $277,000,000, slightly more than the value of the wheat crop. In Nebraska the sale of cattle and calves brought farmers 40.3 per cent of their cash income in 1952.

This area is not only a great producer of stock cattle, but three of the states, South Dakota, Nebraska, and Kansas, finish thousands of head in feed lots. No one can travel through eastern Nebraska, for example, and not be impressed with the great number of cattle on feed. On January 1, 1952, Nebraska farmers had 522,000 head in feed lots, ranking behind only Iowa as a feeding state. At the same time, Kansas and South Dakota had 265,000 and 198,000 head, respectively, on feed. Lamb feeding is also an important aspect of the livestock industry. Kansas and Nebraska both rank high in the number of lambs and sheep in feed lots. In fact, Nebraska with some 632,000 head, exceeded all other states in the lamb-feeding enterprise in 1952.

The value of farm products sold in the Great Plains States emphasizes the importance of the livestock industry in the agricultural economy of the region. In Montana, South Dakota, Nebraska, and Kansas, the value of livestock and livestock products made up 58.6, 71.4, 66.6, and 57.1 per cent, respectively, of the value of all farm products sold in 1949. Oklahoma farmers also usually get over 50 per cent of their income from livestock, but the figure dropped to about 46 per cent in 1949. In the over-all picture of the region, cattle and wheat predominate. Sales of cattle and calves in the Dakotas, Nebraska, Kansas, and Oklahoma brought a total of $953,000,000 in 1949, and the wheat sold amounted to about $675,000,000. The total value of farm products sold in these five states was approximately $2,846,000,000, and cattle and wheat brought about $1,628,000,000, or around 57 per cent of the total.

TABLE 74.—*Value of farm products sold in the Wheat Belt, 1939–49, and the per cent represented by crops and by livestock and livestock products.*

	Value of farm products sold		*Per cent of value of farm products sold*			
			Crops		*Livestock and livestock prod.*	
	1949	1939	1949	1939	1949	1939
Mont.	$ 279,058,735	$ 84,076,381	41.1	46.8	58.6	53.0
N. D.	400,822,179	100,401,313	66.3	61.0	33.7	38.9
S. D.	430,399,867	96,192,307	28.5	34.2	71.4	65.7
Nebr.	779,521,289	192,038,981	33.4	32.0	66.6	68.0
Kans.	764,728,153	203,517,425	42.9	42.7	57.1	57.2
Okla.	471,002,370	145,844,771	54.1	52.8	45.8	47.0
Tex.	1,753,052,010	439,063,949	64.7	48.8	35.1	50.9

Source: *United States Census of Agriculture, 1950,* II, 754.

Dairy products are also an important source of farm income in the Wheat States, especially in the eastern part, where most of the milking is done. Milk and cream brought Oklahoma, Kansas, Nebraska, and Dakota farmers over $164,000,000 in 1949. Dairying, however, is mostly a sideline enterprise. Farmers keep only a few cows for milk, less than ten in most cases, and they are largely dual-purpose animals suitable for both milk and beef production. In the Dakotas and Nebraska, dairying is primarily concerned with the sale of farm-separated cream. The relatively sparse population limits the demand for whole milk. In 1952 the Dakotas, Nebraska, and Kansas produced about 15 per cent of the creamery butter in the United States. But in Kansas and Oklahoma, farmers sell less cream and more whole milk. Cream represented only 35 per cent of the value of dairy products sold in Kansas in 1952.

It is not likely that dairying will increase much in this section. The number of milk cows has been declining and is much below what it was in the nineteen thirties. So long as conditions are favorable to the production of beef and grains, the decline in dairying is likely to continue. An extended period of unfavorable prices, however, would probably encourage more dairying in these states, as it did in the depression-ridden thirties. In some local areas of this region, farmers who had practically stopped milking altogether during the high-price period of World War II and thereafter were resuming this enterprise in 1953 and 1954, when beef-cattle prices fell so drastically.

Today, many farmers in the Wheat Belt States are fabulously prosperous. Buicks and Chryslers, and sometimes Cadillacs, have replaced many of the Fords and Chevrolets on the main streets of towns all the way from Amarillo to Grand Forks. Of the commercial farmers in North and South Dakota, Nebraska, and Kansas, 15.1, 16.9, 18.6, and 15.6 per cent, respectively, sold products valued at above $10,000 in 1949. The years after 1940 saw a long period of favorable prices and good crops. The banking position was sound and remains so today. Farm-mortgage debt has been cut down materially. In Kansas the decrease was from $284,000,000 in 1940 to $143,000,000 in 1948, or a drop of about 50 per cent. The decline was 54, 50, and 45 per cent, respectively, in Nebraska, North Dakota, and South Dakota in the same period. And even though most farm prices dropped below parity in the middle fifties, many farmers continued in comfortable circumstances. But what of the future—both of the land and of prices?

Despite the terrible lesson of the Dust Bowl, and despite the fact that history shows droughts and windstorms to be the natural recurring phenomena of this region, and even though in the memories of many living men the plow-up of the Plains after World War I is still bitterly vivid, millions of acres of too thin grassland

TABLE 75.—*Per cent of commercial farms by economic class in the Wheat Belt, 1949.**

	Per cent of total farms considered commercial	*Economic class* I	*II*	*III*	*IV*	*V*	*VI*
Mont.	85.5	6.1	20.3	27.6	23.0	16.0	7.0
N. D.	95.9	1.6	13.5	32.5	32.4	15.0	5.0
S. D.	94.6	2.4	14.5	33.7	30.1	14.2	5.1
Nebr.	93.2	3.5	15.1	32.9	28.8	14.0	5.6
Kans.	85.5	3.2	12.4	25.8	29.3	20.1	9.2
Okla.	65.3	1.9	8.9	18.2	24.6	26.3	20.0
Tex.	68.4	5.6	13.4	18.3	23.1	23.1	16.6

Source: *United States Census of Agriculture, 1950,* II, 1132–33.

* See Table 5 for basis of classification.

have again gone under the prairie plows. This is land that should never be worked under any now-known farm practice. The government experts have warned. Local conservationists have recalled the previous tragedies. State officials, farm-organization leaders, bankers, and businessmen all have protested. But there is no law that prohibits a free-born American from abusing his own land if he wants to.

During World War II, it was a matter of considerable wonder and much satisfaction that, in spite of abnormal demands, the Plains farmer was not making the mistake of World War I, when he plowed unwisely, planted over 73,000,000 acres of wheat by 1919, and reaped the whirlwind. It seemed that only the lands that could be held in place were being worked. But after the war, when Europe's needs sent the price of grain soaring, strangers appeared with cash money in their pockets. Two-dollar grazing land suitable only for livestock became five-dollar wheatland. The five-dollar land jumped to fifteen and twenty. In 1949 over 76,000,000 acres of wheat were planted.

However, many of the newcomers owned no buildings, no fences —nothing but land. Their homes were in cities far away, in Ft. Worth, Kansas City, St. Louis, and other remote communities. They fitted the seed bed and did their planting by custom operator. When the crop was ripe, a custom harvester gathered it in. A custom trucker took it to the elevator. If the yield was only sixteen or seventeen bushels per acre, the whole investment could be paid back in one year. Another year of any kind of crop at all would produce a sometimes fantastic return on the money expended. But one year the rains will not come. Then the land, tied down so loosely or not at all, will be whipped into clouds of dust as the winds rush across the Plains, and another Dust Bowl will result.

The investor, "suitcase farmer" as he is called, will not be put out. He has made his killing and has no further interest. In many cases he may not even keep up his taxes, but will let the local government recapture the land, or what little is left of it. It may be a generation, or never, before the land will even grow grass again. It is useless to the nation, a handicap to local government.

Worse than that, the experienced farmer down the road, or in the next county, who has practiced conservation and has husbanded his land will be penalized for the sins of the land-robber. For once the thin soil starts to blow, no man can order where it will fall. It may punish farmers who have maintained the highest order of citizenship. And no law on the books protects these innocents.

It seems inconceivable that selfishness so great could prevail in such a situation. A generation ago, when it first happened, many a transgressor could be forgiven on the grounds of ignorance. There is no such excuse today because of the very experience indicated. Much as anyone who loves freedom loathes to see more government controls, it does seem that this instance presents a problem of such importance to the public good that restraining legislation must be created. If we found that water conservation, stream rights, and river usage must be regulated by law for the greatest good of the commonwealth, surely we cannot long ignore the even more important item of the soil itself upon which the future of this, or any other, nation rests.

However, where the land can properly be tilled, it has been fortunate, not only for this country but for the world, that the High Plains are suited more for wheat than anything else. Millions of people that otherwise might have starved were fed on American wheat after World War II. Between 1945 and 1950 the United States exported anywhere from 300,000,000 to 500,000,000 bushels of wheat annually, while in eight of the years between 1930 and 1944 we exported less than 50,000,000 bushels. But now that the huge export business is about finished, the old problem has again come up. Wheat is a major export crop, and what shall be done with the surpluses?

In general, we can annually consume or export only around 700,000,000 bushels of the golden grain, but our productive capacity has gone up to well past 1,000,000,000 bushels. The average annual production between 1940 and 1949 was 1,071,310,000 bushels. The great bulk, about three-fourths of this production, is in winter wheat, the balance in spring and durum wheat. The latter grow on soils and in climates generally north of the winter-wheat belt where the winters are so severe that a fall-planted crop cannot germinate economically. Spring wheat has specific uses in the baking business, but the demand is easily met. Surplus winter wheat can partly be used for feed, but if there is too much, as often happens, it drops to disastrous prices. One of the authors hauled wheat to the elevator in the fall of 1931 and received only twenty-five cents a bushel for it! In some places it sold for as little as seventeen cents.

The International Wheat Agreement was designed to provide wheat for needy countries and, at the same time, to relieve the surplus problem among the principal exporting countries. The United States sold some 248,000,000 bushels in 1950–51 under the terms of the agreement at prices around sixty to seventy cents below the government support price. The federal government shouldered the losses, but wheat *was* moved out of American granaries and terminals. Nevertheless, even this heruclean effort has not been enough to maintain full American production.

The alternatives seem to be acreage reductions and crop shifts, unless some unforeseen export markets develop, or unless some new industrial use can be found for the excess wheat. Distilling it into alcohol for farm motor fuel has been a dream of a generation, but neither motor manufacturers nor oil companies have helped the scheme along. Maybe a perennially petroleum-short future could bring some change in this situation, but at the moment alcohol-from-farm-surpluses does not seem to have a bright outlook. So far, the only real answer offered has been acreage restriction. Under the government's price-support programs, wheat acreage had been cut to around 55,000,000 acres by 1955.

In the nineteen thirties, attention in this area was turned toward the grain sorghums. These plants, once natives of Africa and Asia, are noted for their drought resistance. They make a comparatively better growth than wheat in dry years, and their feed value is almost as good as corn. One drawback was that the sorghums did not lend themselves to mechanization until American plant-breeders literally tailored the crop to fit our machines. Now they are as mechanized as wheat.

From the Río Grande to Canada, right through the heart of the wheat country, especially the southern part, runs the area of greatest sorghum concentration. Texas had 4,658,188 acres and Kansas

2,266,586 in 1949, and sorghum occupied 16.6 and 10.5 per cent, respectively, of the cropland harvested in those states. The wheat that is grown, despite surpluses, can provide fall pasture for livestock. The accompanying sorghum crop can provide winter feed and even make some finish. This new help to Plains agriculture can certainly contribute toward stability of operations, and, since a wheat grower does not spend over forty days a year in employment on his farm, it will provide the year-round employment which is lacking in a strictly wheat operation.

The effect of a sorghum-feeding program would be to aid the wheat country, but probably at the expense of some other areas such as the rich corn-producing regions. The outcome of such a program depends upon how important livestock products will be in the diet of the future. If the demand goes to new highs because of a generally higher standard of living and an increased population, then we shall need more livestock than our present ranges can provide. In that case, the Wheat Belt, with the aid of sorghums, might produce the extra animals. Less emphasis would then be placed on so much cash-crop farming in some areas and more emphasis would be given to the production of livestock. The shift is usually a desirable one in any agricultural economy, but it takes away the possibility of making huge profits in any one year.

A factor that may militate against this idea is the character of the people. Boom and bust psychology is still strong here, although several authorities believe that residents of the Plains have become less and less a "next year" people. But the old saying is "Give me just one good year out of seven and I'll get by." For generations, out of necessity, Wheat Belt farmers have had to endure the hard years waiting for the good years. When a good year does arrive, the urge is not to conserve for the sure-to-return bad times, but to go on a buying spree. High-priced automobiles sell easily where a fifth-hand wreck sold hard a year before. Trips to California and Florida become the style of the land. Everybody is rich and everything is rosy. Then, as surely as the climatic cycles, bad times return.

If greater stability is to come, a significant change in the minds of the people must precede it. When the weather is favorable and prices are good, farmers in the Great Plains must build up reserves to tide them over the inevitable bad times. Not only do they need monetary reserves, but they must provide themselves with reserves of feed and seed. At all times, farmers in the western Wheat Belt must follow practices in their farm operations which will conserve moisture. Soil must be protected from blowing, and marginal wheatland should be turned back to grass. And, of vital importance, farmers in this region must develop flexibility in their operations if they are to achieve stability. This would include having a flexible livestock herd and being able to shift crops quickly to take advantage of changed conditions. The idea must be to cut off the peaks and fill in the valleys of income. Provision must be made for weathering the lean years which come so often to the Great Plains. It is likely that, over a twenty-five- or thirty-year period, farmers in the western prairies and Great Plains have an income which exceeds that of farmers in most other sections of the country. The greatest danger in the future is a coincidence of dry years and low prices like that which occurred in the early and middle nineteen thirties.

Yet, if wheat prices again skyrocketed for whatever reason, it would be a rare man who knows the history of this region whose pulse would not quicken. They would indeed be a people of enormous self-control and almost godlike foresight who would not rip up the land and plant wheat, for even gold mines hardly make the quick returns that good wheatland, a sufficiency of moisture, and a high price can produce.

There is hope that a more mature outlook is in the making. In recent years there has been a small expansion of irrigation, and the Missouri Valley projects will make even more irrigated acres. In addition, portable irrigation has appeared on the Great Plains and has become a widely accepted innovation.

This latter technique was born in Florida and New Jersey. Instead of depending upon ditches and laterals, its basis is a network of surface pipes. The water is distributed by sprinkler heads very similar to those used on urban lawns. The sources are streams, stock tanks, and wells. While the idea is old, one new aspect, the use of magnesium and aluminum pipes, give it fresh interest. Previously, the weight of the ground system and the difficulty of moving such weights has been a drawback, but the very light modern pipes possess a high degree of portability, as well as economy.

Because of inadequate water supplies, not all the land in the Great Plains can be adapted to this system. Where there is enough sub-surface supply, or where ground configuration makes it possible to erect dams cheaply and to hold back reasonably large quantities of runoff, the portable irrigation method offers some exciting possibilities for a much wider range of farming than just wheat and summer fallow. It is too early to estimate how successful the idea may be or over how large an area it may spread, but it is a straw in the wind indicating that this whole region may not be as eternally committed to wheat as it was once thought to be. According to the *United States Census of Agriculture, 1950,* Nebraska and Kansas had 8,295 and 3,121 acres irrigated by sprinklers in 1949. But this was only the beginning, and the system has spread rapidly since that time.

Even more pregnant with possibility is the proposition of harnessing the long, muddy, and often cantankerous Missouri River and its dozens of tributaries. Countless plans have been floating around for years as to what should be done about a river that frequently destroys more land values in a few days' flood, as in 1951 and 1952, than the adjoining land will produce in seasons of crops. At the present time, some water for irrigation is being taken from the tributaries and from the Big Muddy itself, but only a fraction of the potential has been realized. Nearly 5,000,000 acres were proposed for irrigation in the Missouri Valley under the Flood Control Act of 1944. About half of this new irrigation was to be in the Dakotas. At this juncture only about one thing is certain: the cost will be very high. The Missouri Basin Survey Commission reported in 1953 that the minimum cost of bringing new land under irrigation would be $100 per acre. To get water on the first 750,000 acres of the proposed irrigation would cost $400 an acre, and on the next 740,000 acres it would cost from $400 to $700. History of the various reclamation projects shows that water users could not repay such costs, and there is even serious doubt that revenues from power would be able to pay the power costs and, in addition, a large part of the irrigation cost. There is also the question whether irrigation, at public expense or otherwise, should be encouraged at a time when the country is struggling to get rid of surpluses in several basic crops.

Just what will be done is not now known, but it is extremely dubious today that a Missouri Valley Authority on the model of the TVA will ever be set up. However, some dams and irrigation and river-control projects are already under way and will continue. With added power it is not impossible that industry, now nearly entirely absent, will seek locations in the area. This should make markets nearer home, and markets for vegetables and livestock products. But these things are very much in the problematic stage.

The forseeable future seems to be that the Wheat Belt will stay the Wheat Belt, but with forced acreage contraction. Sorghums should be the great secondary crop over much of the area, unless a surfeit of corn breaks that market so badly that there would be literally no market for any other feed grain. Some of the land will be ruined and out of cultivation permanently because of the depredations of the "suitcase farmer." A broken wheat market and a consequent reduction in land prices may turn attention even more strongly toward livestock. If plant-breeding work such as is going on now brings new arid-land grass strains, and particularly if a forage crop can be found, livestock favor will grow. Presently, an African grass called weeping lovegrass is receiving high interest, but no variety has been found that will do the job that native hay does in the Sand Hills of Nebraska.

There is still another possibility that would have seemed to be only a Jules Verne dream a few years ago. That is the matter of rain making by seeding dry ice or silver iodide in certain types of clouds. Theoretically, a degree of control over precipitation might be secured in this land where rain is the most valuable of all things. But so far the value of artificial rain-making has not been definitely proven.

While such notions are not impossible or even improbable, the one course of action that we now know to be necessary, even mandatory, is to get all the wheatlands back on summer fallowing—at least until some brand-new climate changer or man-made moisture producer comes along. If all the lands that should be in fallow are maintained under that program, a large part of the probable surplus will be eliminated. A more normal price will suggest to many owners that their lands should be in grass or that they have enough money to retire to California. No doubt such a voluntary retirement of lands and a migration westward will take place when the first dust-laden wind sweeps down out of the Rockies. So in one more area it seems that some prosperity in farming is partly dependent on some catastrophe—a curious commentary on the race that owns the richest farm in the world.

CHAPTER 10

The Southwest: Far Distances and Dry Skies

(Oklahoma, Texas, New Mexico)[1]

NOT MANY years ago it was easy to describe this section, its crops, and its life. Utter simplicity was the rule. Beef, sheep, money crops, and native grasses such as grama made up its agricultural economy. Efforts were made to grow corn, but, for the most part, the low precipitation foiled this move. Cotton was imported into parts of the area and, unfortunately, was successful until much of the soil eroded away and gave out. Today simplicity has been replaced by a complex of crops and techniques, no one of which can be said to be dominant over the whole region, although beef cattle are found in almost every minor subdivision.

Once Oklahoma was among the very top cotton states in the country, producing over a million bales a year between 1924 and 1929. The white lint was the big money crop. But the rolling lands, subject to flash rains of great intensity, and the usual land-killing character of the crop slowly drove much of the state out of the cotton business. Cotton acreage reached a high of 5,396,000 acres in 1925, but had declined to only 1,045,000 acres by 1953. Cotton made up about 75 per cent of the income from all farm crops in

[1] For statistical data on Oklahoma, see Chapter IX; for Texas, Chapter VI; and for New Mexico, Chapter XI.

1925, but it had declined to 15 per cent in 1952. In Cleveland County, in the central part of the state, there were twenty cotton gins in the nineteen twenties; only three remained in 1954. Cotton is still a leading money crop in southwestern Oklahoma, where, although rainfall must be depended upon, some 44,000 acres were grown under irrigation in 1953. Irrigated cotton there produces as much as a bale and a half per acre. But in the central, south central, and southeastern parts of the state, the white lint is only one of several crops, including peanuts, corn, vegetables, and grain sorghums. Livestock is playing a greater relative position in the agricultural economy of those parts of the state where cotton was once king.

Destructive erosion and the Depression, coupled with the drought, brought Oklahoma's big cotton days to an end. Thousands of eroded acres were abandoned. The crop rows usually had run up and down the hills, and each row had made a little gully. The one-time grass soil washed away, leaving nothing but the red subsoil. Yields fell off to a mere 100 to 200 pounds per acre. When credit for seed was not to be had, the growers, most of them sharecroppers, gave up and became Ishmaelites, wandering the highways of the Pacific Coast in search of any kind of work. They said they had been "tractored out." A more correct statement is that they were "cottoned out" and "eroded out."

At length conservation got underway. Grasslands were restored in part. Brush and rock dams stopped up some of the gullies. Land was held by terracing and contouring. Livestock numbers increased. Once-sick Oklahoma started on the comeback trail.

One of the facts about Oklahoma which attracts student interest is the tremendous agricultural changes which have occurred since the dark days of the nineteen thirties. The value of land and buildings per acre declined to an average of $22.20 in 1935. By 1953 it had risen to $63.35, with some choice land bringing $200 an acre, and more. But despite some favorable and healthy changes, many Oklahoma farmers have only a mere subsistence living. The per capita income in a number of eastern Oklahoma counties, where much of the land is poor and most of the farms are small, was less than $500 in 1950. In 1954, partly, but only partly, because of the drought, people there were actually starving before govern-

GENERAL PATTERN OF GREAT SOIL GROUPS

The Southwest

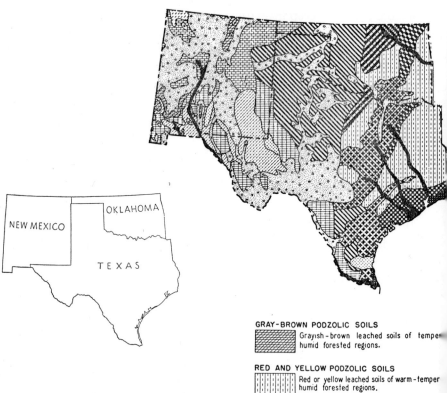

NEW MEXICO
OKLAHOMA
TEXAS

GRAY-BROWN PODZOLIC SOILS

Grayish-brown leached soils of tempe humid forested regions.

RED AND YELLOW PODZOLIC SOILS

Red or yellow leached soils of warm-temper humid forested regions.

PRAIRIE SOILS

Very dark brown soils of cool and temper relatively humid grasslands.

REDDISH PRAIRIE SOILS

Dark reddish-brown soils of warm-tempe relatively humid grasslands.

REDDISH CHESTNUT SOILS

Dark reddish-brown soils of warm-tempe semiarid regions under mixed shrub and g vegetation.

BROWN SOILS

Brown soils of cool and temperate, semiarid gr lands.

REDDISH BROWN SOILS

Reddish-brown soils of warm-temperate to semiarid to arid regions, under mixed shrub grass vegetation.

ment relief was provided. Oklahoma's contribution to the nation's total agricultural output on the basis of value was slightly less percentage-wise, in 1949 than ten years earlier.

Despite the relative decline of cotton in Oklahoma's farm economy, it is still a highly important crop. But today both wheat and cattle bring farmers much more money. In 1952 cotton, wheat, and cattle brought $52,000,000, $178,000,000, and $234,000,000, respectively. Total cash receipts amounted to $673,000,000, of which about 61 per cent came from cattle and wheat.

Nevertheless, Oklahoma produces a wide variety of crops. In the eastern part of the state, where precipitation is modestly heavy, corn is a common crop. However, corn acreage declined from about 3,000,000 acres in 1929 to only 777,000 in 1952. Most hay crops grow well and have been expanding. In 1949 hay was harvested from 9.7 per cent of the cropland, an increase of 2 per cent over 1939. Alfalfa and lespedeza are important for both hay and seed, as is vetch. The state harvested 221,091 bushels of alfalfa seed in 1949, ranking second in the nation. Peanut acreage has been increasing and reached over 200,000 acres in 1950. Vegetables, nuts, especially pecans, and small fruits like strawberries and black-

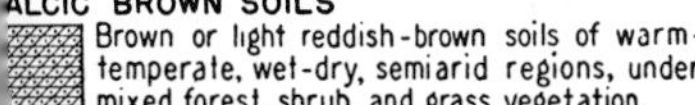

ALCIC BROWN SOILS
Brown or light reddish-brown soils of warm-temperate, wet-dry, semiarid regions, under mixed forest, shrub, and grass vegetation.

ZEM OR GRAY DESERT SOILS
Gray soils of cool to temperate, arid regions, under shrub and grass vegetation.

ESERT SOILS
Light reddish-brown soils of warm-temperate to hot, arid regions, under shrub vegetation.

SOLS
Soils with strongly leached surface horizons over claypans on nearly flat land in cool to warm, humid to subhumid regions, under grass or forest vegetation.

INA SOILS
Dark grayish-brown to black soils developed from soft limy materials in cool to warm, humid to subhumid regions, mostly under grass vegetation.

WIESENBÖDEN (1), GROUND WATER PODZOL (2), AND HALF-BOG SOILS (3)
(1) Dark-brown to black soils developed with poor drainage under grasses in humid and subhumid regions.
(2) Gray sandy soils with brown cemented sandy subsoils developed under forests from nearly level imperfectly drained sand in humid regions.
(3) Poorly drained, shallow, dark peaty or mucky soils underlain by gray mineral soil, in humid regions, under swamp-forests.

BOG SOILS
Poorly drained dark peat or muck soils underlain by peat, mostly in humid regions, under swamp or marsh types of vegetation.

LITHOSOLS AND SHALLOW SOILS (ARID-SUBHUMID)
Shallow soils consisting largely of an imperfectly weathered mass of rock fragments, largely but not exclusively on steep slopes.

SANDS (DRY)
Very sandy soils.

ALLUVIAL SOILS
Soils developing from recently deposited alluvium that have had little or no modification by processes of soil formation.

berries contribute to farm income. Spinach is one of the main vegetable crops, and over 9,000 acres were harvested in 1949, an acreage which was exceeded only by Texas. And of course Oklahoma is famous throughout the entire country for its watermelons. In 1950 over 1,000 carloads were shipped out of the state, plus hundreds of truck loads. Grain sorghums are grown widely in the western part of the state, but less acreage is now devoted to these crops than in past years, which reflects a greater emphasis upon wheat. Broomcorn is an important crop in the south central part of the state. Indeed, the little town of Lindsay is the broom capital of the nation.

In the last few years that part of the old Dust Bowl which was in Oklahoma has been planted to wheat when it should not have been. In 1949 Oklahoma farmers planted over 7,000,000 acres of wheat, the highest acreage on record. But government acreage restrictions cut the total, especially in 1954 and 1955. Probably much of the land taken out of wheat will go into forage crops and grain sorghums. In some places restored land is going back into cotton, with the rows once again running up and down the hills, a clear case of flying in the face of Providence. But enough of the citizenry is soil-conscious to give hope that those who have not learned the

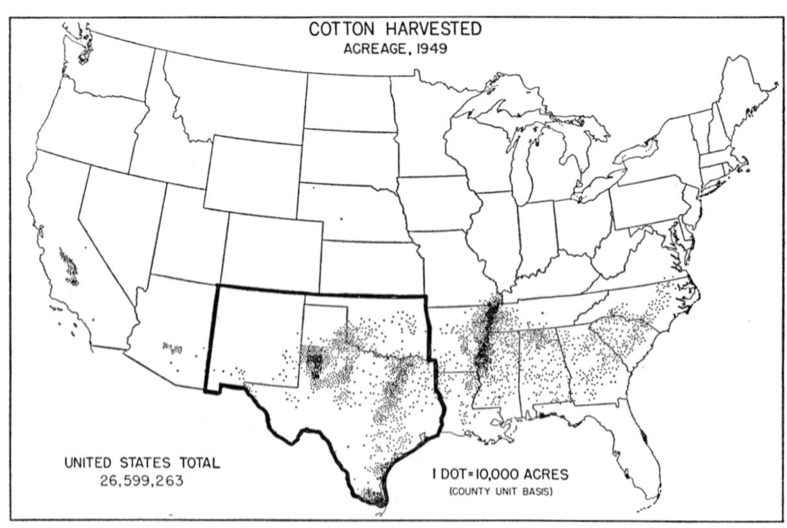

lesson of history will not again debauch large areas. One advance has been to plant cover crops between the cotton rows, thereby holding the soil and also providing winter and early spring pasture.

Oil money, so greatly cursed by some people, has been an agricultural blessing to much of Oklahoma. It has become the fashion for oilmen to go into beef-cattle raising. One of their prime interests has been to grow the best possible pastures and hay lands of bluestem, an erosion fighter and a native Oklahoma grass of high nutritive value. Besides promoting the spread of this and other grasses, the cowmen keep a watchful eye for grass fire, which, next to erosion, is the great threat of the prairies. One of the richest and most notable beef-cattle areas in the nation is in south central Oklahoma, appropriately called Hereford Heaven, where former Governor Roy J. Turner owns one of the most famous ranches.

Throughout much of the state, additional pasture could be provided if sufficient capital and ambition were available. It is estimated that there are around 10,000,000 acres of brushland in the state which, if cleared, could supply pasture to produce 150,000 tons of dressed beef a year. Some owners in recent years have cleared hundreds of acres with machines and chemicals, adding good grazing land to the farms and ranches.

The agronomists at Oklahoma A. and M. College favor the cattlemen, but feel that cattle ranches are not the only answer to the state's need. Cattle require lots of land and a high capitalization to be profitable. Most small farmers can secure neither. That is one reason why cotton was so widely cultivated even when its depredations could be clearly seen. Crops and farming methods not yet fully envisioned must be found if the small farmer is to have a permanent and profitable business.

There seems to be an unwillingness to admit that possibly the land in this region was never made to support small operations. The tradition of the 160-acre homestead still holds its destructive grip on much farm thinking, but on the whole, farmers must rely on extensive operations. Tears have been shed over the plight of the small farmer in areas where nature decreed against small acreages, except where irrigation is possible. There may be some good reasons for maintaining a big population of "honest yeomanry" on the soil, but economics is not one of them. Neither contiguous markets nor the soil-climate combination suggests a future for an intensive agriculture. There are certain irrigation possibilities which have come to fruition, and they may expand. As previously mentioned, irrigated agriculture is growing rapidly in southwestern Oklahoma, reaching about 70,000 acres in 1954.

It may be that cotton and wheat will decline to even less importance because of government controls on surplus crops, or possibly for other reasons. Grain sorghums and broomcorn, where adaptable, will stay or perhaps increase in favor. Beef will continue to be popular. Intensive crops will depend upon greater industrialization, and in this field Oklahoma is doing a very assertive and aggressive job. Oklahomans not only lose no chance to point out the centralized location and the generally mild climate (but extreme heat in summer) of their state, but also go on the road in special trains to sell the industrial advantages to other regions such as Detroit and Pittsburgh. Huge water-users, however, are ruled out by the generally dry character of the state. During the frequent hot, dry periods, many towns in the central and western parts of the state commonly have to ration or restrict the use of water. This problem was pointed up in late 1954 when the Okla-

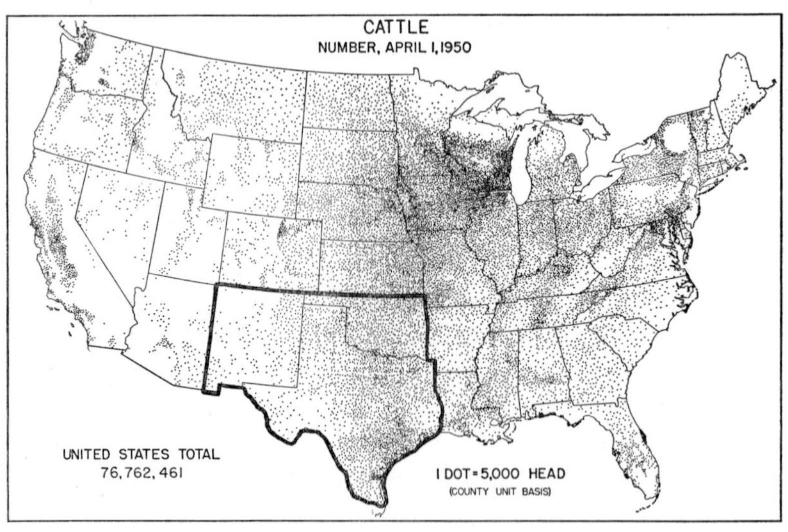

homa City Council gave preliminary approval to a long-range water program which would bring water from the Kiamichi Mountains, over 100 miles southeast of Oklahoma City. The estimated cost was given as $109,000,000.

One of the most significant features of the current trends in Oklahoma agriculture is the increasing importance of livestock and livestock products. Except for 1949, livestock brought farmers more money than crops did in every year from 1935 to 1952. This change began after 1929. In the nineteen twenties crops often brought two or three times the income derived from livestock, largely because of the value of cotton. For example, livestock and livestock products represented only 22 and 27 per cent of the cash receipts from farm marketings in 1924 and 1925, respectively; in 1951 and 1952, farm income from this source had grown to 63 and 56 per cent, respectively. Cattle have played the major part in bringing about this change. In fact, most other kinds of livestock, including hogs and sheep, are declining in numbers.

Texas is an empire in itself when it comes to agriculture. There is an extremely wide diversity and variation of climate, soils, and crops. The average annual rainfall varies from as much as fifty inches along the eastern Gulf Coast to as little as ten inches in the extreme western part of the state. Farm lands range from sea level to about a mile high. And in the lower Río Grande Valley the nearly year round growing season is in sharp contrast to the less than 180-day season in the northern Panhandle. Nearly all kinds of crops and livestock raised anywhere in the United States are to be found in this huge agricultural domain. In 1939 Texas ranked third in the value of farm products sold, being exceeded by both Iowa and California. In 1944 it ranked second, and in 1949, according to the 1950 census of agriculture, it ranked first in the value of farm products sold, with a whopping $1,753,052,010. By 1952, farm income exceeded $2,000,000,000.

In the irrigated Río Grande Valley, citrus and vegetables burgeon in lushness unsurpassed by even Florida or California, which the region most nearly resembles. Hidalgo County was the nation's number one county in acres of vegetables harvested for sale in 1949. This fabulous county not only ranks first in tomato acreage, but has more grapefruit trees than any other county in the country. The future of some southern Texas land is limited by the amount of water that can be put on it and, paradoxically, the amount that can be drained off. Near the Gulf the lands tend to waterlog from the excess which drains down on them from the upper watersheds and irrigated lands.

As previously shown, the eastern part of Texas is very akin to the Cotton South. It has the typical piney woods, large acreages of cotton, and a tendency toward a cash-crop economy. Central Texas grows a variety of crops where precipitation is sufficient, and, where it is not, a flourishing cattle, sheep, and goat industry exists. A bit farther west is the greatest concentration of feeder lambs in the country. Still farther west on the eastern edge of the Staked Plains are grain sorghums and cotton. The area around Lubbock, where there is a great amount of deep-well irrigation, is one of the most outstanding cotton-producing regions in the world. In 1949 Lubbock County ranked first in cotton acreage with 359,548 acres. Production was 253,469 bales. The northwestern Panhandle region, as shown in the previous chapter, belongs to the Plains Wheat Belt. And everywhere from the great King Ranch in southern Texas to the wheat country north of Dalhart are beef cattle.

Texas is first in many things because of sheer size. It leads in the production of beef cattle and probably will continue to do so because such vast quantities of the land are suitable for no other uses. The traveler literally can drive for hours and see nothing but grazing land marked only by dry river beds which do not suggest even a sometime irrigation—land so arid that no summer fallowing could make grains profitable. Forage-consuming animals seem to be the only possible users of thousands of square miles of this gargantuan pasture.

One of the world's greatest ranching empires, commonly called the Southern Plains region, stretches throughout central and western Texas and into southeastern New Mexico. A combination of short grasses, semidesert grasses, and browse shrubs provide good grazing for thousands of sheep and cattle. This range will support livestock the year around, although protein concentrates are used in winter feeding. The Southern Plains have, within recent years, undergone a change in appearance from grasslands to brushlands. The decrease in perennial grasses and the increase in brush have caused a partial shift of cattle population eastward, with sheep and goats, the latter frequently used to help keep down the growth of brush, increasing in importance, especially on the Edwards Plateau. The number of sheep in Texas increased from 2,573,485 in 1920 to 7,750,395 in 1950.

Sheep and goats are pretty well concentrated on the Edwards Plateau, which occupies a region east of the Pecos River nearly to Austin. San Angelo and Del Río mark the approximate north-south boundaries of the area. Val Verde County (Del Río) has more sheep and lambs on its farms, and sells more, than any other county in the United States. North central Texas, the Gulf Coast, and the "west of the Pecos" regions are other leading ranching areas. In the Gulf Coast area between Guadalupe and Río Grande rivers, cattle ranches predominate. Here the Brahman is crossbred with beef breeds to produce an animal better adapted to the heat and more resistant to parasites. The famous King Ranch, with its 900,000 acres and around 85,000 head of cattle, is in this area.

Texas had 8,940,000 head of cattle in 1952, which was about 11

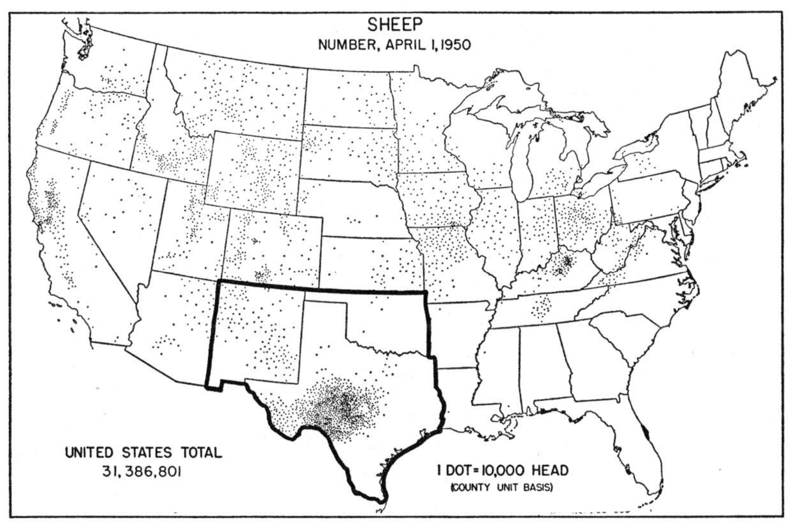

per cent of the nation's total. The state also ranked first in sheep population, with over 6,000,000 head, although this was less than the number in 1950. But, in any event, Texas had around 22 per cent of all sheep and lambs in the United States; and most of the country's angora goats are in Texas. In 1950, 2,350,000 goats were clipped, producing 12,643,000 pounds of mohair out of a total national production of 13,245,000 pounds. Texas also ranks first in wool production. The 1950 crop was over 51,000,000 pounds, nearly 25 per cent of the domestic output.

The low productivity of much of Texas ranch land necessitates fabulously large operations. In many areas they do not figure land-grazing capacity in acres but in sections. In most of the region west of San Angelo, ranches run to thousands of acres. Residents of Crockett County (Ozona) have been heard to boast that there is not a single acre of plowed land in the county—and it is only a very slight exaggeration. West of the Pecos River, where cattle ranching, as well as sheep ranching, is important, the average ranch is around 15,000 to 20,000 acres or more. Ranches of 50,000 or 60,000 acres are not uncommon. For example, the average-size farm in Brewster and Jeff Davis counties in the Big Bend country of southwestern Texas was 18,169 and 22,345 acres, respectively, in 1950. Hudspeth County east of El Paso had farms which averaged 15,511 acres. These extensive holdings have a relatively small value per acre, but the tremendous acreages make the average investment very heavy. The value of land and buildings averaged from $4.71 an acre in Winkler County around Kermit, Texas, to $9.96 in Hudspeth County. Generally, the value of land and buildings per acre was less than $15.00 in that great ranching empire west of the Pecos.

Livestock and livestock products made up about 35 per cent of the value of farm products sold in 1949. This was a smaller proportion than in either 1939 or 1944, due partly to the increased position of cotton. The income from cotton far exceeds the income from any other crop, and, after it, rice, truck crops, wheat, and grain sorghums rank in that order as sources of farm income from crops. In 1952 livestock and livestock products brought farmers between 46 and 47 per cent of their total farm income. Cattle and calves furnished most of the income from livestock, followed by poultry and dairy products. The value of farm products sold in some of the counties plainly reveals the emphasis upon a ranching economy. In 1949 Brewster County farmers and ranchers sold $3,702,722 worth of farm products, of which $2,887,346 was represented by livestock sold alive. For the entire state, there has been an occasional year when cash receipts from livestock and livestock products have exceeded that from crops.

Today important changes are taking place in Texas agriculture. Continuous row-crop production and overgrazing of the ranges have lowered the productivity of much of the land and have pointed up the need for conservation. And conservation practices are being eagerly adopted. Soil-building crops are being planted, contour farming and other conservation techniques are finding more favor, and diversification is progressing rapidly. Brush is being eliminated on thousands of acres of ranch land. In much of the state, especially in the east, there is a trend away from the predominance of cotton farming and a move toward producing livestock and special crops. Livestock breeds are being steadily improved, and better feeding practices are being followed. The result has been a significant higher level of farm living for many Texas farmers. In 1949 about 19 per cent of the commercial farmers sold products valued at $10,000 or above.

However, a long and severe drought in West Texas in the early nineteen fifties cut deeply into farm income. By 1953 and 1954 many ranchers were forced to sell part of their breeding herds, while others had gone heavily in debt to buy expensive feeds. The combination of drought and overgrazing made ranges in some areas of West Texas "as bare as a well-swept cabin dooryard," according to one widely known observer. In order to combat the lack of water, officials of the Bureau of Reclamation have suggested that a great canal should be dug some sixty to seventy miles inland from the Texas Gulf Coast to take surplus water from East Texas rivers to the semiarid Gulf Coast in the south. But even this billion-dollar scheme, if developed, would not help the parched plains hundreds of miles north and west. As the water problems of this region are brought more and more into focus, the dream of the erratic sculptor, Gutzon Borglum, of bringing water from the Missouri River to the Southern Plains seems less fantastic than once thought.

New Mexico is another state of great extremes and sharp limitations. It can hardly be said that it is of major importance agriculturally. In 1949 the total value of farm products sold was only about $154,000,000, less than that of Los Angeles County alone. In the northeast, the state belongs to both the Wheat Belt and the ranching region, as well as to the Dust Bowl. In the central east and southern east of the Pecos Valley, irrigation makes an oasis for peanuts, cotton, alfalfa, some fruit and vegetables, and, of course, the omnipresent beef cattle. The south central Mesilla Valley on the Río Grande is another irrigated sector, with crops similar to those in the Pecos Valley.

The mid-Río Grande Valley has been irrigated for generations, but waterlogging of much of the valley lands has caused a high rate of abandonment. In the twenties a Middle Río Grande Conservancy District was set up to drain these lands, leach out the alkali that had been deposited in them, and return them to cultivation. Some progress has been made, but the project has been so beset by politics that a full potential has not been realized. Outside of a few small irrigated projects (Mimbres, Bluewater, San Juan, etc.), the rest of the fourth largest state in the Union is mostly grazing land with trees-and-grazing in the mountain areas. It is sad to report that these millions of acres of land have been grazed almost to the soil. In some sections as many as eighty acres are needed to support one head of beef cattle. And examples of vicious erosion can be seen from almost every mile of highway in the state.

The outlook would be tragic to the extreme had not some new ideas appeared in recent years. One already mentioned is the breeding of new drought-resistant grasses such as the weeping lovegrass. Another is the building of stock tanks and the damming of gullies both by public and private agencies. Very recently an inventor of an airplane-seeding process for reclaiming range lands under government and individual sponsorship has been at work. This suggests that a real attempt is being made to reclaim the vast areas of the dry Southwest for better and more carefully managed grazing in the future. If this is not done, large quantities of the lands in these three states will become a national liability.

There is little doubt that one of the highest land uses for many places in the Southwest is in recreational and educational areas. Tourists even now are a highly important cash crop. Where so many natural wonders abound and so much history has been made, where cliff dwellings, caverns, ruins, and historic buildings and battlegrounds are dotted thickly, agriculture-under-handicaps might well give way to the tourist, who takes nothing and leaves his dollars behind.

The symbol of the future for most of this area seems to be the beef animal, and to a lesser extent the sheep. International difficulties give the high-cost range-raised American sheep a poor competitive position for the long term, as is evidenced by the decline to a sheep population of 31,000,000 in 1949, the lowest since about 1870. Texas has been the major exception to this trend. With only 1,889,298 head of sheep in 1900, Texas, as mentioned before, reported over 7,000,000 a half-century later. Government subsidies provided for wool growers in the 1954 farm law may encourage sheep production.

The one thing that can be prophesied without quibble is that this region will remain one where water is more precious and just about as scarce as rubies, and where the beholder can look farther and see less than anywhere else in the United States.

CHAPTER 11

The Rocky Mountain States: A Farm in the Sky

(New Mexico, Colorado, Wyoming, Montana, Idaho)

A COMMON NAME for this region is the American Switzerland, a designation which is less than exact. True, mountains are the dominant feature and tourists a rich cash crop. But there the similarity ends. Dairy products are not the important agricultural part of the economy. The well-deserved fame of the cuisine and hostelries of Switzerland is not duplicated, except in a very few and exceptional areas. Small manufacturing is negligible here, unlike the land of watches and alarm clocks. And instead of the cheese-making dairy animal of the Alps, the white-faced beef cow, in addition to the sheep, has long been the mainstay of this high country.

From Lake Louise in the Candian Rockies to Santa Fé in the southern Rockies, this region was once the home of game, Indians, and the Mountain Men. The cash export was skins. The social contribution was miscegenation between hunters and Indian women. The permanent effects were a depletion of native meat and fur-bearing animals, mongrelization of the races, and practically no worth-while residue.

GENERAL PATTERN OF GREAT SOIL GROUPS

The Rocky Mountain States

REDDISH BROWN SOILS
Reddish-brown soils of warm-temperate to hot, semiarid to arid regions, under mixed shrub and grass vegetation.

NONCALCIC BROWN SOILS
Brown or light reddish-brown soils of warm-temperate, wet-dry, semiarid regions, under mixed forest, shrub, and grass vegetation.

SIEROZEM OR GRAY DESERT SOILS
Gray soils of cool to temperate, arid regions, under shrub and grass vegetation.

RED DESERT SOILS
Light reddish-brown soils of warm-temperate to hot, arid regions, under shrub vegetation.

LITHOSOLS AND SHALLOW SOILS (ARID-SUBHUMID)

(HUMID)

Shallow soils consisting largely of an imperfectly weathered mass of rock fragments, largely but not exclusively on steep slopes.

SANDS (DRY)
Very sandy soils.

ALLUVIAL SOILS

Soils developing from recently deposited alluvium that have had little or no modification by processes of soil formation.

ROWN SOILS
Brown soils of cool and temperate, semiarid grasslands.

AY-BROWN PODZOLIC SOILS
Grayish-brown leached soils of temperate, humid forested regions.

ESTNUT SOILS
Dark-brown soils of cool and temperate, subhumid to semiarid grasslands.

DDISH CHESTNUT SOILS
Dark reddish-brown soils of warm-temperate, semiarid regions under mixed shrub and grass vegetation.

Then this region, from the Great Plains on the east to the Pacific valleys on the west, became a hard, strange, and dangerous barrier that Coast-bound pilgrims had to cross at risk of life and limb. Many besides the Donner Party never reached California. Indians, starvation, accidents, and the rigors of a country tougher than anything previous waves of migrants from the Atlantic westward had even known thinned the survivors, but did not discourage the desire to move west or the seemingly endless number of new aspirants. Except in a few trading stations such as Santa Fé, this second wave of white men left little behind but history.

The miners, always an "exploit-and-get-out" crew, came next. They had little ambition to leave anything except holes in the ground and inert, worthless heaps of tailings. Even though as individuals they had no intention of forming a permanent society, they unwittingly led to the establishment of one. The miners were paying fabulous prices, more than their precious metals were worth in many cases, for supplies transported across the thousand miles from the Mississippi Valley to the diggings. Yet here and there in the vast jumble of the mountains were fairly level, richly productive patches of silt deposition, well watered, that would grow excellent crops, high yielding though low in gross tonnage. Rarely does a pioneer economy show any signs of sticking until the plowman or stockman appears, and a few men, plowmen at heart and probably disappointed gold-seekers, began to see the opportunity offered by the land. Others followed their lead, and agriculture was born in the sky.

To this day, in remote valleys, such small-scale agriculture still persists, and the farmers sell their fruits, vegetables, and animal products to miners, lumbermen, and now dude ranches and resorts. But the very disposition and general lack of mountain land suitable for intensive cropping have been deterrents to any significant expansion. More recently, irrigation in the larger but not naturally watered valleys has expanded row-crop and forage-producing farming.

Where cloven-hoofed mountain sheep grew naturally, it was inevitable that some farmer would think that domestic woolies might flourish. And if grass-eating buffalo, deer, and elk waxed fat during the summer months on pasture a mile in the sky, someone was going to consider the hardy beef animal as their successor. Hence, from southern Texas, Mexico, and the Pacific Northwest, both sheep and cattle moved into the mountains, never to retire, although present world conditions are forcing a slow retreat of the sheepman and his products.

TABLE 76.—*Number of farms in the Rocky Mountain States, 1870–1950.*

	1950	1940	1930	1920	1910	1900	1880	1870
Mont.	35,085	41,823	47,495	57,677	26,214	13,370	1,519	851
Idaho	40,284	43,663	41,674	42,106	30,807	17,471	1,885	414
Wyo.	12,614	15,018	16,011	15,748	10,987	6,095	457	175
Colo.	45,578	51,436	59,956	59,934	46,170	24,700	4,506	1,738
N. M.	23,599	34,105	31,404	29,844	35,676	12,311	5,053	4,480

Source: *United States Census of Agriculture, 1950,* II, 55–56.

The five Rocky Mountain States under consideration contain some 353,000,000 acres of land, nearly 20 per cent of the entire land area of the United States. Yet this vast region had only 157,-160 farms in 1950, about the same as Michigan. Agriculture in this area is characterized by relatively few, but many very large farms. The average size varied from a low of 832 acres in Colorado to 2,728 acres in Wyoming. Only Arizona had a larger state average per farm than Wyoming. Most of the farm land is used for range and pasture, emphasizing the importance of the livestock. A great deal of the land in these states is, of course, in national forests and other public lands. Only 25 per cent of Wyoming's total land area is in farms. In Montana, farms occupy 63 per cent of the total area.

TABLE 77.—*Average number of acres per farm in the Rocky Mountain States, 1870–1950.*

	1950	1940	1930	1920	1910	1900	1880	1870
Mont.	1,688.7	1,110.7	940.3	608.1	516.7	885.9	267.1	164.0
Idaho	328.3	235.8	224.3	198.9	171.5	183.4	173.9	186.3
Wyo.	2,728.8	1,866.2	1,469.3	749.9	777.6	1,333.0	272.3	24.8
Colo.	832.7	612.9	481.6	408.1	293.1	383.6	258.6	184.3
N. M.	2,013.7	1,139.4	981.5	817.9	315.9	416.8	124.9	186.1

Source: *United States Census of Agriculture, 1950,* II, 55–56.

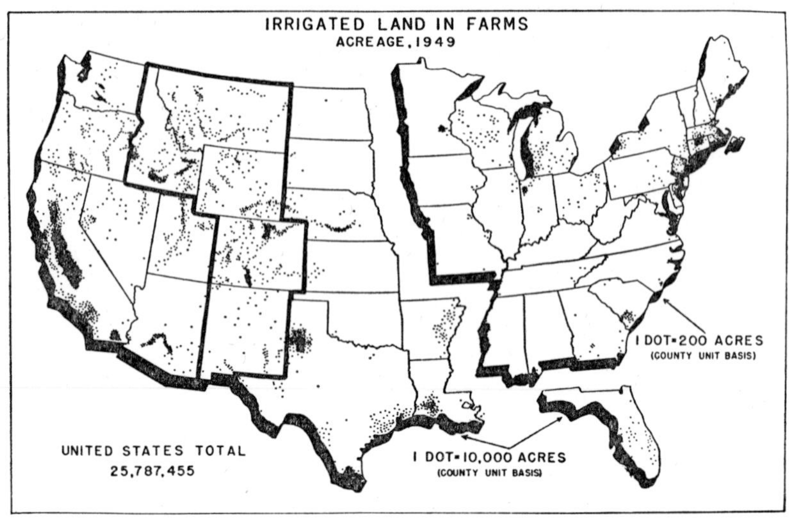

Only a small percentage of the land is in harvested cropland. Just 4 per cent of New Mexico's farm land is in this category; in Wyoming the figure is 5.5 per cent. Idaho has 27.6 per cent of its farm land in harvested cropland, which is the highest for any of the Rocky Mountain States. Of the cropland harvested, a sizable percentage is irrigated. Over the whole region about 57 per cent of the farms (not of the farm acreage) are irrigated. Of the farms reporting in 1950, irrigated cropland represented about 18 per cent of the total cropland harvested in Montana, but it was a high of over 57 per cent in Wyoming. Montana had the lowest percentage of cropland harvested under irrigation because of the large amount of dry-land farming, particularly wheat, in the eastern part of the

TABLE 78.—*Average value of land and buildings per acre in the Rocky Mountain States, 1870–1950.*

	1950	1940	1930	1920	1910	1900	1880	1870
Mont.	$16.86	$ 7.54	$11.81	$22.15	$18.58	$ 5.24	$ 7.97	$ 4.18
Idaho	69.82	32.94	44.64	69.43	46.38	13.20	8.64	5.11
Wyo.	13.21	5.67	8.79	19.88	11.46	3.32	6.72	3.35
Colo.	31.93	12.32	21.79	35.40	30.19	11.22	21.55	8.46
N. M.	15.01	4.83	6.74	9.09	9.92	4.07	8.74	2.17

Source: *United States Census of Agriculture, 1950,* II, 55–56.

state. Even the irrigated land per farm is substantial. In 1950 it averaged 127, 72, 182, 105, and 51 acres per farm in Montana, Idaho, Wyoming, Colorado, and New Mexico, respectively, and, as in other areas of the United States, the irrigated farms are steadily increasing in size.

This vast Rocky Mountain region is a sheepmen's and cattlemen's paradise. Most of the farm income is derived from livestock and livestock products, mainly sheep and beef cattle. In the five states under consideration, the value of crops sold in 1949 was 41.2 per cent of the total. Livestock and livestock products, on the other hand, represented over 58 per cent of the value of all farm products sold. Only in Idaho did the sale of crops bring more money than the sale of livestock and their products. This was due to the large cash crops of potatoes and wheat. The rich Snake River Valley usually places Idaho second only to Maine as a potato producer, and northwestern Idaho is part of the fabulous Palouse wheat country.

Wyoming is predominantly a livestock state. Over 76 per cent of the value of farm products sold in 1949 came from livestock and livestock products. It is of interest to note, however, that each of three California counties, Los Angeles, Fresno, and Kern, sold a

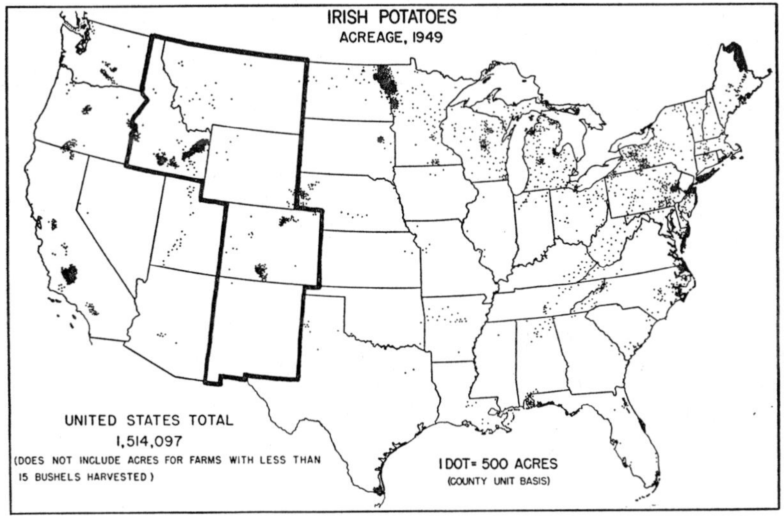

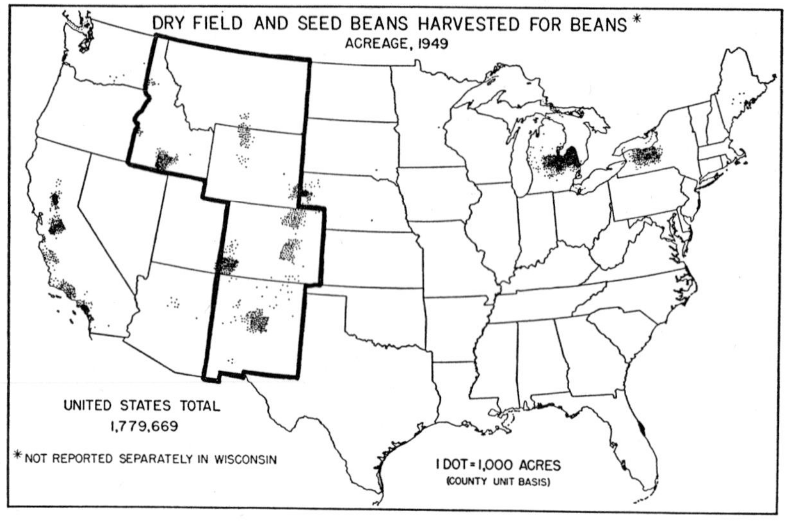

greater value of farm products than the entire state of Wyoming. About 58 per cent of Montana's and Colorado's farm income was derived from livestock. Although ranching is very important in New Mexico, crops seem to be increasing in the total farm-income picture. This apparently is due to the greater value of the cotton crop, which is grown under irrigation. Between 1939 and 1951 cotton production jumped from 100,138 to 272,000 bales.

TABLE 79.—*Value of farm products sold in the Rocky Mountain States, 1939–49, and the per cent represented by crops and by livestock and livestock products.*

	Value of farm products sold		*Per cent of value of farm products sold*			
			Crops		*Livestock and livestock prod.*	
	1949	1939	1949	1939	1949	1939
Mont.	$279,058,735	$ 84,076,381	41.1	46.8	58.6	53.0
Idaho	281,025,323	83,890,896	54.7	51.3	45.0	48.3
Wyo.	121,835,629	45,939,704	23.6	19.1	76.3	80.8
Colo.	426,447,889	101,587,195	41.9	40.0	58.0	59.9
N. M.	154,740,229	42,656,795	44.8	35.3	55.1	64.3

Source: *United States Census of Agriculture, 1950,* II, 752–54.

A high percentage of the commercial farms in these states are classified as livestock farms other than dairy or poultry. The census of 1950 placed over 43 per cent of Montana's commercial farms in this category. The figures were 54, 40, and 34 per cent in Wyoming, New Mexico, and Colorado, respectively.

Both the dry-land and the irrigated farming in this area are closely associated with the livestock industry. Hay is a leading crop and occupies a large amount of the cropland harvested. It made up 24.8 per cent of Montana's harvested cropland in 1949 and 28.3 per cent in Idaho. On many of the 90,513 irrigated farms in this region, alfalfa is a very important crop. It is considered one of the very best sheep feeds. Although sugar beets are a major cash crop, especially in Colorado, Idaho, and Montana, the tops are made into hay or silage and the beet plup is hauled back to the farm and used for livestock feed. Oats and barley are among the other crops on irrigated acres which add to the total feed supply.

TABLE 80.—*Number of sheep in the Rocky Mountain States, 1900–50.*

	1950 (*April 1*)	1930 (*April 1*)	1920 (*Jan. 1*)	1900 (*June 1*)
Mont.	1,336,612	4,027,457	2,082,919	6,170,483
Idaho	1,508,690	3,301,754	2,356,270	3,121,532
Wyo.	1,828,838	3,417,460	1,859,775	5,099,613
Colo.	1,657,425	2,505,159	1,813,255	2,044,814
N. M.	1,196,562	2,291,426	1,640,475	4,899,487

Source: *United States Census of Agriculture, 1950,* II, 430.

The Rocky Mountain area is one of valley and foothill ranches. In the spring, as the snow recedes under the warm chinook wind, the livestock are moved from the sheltered valleys toward the high country. Tender, juicy, and highly nutritious grasses pop up in little glades between the rocks and under the trees to make a forest carpet. The prevalent bunchgrasses make excellent pasture for both sheep and cattle in the spring and fall. The so-called "pine bunchgrasses" are found in the higher range, 4,000 to 6,000 feet above sea level, and are best suited for cattle because of their coarseness. Higher up the mountains, around 8,000 or 9,000 feet, the grasses, weeds, shrubs, and creek meadows make excellent sheep grazing. Even higher, the Alpine area is good for only two or three months of pasture and is also used mostly for sheep.

TABLE 81.—*Number of cattle in the Rocky Mountain States, 1900–50.*

	1950 (*April 1*)	1930 (*April 1*)	1920 (*Jan. 1*)	1900 (*June 1*)
Mont.	1,758,243	1,290,353	1,268,516	968,387
Idaho	948,802	622,170	714,903	363,534
Wyo.	1,027,723	824,039	875,433	687,284
Colo.	1,775,540	1,454,352	1,756,616	1,433,318
N. M.	1,138,478	1,055,327	1,300,335	991,859

Source: *United States Census of Agriculture, 1950,* II, 401.

On these mountain ranges livestock develop strong bone structures, for calcareous soils are the rule, while the animals' general thrift seems to surpass that of animals grown at lower and outwardly more beneficent elevations. In late summer, as the mountain pastures grow sparse and the nights more chilly, the animals are worked back to the lower altitudes and reach the valley ranches

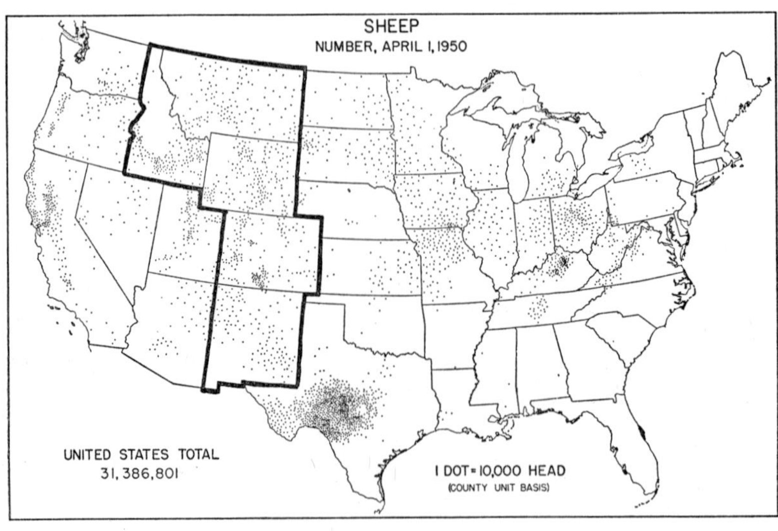

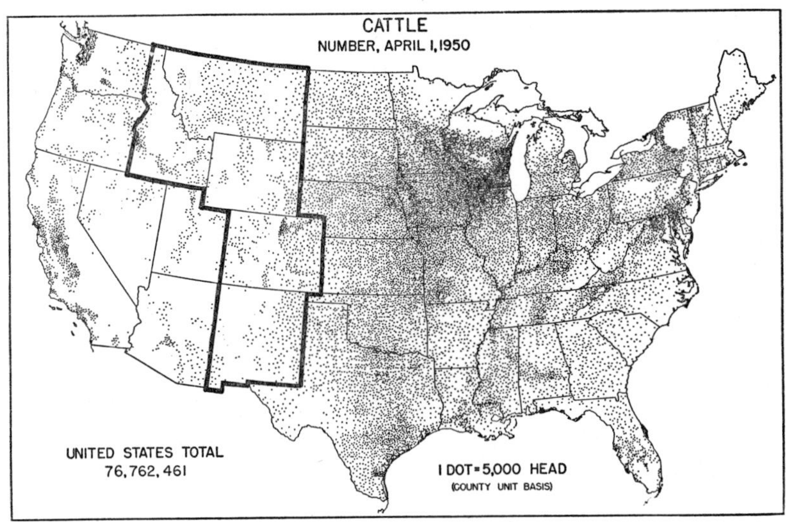

by September. In the meantime the rancher has been making hay in the lower valleys, hay that is watered by subirrigation or by man-made methods. As previously mentioned, much of the irrigated farming in the mountain valleys is done in conjunction with the livestock industry.

Of course not all of the ranching by any means is done in the high mountain country. On the Plains, east of the mountains, in eastern Montana, Wyoming, Colorado, and New Mexico, thousands of head of livestock dot the ranges. Beef cattle are more predominant in the Plains region, while sheep are more confined to the mountains proper.

Lambs and calves are shipped out of the mountains and the Plains as the cash crop of these states. The brood herds are put on late pasture, then moved to sheepsheds or cattle windbreaks for the winter. Summer-made hay and some cottonseed cake are fed by hand or self-fed from scattered hay stacks and racks when the weather is most severe. When the snow is not too deep to plow, winter grazing is often made possible by pulling a V-plow over the fields to reduce the depth of the snow. The mountain-wise animals do an excellent job of finding grass even though normal grazing appears impossible.

Because of a climate which prohibits alternate enterprises, it is not likely that the dominant grazing character of the high country will change in foreseeable times. It is likely, however, that it will be definitely curtailed if the long-time tendency to overgraze is not curbed. Rangelands in the mountain country and in the arid or semiarid grassy Plains have all been extremely overworked since wartime's huge demands and peacetime's no lesser compulsion of record-breaking prices. Pastures have had no rest. A little reseeding has been done here and there, it is true, but not a fraction of what is needed.

Mont H. Saunderson of the United States Forest Service has pointed out that much of the western range is a declining resource. "Some parts of it," he says, "can be written off as having passed or rapidly passing the point of feasible rehabilitation." Other authorities believe that this is an overstatement, but there is no question that erosion and shifts to plant life not as good as the original range forage have seriously decreased the value of many mountain ranges. Where bunchgrasses have been overgrazed, weeds and annual grasses have taken over. Not only is this forage less nutritious, but overgrazing and the destruction of the original plant life endanger the watersheds. It is of utmost importance to the agricultural economy of the mountains and the adjoining areas that the upland watersheds be properly used.

Although the outlook for sheepmen is an unhappy one, the growing abandonment of their enterprise is a help toward range maintenance. The split-mouthed, sharp-hoofed sheep grazes closer and more intensively than any other animal, and the cutting edges of a band's small hoofs can literally destroy a restricted pasture. This is not to say that the cattleman is guiltless—far from it. Too many cows for the carrying power of the range will ruin it just as much, if not just as fast, as too many sheep.

Of recent years irrigation has been expanding in this region, and several hundred thousand acres have been added to the amount of irrigated land in farms. And despite the long distance from concentrated markets and the consequent prohibitive transportation cost which held back agronomic cropping so long, promotion, special taste appeals, and the growth of markets nearer home have helped promote this type of agriculture.

From Idaho's potatoes in the north, through sugar beets, vegetables, alfalfa (and other forage crops), to the pinto beans and chili peppers of New Mexico's mountain valleys, more intensively tilled crops have come to stay. Weld County, Colorado (Greeley), ranked seventh among the nation's counties in the value of farm products sold in 1949. This county alone had 8.1 per cent of the total national sugar-beet acreage. Colorado's Pascal celery brings a premium wherever it is sold, and Rocky Ford melons are sought eagerly. The pickle makers regularly buy all the New Mexican chili peppers they can get, while pinto beans have built their own market, not only in the growing Southwest but in the outlands.

In Colorado, and to a lesser extent in Wyoming, a prosperous lamb-feeding business has come into being. The farms are put on a rotation program that annually devotes a small fraction of the land to sugar beets, a crop which has a high labor and water requirement. The balance of the arable land is devoted to alfalfa, small grains, vegetables, and often turkeys, for, as the latter have grown in national favor as a year-round meat, the Mountain States have grown in prominence in turkey ranging (in contradistinction to the fenced pastures or the dry-wire culture of the East). Lambs, and sometimes calves, are fattened during the winter months, giving year-round employment and a fine diversity. If any hay in excess of the farm needs, has been raised there is always a sure cash sale where forage-consuming livestock numbers are perennially greater than mountain-raised supplies.

It has been noted that irrigation is expanding in this region, but it should be stated, however, that lack of water is a definite limiting factor in developing additional irrigation projects. Most of the water resources of the Mountain States are already developed, except for some high-cost possibilities of complex structure. One of the problems is that in many places the excess surface water is not favorably located in relation to suitable land or is in areas where the cost of irrigation would be exceedingly high. It is extremely important for the future of agriculture in the Mountain States that the limited supply of water be conserved and wisely used. As mentioned earlier, better land-practices are needed on many of the mountain watersheds.

The richest irrigated sectors now are in the eastern foothills, extending, but not continuously, from just east of Watrous, New Mexico, to Fort Peck, Montana. In Colorado, water is being diverted from Grand Lake (west of the Continental Divide) for a distance of thirteen miles through the mountains into the Big Thompson River near Estes Park. There are also many small, naturally irrigated sections west of the Continental Divide in the mountain states. It has been proposed that the waters of the Gunnison River be diverted under the mountains to the eastern slope, eventually debouching into the Arkansas. This is intended to make a garden spot of the grazing lands of southeastern Colorado, as has been so successfully done farther north and around Golden and Boulder.

TABLE 82.—*Total acres of cropland harvested, and acres of irrigated cropland harvested in the Rocky Mountain States, 1949.*

	Acres of cropland harvested	*Acres of irrigated cropland harvested*	*Per cent of total cropland harvested which was irrigated*
Mont.	7,576,173	1,366,851	18.0
Idaho	3,647,885	1,703,601	46.7
Wyo.	1,900,646	1,092,122	57.5
Colo.	6,892,904	2,253,868	32.7
N. M.	1,897,813	577,767	30.4

Source: *United States Census of Agriculture, 1950,* III, 38.

Even farther west, the long-established Mormon projects of central and northern Utah and the prosperous development of the Snake River act as show windows for public-water proponents who have a hundred other schemes they want Congress to approve. Too few voices are raised in protest, not against progress, but in fear of surpluses. For the moment we can use most of our farm production but *not in all crops.* Some of the crops of high yield and per-acre value which are needed to make an irrigation project pay seem to be the very crops that are either in surplus or soon will be.

No doubt more irrigation is underway for this section, in spite of history and economics. It is too politically potent to miss. Because of the fantastic growth of the Pacific Coast market in recent times, perhaps the future projects will not fare so badly as have some in the past. Maybe these growers, unlike the early irrigators, can find a market to which transportation costs will be low. In that case farmers farther east may feel the diminution of the gross market and have to change their patterns to fit the new situation. However, even with more acreage under the ditch, the general character of the Mountain States' predominantly livestock economy (as far as land use is concerned) will remain unchanged.

One new development has come about for the high country in recent years that is only now in its early stages, but which deserves a full-dress expansion. That is tree culture.

While most of this vast area can be grazed, much of it only after a fashion, the preponderant portion is best suited for trees. In the past we have cut, burned, and made farms of innumerable sections where no farming should have been attempted. The mountains are dotted with abandoned projects. In all of the Mountain States, these writers have found cabins and barns thickly surrounded by second-growth trees, and often with trees literally growing through roofs and walls. Too often they are of the weed variety.

Many forested areas once provided, and in some instances still provide, grazing of a substandard type in which the browse is not the best, or even the most economical foodstuff. Over the longer term such lands would be better off in trees.

Year after year we are cutting more trees than we are replanting. If this is not stopped sheer mathematics will put an end to our timber resources. Enlightened lumbermen, whatever their sins of yesteryear, are now trying to stem the tide on their own lands. They are replanting, setting up sustained-yield bases, cutting to thin (thus allowing more usable growth to develop), cutting in blocks for certain varieties, leaving seed trees to reforest, and setting up tree farms. Unfortunately, not all lumbermen are doing this, and not even the larger part of the forest lands is under the control of the tree farmers.

The vast portion of the lands that must provide tomorrow's lumber belongs to farmers, ranchers, and private nonfarm owners. On most of these lands no attempt is made at fire prevention, insect control, or scientific harvesting, to say nothing of reforestation. Yet the lands could be put on a crop basis and yield income-producing timber for generations, if not for eternity. Grazing should be cut down and in some places eliminated. While this would subtract from today's income, it would preserve tomorrow's capital.

Hence the greatest agricultural change in this area is not one that is well under way, but one that is already late in starting. Every day that goes by without such a nationally progressive land-use policy being put into effect is a day when some part of our basic heritage has probably been lost forever.

The changes which need to be made in this most scenic part of America are no more, and probably less, cattle; a little more but not too much irrigation; and enormously greater tree-farming acreages. If it were possible, what the overexploited West really needs is an overdose of soil husbandry.

CHAPTER 12

The Western Slope: Land of Tomorrow

(Arizona, Utah, Nevada, Idaho, California, Oregon, Washington)

AT THE BEGINNING of this book mention was made of the difficulties of writing about contemporary American agriculture. Whether or not the statements presented were accepted, the difficulties of organization, emphasis, and presentation will be abundantly clear as one reaches the area of the Far West. Indeed, the problems reach imposing and complex proportions. Here geologic factors are strong. Physiographic factors cannot be denied. But economics, obviously, will have more to do with the future than either geology or physiography. Field and machine technology take on a dynamism which is not even equalled in the Corn Belt. Psychology, historically important elsewhere as an effect rather than a cause, is here at the very roots of the problems and the probable outcomes of agricultural change.

In short, any writer faces a separate and very acute challenge when he grapples with the Far West, its present and its pregnant future. The usual treatment of the West, a historical threshing of fact and fancy, does not fit the purpose of this book. The rapidly changing present and the probable future matter most. Although one of the writers is a native of this region and has specialized in

GENERAL PATTERN OF GREAT SOIL GROUPS

The Western Slope

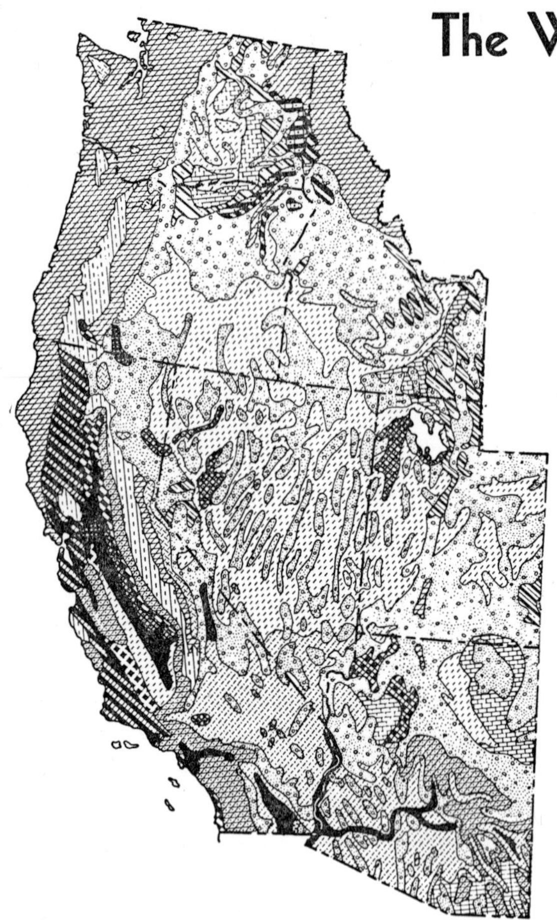

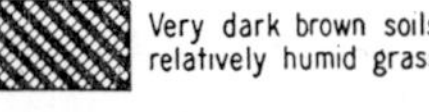

GRAY-BROWN PODZOLIC SOILS

Grayish-brown leached soils of tem humid forested regions.

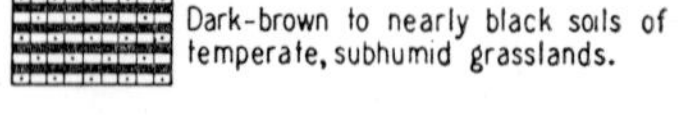

RED AND YELLOW PODZOLIC SOILS

Red or yellow leached soils of warm-ter humid forested regions.

PRAIRIE SOILS

Very dark brown soils of cool and te relatively humid grasslands.

CHERNOZEM SOILS

Dark-brown to nearly black soils of c temperate, subhumid grasslands.

CHESTNUT SOILS

Dark-brown soils of cool and tempera subhumid to semiarid grasslands.

BROWN SOILS

Brown soils of cool and temperate, semia lands.

reporting its mutations for twenty-five years, still we face our self-assigned job with no little queasiness in our intellectual stomach.

Others may question the division of subject matter. Still another group may find much to criticize in the subdivisions. Our adumbrations and findings may call for rejection or pugnacious dispute. Whatever the reaction, someone has to set forth a new plat or investigational scheme that is more in concordance with the tremendous changes that are taking place in this area with every edition of the newspapers than the historiographic patterns used by students of "Only Yesterday."

Perhaps our breakdown is not the most successful. It is probable that someone else can find a better one. But as the forty-niners so long before us made a trail and took what came of it, so we arbitrarily set on our way and only hope we will find Sutter's Creek or Fort Astoria at the end.

To us the Pacific Coast as such is not a comprehensive agricultural area. Even as the local people themselves instinctively make a broader division, so to us the general prefacing urge, desire, accomplishment, and drawbacks involve an area roughly from the Continental Divide to the actual lapping waters of the ocean so

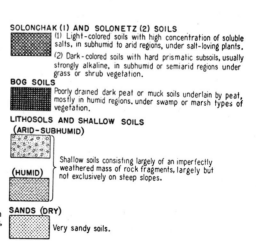

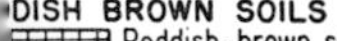

DISH BROWN SOILS
Reddish-brown soils of warm-temperate to hot, semiarid to arid regions, under mixed shrub and grass vegetation.
CALCIC BROWN SOILS
Brown or light reddish-brown soils of warm-temperate, wet-dry, semiarid regions, under mixed forest, shrub, and grass vegetation.
OZEM OR GRAY DESERT SOILS
Gray soils of cool to temperate, arid regions, under shrub and grass vegetation.
DESERT SOILS
Light reddish-brown soils of warm-temperate to hot, arid regions, under shrub vegetation.
OSOLS
Soils with strongly leached surface horizons over claypans on nearly flat land in cool to warm, humid to subhumid regions, under grass or forest vegetation.
ZINA SOILS
Dark grayish-brown to black soils developed from soft limy materials in cool to warm, humid to subhumid regions, mostly under grass vegetation.
SOLONCHAK (1) AND SOLONETZ (2) SOILS
(1) Light-colored soils with high concentration of soluble salts, in subhumid to arid regions, under salt-loving plants.
(2) Dark-colored soils with hard prismatic subsoils, usually strongly alkaline, in subhumid or semiarid regions under grass or shrub vegetation.
BOG SOILS
Poorly drained dark peat or muck soils underlain by peat, mostly in humid regions, under swamp or marsh types of vegetation.
LITHOSOLS AND SHALLOW SOILS
(ARID-SUBHUMID)
(HUMID)
Shallow soils consisting largely of an imperfectly weathered mass of rock fragments, largely but not exclusively on steep slopes.
SANDS (DRY)
Very sandy soils.
ALLUVIAL SOILS
Soils developing from recently deposited alluvium that have had little or no modification by processes of soil formation.

ironically named Pacific. The lack of sweet water is to us more indicative than the riches of valley agriculture. The absence of markets at one time and the creation of markets at another is as significant as the coming and going of the Dust Bowl in the Great Plains sector. And the as yet completely befogged future of Alaska and Asia cannot be disregarded even though little solid fact or soundly based conjecture can be evoked.

Accordingly, to present the clearest picture, for this portion of the book alone we are using a subdivisional form that grows out of the peculiarities of the region itself. Because there are more likenesses than dissimilarities here in soil, climate, and markets, we choose to break down the huge region by other than political boundaries.

Clouds, Rivers, and Wells

East of the Mississippi River, the general problem of water is how to control too much of it and how to get rid of it. Droughts occur, sometimes very severe, but they are not the usual thing. In the past, irrigation has been almost nil except for spots in New Jersey and Florida, although supplemental irrigation is now rapidly growing. This rapid increase, especially since about 1950, has developed to meet regional drought conditions, but even more to increase production within acreage controls.[1] But generally speaking, annual precipitation is so regular that, within relatively small bounds, a near-correct prophecy can be made for most seasons. Consequently, in the portions of this book given over to the eastern half of the country, little attention has been paid to water, except to note the misuse of it or the lack of controls over a superfluity.

West of the Mississippi, the discussion of water has received more and more attention the farther we have proceeded from the great river. By the time we get to the High Plains, water becomes one of the major interests, with wind, soils, and distances also

[1] In 1954 a Dickson County, Tennessee, farmer grew two crops of tobacco on the same land by planting early, fertilizing, and irrigating heavily. It has been estimated that Missouri's irrigated acreage increased 440 per cent between 1950 and 1954. Georgia tripled its irrigated acreage between 1952 and 1954. This increase in irrigation is going on all over the Middle West, East, and South.

Courtesy United States Forest Service

Sheep find luxuriant summer pasture in the mountain meadows of Idaho.

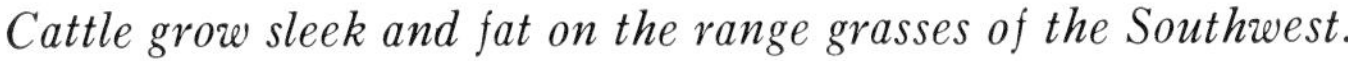

Cattle grow sleek and fat on the range grasses of the Southwest.

Courtesy Bureau of Reclamation

In many parts of the arid West, irrigation has made the desert bloom, as in this Wyoming scene.

Courtesy Seabrook Farms

Portable irrigation equipment provides the supplementary moisture needed for the proper development of many vegetables.

Picking the fruit is one of the few hand operations still used in orchards. Here, choice pears are stacked on a pallet aboard a forklift, which will load them on trucks bound for the cannery or the market.

Courtesy Standard Oil Company of California

Courtesy Standard Oil Company of California

Harvesting lettuce in California's Salinas Valley. Cut by hand labor, the lettuce is placed on a conveyor belt for loading onto the truck.

Four men can plant many acres of broccoli in a day with a machine like this one, shown at work in the Santa Clara Valley, California.

Courtesy Standard Oil Company of California

A twelve-row cotton-planting rig. On this particular farm, near Huron, California, 19,000 acres were planted to cotton in 1951.

A land plane in California's San Joaquin Valley.

Courtesy Standard Oil Company of California

Harvesting seeds at the Ferry-Morse Farms, Salinas Valley, California.

The deep-well pump in the background delivers 2,000 gallons per minute from over 500 feet below the surface to irrigate land in California's San Joaquín Valley.

Courtesy Kouchy and Long

Courtesy Standard Oil Company of California

Sugar beets are a major crop in California. The beets are picked by machine and processed at one of the refineries in each growing area. Pulp left after sugar has been removed becomes valuable stock feed.

assuming great importance. In the mountain region, for the moment, water is a great political question. But when we reach the Western Slope of the Great Divide, water becomes paramount.

A crop will or will not be made—with emphasis on the negative—depending upon the greatest-used phrase in that country: "If it rains"—or if enough irrigation water is available. The transitoriness or permanency of settlement more and more rests on man-aided water distribution. The Great American Desert dominates much of the region, a land once thought to be eternally useless, but of later years of high potential agricultural output *if the water supply holds up*. Water is the West's life blood. A sufficiency or lack of this life-giving fluid can make or break the West. Water can be the difference between boom and bust. Southern California is a potential desert, as it once was, if anything goes awry with its expensively constructed water sources. Fresno, located in California's fabulously rich Central Valley, gets less than 10 inches of rainfall a year. Even supposedly wet Oregon and Washington have a much greater acreage in present or onetime desert or near-desert than in naturally watered arable lands. For example, the average rainfall at Vale in eastern Oregon is less than 9 inches; at Hanford, Washington, on the Columbia River, there is often only about 6 inches of precipitation, compared to over 140 inches in parts of the Olympic Peninsula.

Although there seems at first glance to be little in common between Idaho and Southern California, and Arizona and Washington, actually none of these regions would contribute any great amount to national farm production if all of them had not constructed the most extensive irrigation systems in the world. Water is one of the several things that tie together all of this huge area of some 453,000,000 acres, or about 24 per cent of all the lands in the United States.

The romance of water and dry land goes back long before Columbus came to this country, possibly as early as A.D. 500. The best account we have centers around the several-storied ruin of a building, probably a combined granary and fort, near the town of Florence, Arizona, in the valley of the Gila River. The name of this building and its surrounding excavated ruins is Casa Grande.

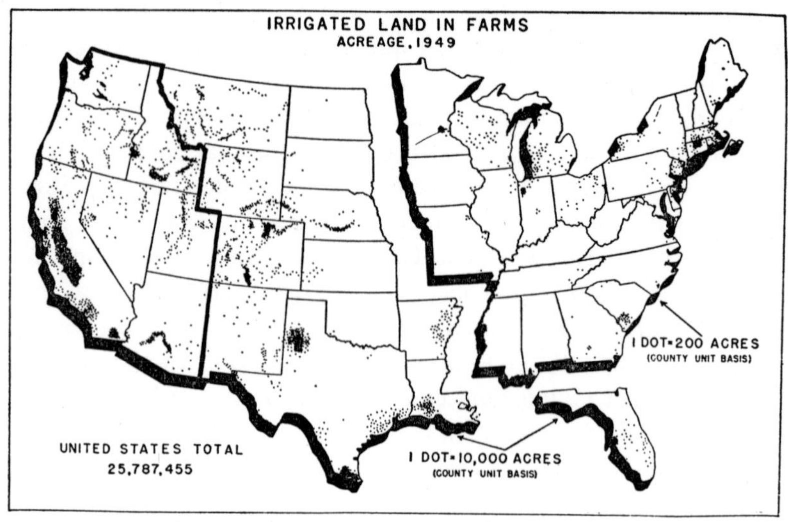

Here, a thousand years ago, lived a people called the Hohokam, or Water People. They were an agricultural people, not a nomadic pastoral folk, as were most of their neighbors. From what source we do not know, they had gained a rather good, albeit primitive, knowledge of engineering principles and hydrology. They harnessed the Gila, dug ditches and laterals, and created a garden in the desert. Corn, beans, and melons flourished under their husbandry and the magic of water on soils that were in a condition of unleached richness, soils that contained the best plant-food values washed or blown down and deposited in the broad valley.

What happened to them and their culture is not known. That they were good farmers and knew how to weave and make pottery we have evidence. The thick walls of the still-standing central building indicate they knew how to protect themselves up to a point. Whether a long series of droughts and drying up of their major water supply drove them away, or whether such marauders as the Apache cut down their numbers until they were no longer able to defend themselves, the calendar sticks of present-day Indians, by which they collect history, do not tell authentically. However, although some misfortune drove them away, the engineering that went into their ditches was so correct that some forty miles of onetime Hohokam ditch-line are in use today as part of the great Salt River Valley project. Modern engineers could not improve upon the ancients.

Although no such extensive works have been found elsewhere in the West, still there is evidence that the meager though sufficient waterworks of other Indians, notably the Pueblos, go far back into time. Somehow they discovered the problem of the predominantly arid West and worked out a solution which has not changed too much even today. The West has vast quantities of water suitable for agriculture and millions of acres of land rich in nutrients, slow to leach, inviting in topography. But the best water and the best land were not naturally married by nature. Usually the water flows through lands that are inhospitable to any crop, or else is separated from good croplands by natural barriers such as mountains, alkali sinks, or sterile basalt.

The problem today is still as it was centuries ago: how to get sweet water and rich land together. On top of this is a new problem the Indians, other than the Hohokam, did not have. It is how to continue an adequate flow of water, once the barriers are surmounted, to give life permanently to all the acres man would put to use.

Although the first huge success in diverting waters to the desert, the Salt River Valley project, was only finished in 1911, by 1946 worry over the permanency of the project was starting, almost in secret, among valley owners. True, the crop yields were in the realm of the fantastic. True, endless problems had been met and conquered. True, many failures in crop choice had come along before proper and seemingly correct usage was discovered. Two-dollar desert land had leaped to four or five hundred dollars in value. And even the most rambunctious of the pronouncements of the Phoenix Chamber of Commerce were backed by more fact than fiction. By 1949 Maricopa County ranked fifth among the nation's counties in the value of farm products sold.

Yet the water table slipped slowly downward, for in the valley all irrigation is not by surface flow. There are also many thousands of acres dependent on wells. In 1949 there were 963,560 acres in Arizona's irrigated farms. Over half of the irrigated farms, comprising 524,435 acres, were provided with water from pumped wells. The number of wells pumped for irrigation increased from 999 in 1920 to 1,858 in 1940, and jumped to 4,361 in 1950.

With such extensive pumping, especially in Maricopa (Phoenix) and Pinal counties of central Arizona, the water level has fallen dangerously low. The average pumping lift reported in 1939 was 62 feet. By 1949 it was 134 feet. When the pumping level goes below 160 feet, worry starts unless prices are fabulously high. When it goes below 300 feet, worry is acute no matter how high prices might be. And in some places by the mid-forties the 160-foot mark was general; in other places even the 300-foot mark was becoming common. True, farm-product prices were abnormally high. But how long would prices stay up and the water stubbornly stay down? If a drought occurred, what would happen to the whole rich but threatened valley? Part of the answer has already been supplied. One Arizona farmer declared in 1949 that, ten years earlier, "with one pump and a reasonably good well, you could irrigate 320 acres. Today that same pump will irrigate only about half that. I used to pump from 125 feet. Now I'm down to 235." A Senate subcommittee reported early in 1945 that Arizona's "ground-water table has been so reduced by pumping as to reach the point where irrigation may become uneconomic due to the high cost of pumping water."

The probable re-enaction of the Hohokam's leaving is not something the growers are inclined to pass off lightly, even if the booster element claims there is nothing wrong that a good rain cannot cure. The threat brings up again a legal controversy that has raged on and off for years all over the arid Western Slope: the need for an underground water-rights policy or subsurface water conservation.

Everyone recognizes this need, but nobody wants to be the person hurt by it. The crux of the matter is that only so much water can be put on or pumped from a certain area of land. According to present laws, anyone owning land can pump anything out of his ground to as great an extent as he wants. "A" may own land at the edge of an irrigation district. Part of his water supply —the only part he is permitted to buy—comes from the ditch. The balance that he must have to make crops comes from wells. No doubt some of the well supply is seepage from the ditch.

Then along comes "B" and buys land just above the limit of the ditch service, but nearer than "A" to whatever mountain source of the underground water there is. He puts down wells. To get enough water for his land, he pumps excessively. Soon the wells of "A" start to give out. If "B" pumps hard enough, he may completely dry up the underground supply of "A." If there are enough "B's" around the perimeter of the project, a large part, maybe all, of the project will suffer, or even become uneconomic and have to be abandoned. Yet under present law there is no way to stop "B" from exercising his right to all the water he can raise from under his acres.

More than likely he will not only pump "A" out of the picture, but eventually himself as well. The capital loss of both will be high and probably result in double bankruptcy. And if the cyclical dry spell afflicting the West keeps up, no doubt many of both "A" and "B" will be literally dried out of their holdings.

Where a project is dependent solely on ditch flow, the maximum potential acreage can be set up at the start. But where wells are part of the deal, it is difficult or impossible to estimate what a safe limitation should be. This situation faces much of California's now-rich farm land. If further drain on available supplies is not stopped by law or agreement, then a new source of water must be found. That is the essence of the great Central Valley project. In California the average pumping lift was reported at 57 feet in 1940 and 88 feet in 1950. But in some areas the water level has fallen so drastically that lifts of several hundred feet are common. In Kern County, the nation's leading cotton county, the water level has dropped from 15 to 30 feet annually during the last five to ten years. The average lift there was about 175 feet in 1954, ranging from 60 to as much as 500 feet. Investments in wells, pumps, and related equipment may run as high as $70,000 or more. Some farmers on the west side of the San Joaquín Valley have drilled as deep as 3,000 feet, at a cost of around $75,000, in order to get a well which will produce about 1,000 gallons a minute. Some areas in California have an annual power cost of $35 to $40 an acre just for pumping. Such costs may shock a Corn Belt or a Wheat Belt farmer, but it happens that the deep wells are in localities of good soil types. Therefore crop yields are high and the crops grown are primarily high-income producers. Thus these ventures have been paying off. A serious drop in farm prices, however, would undoubtedly make many of the highly capitalized individual irrigation projects uneconomic.

Farsighted realists declare that the best thing that could happen to western irrigated agriculture right now is a farm depression of not too great magnitude. They do not wish the modern pioneers any bad luck as people—only as competitors for limited water. Many a "fringe" or marginal operation that came into being during the high prices of the war cannot exist under more normal prices, even with water. If such ill-advised people were to leave the land before the water table disappears entirely, resuscitation would not be impossible. But the fear is that the old-timers, as well as the newcomers, will go broke by water starvation before a lowering of prices will force them out of the business. Should this happen, the loss will be more acute and hurt worse.

Still another problem is always present in irrigated areas. If the water diverted onto the land does not have an underground drain, it will eventually back up and drown out the crops, as is happening in the Río Grande debouchment in Texas. Most irrigated soils in the West are underlain with strata of alkaline materials. When those strata are wet by irrigation, their alkaline salts become soluble and take on capillarity. They rise through the soil and feed into the roots of plans. The *pH* goes beyond tolerance and the plant dies. Later, as the process continues, large blotchy areas of white (alkaline sinks) appear on the surface that can only be removed by a thorough leaching, which means more water usage with a built drainage system. So to the cost of building a ditch above the field level is added the cost of digging a ditch below that level. And water that brings moisture to the fields must have added to its cost water to take the results of the first away. Irrigation farming is not the worry-proof business so many laymen consider it to be.

Finally, there is the problem that has assailed western growers ever since production outstripped local consumption: the cost of transportation to faraway markets. Supposing a Grand Coulee project brings 1,200,000 more acres into production, a central Arizona project contributes more, and the dozens of other proposed projects and additions are constructed, who will be the market? If it is to be the traditional eastern marts, some of the presently irrigated acres, as well as the new ones, will have a hard time paying off their costs. As will be discussed later, relatively high freight rates are still a burden to western farmers.

The place of water in western agriculture can best be evaluated by the production figures. Outside of wheat, most of the highest-value crops are produced almost exclusively on irrigated land. The 1950 agricultural census listed the entire California cotton crop in 1949 as having been grown under irrigation, and all but 327 bales of Arizona's cotton came from irrigated fields. The states of California, Arizona, Idaho, Oregon, Washington, and Utah produced 94,993,484 bushels of potatoes under irrigation in 1949, and only 5,047,224 bushels without irrigation. Farmers in the five states of Idaho, Washington, Oregon, Utah, and California raised about 4,556,869 tons of sugar beets, of which all except 15,334 tons were irrigated. In the seven states on the Western Slope over 92 per cent of the alfalfa was grown on irrigated land in 1949. And of course citrus and most of the apples and other fruits are grown with the aid of man-diverted water. Water is indeed the key to western farming.

It is improbable that any more than a minor percentage of available land will ever be added to the dry-farming land. It is more likely that declining yields resulting from bad land-use such as in the Palouse (Washington-Idaho) wheat region will cut actual harvested acreage. But from the figures given above, it can readily be seen that a very few acres more of irrigated lands not only could boost western production tremendously, but even cause national repercussions. A subcommittee of the United States Senate reported in 1945 that as much as 5,000,000 acres could be irrigated in Arizona alone if sufficient water were available. Obviously the future of western agriculture is irrigated farming, but a whole series of economic questions must be answered before any expansion can be successfully undertaken.

Water—Urban or Rural?

Ever since the first Western Slope subsistance farmer found himself with a surplus, the cry has gone up, "Give us more city people!" Boosters' organizations, chambers of commerce, and advertising clubs flourish in almost every hamlet west of the Great Divide. They scheme and toil around the clock to persuade people "back east" to come west and enjoy the various advantages of climate, recreation, and industrial opportunity. In earlier years the latter was soft-pedaled somewhat because of the transportation difficulty. People who had made their money elsewhere and wanted to retire were the No. 1 desirables. Workers were not encouraged unless they were low-cost laborers such as Mexicans or Orientals.

But as long ago as World War I, in Los Angeles, for example, it became apparent that city growth, while making a market for farm products, also competed with farmers for what little water there was. The wells, cisterns, and the small dams on minor watercourses that had served the Los Angeles area when it was an oasis in the desert were not enough. The nearest respectable bodies of fresh water were over 200 miles away at Owens and Mono lakes, which were fed by the melting snows of the Sierras. The genius of an unschooled engineer named William Mulholland showed the way to transport these waters, which served only a few farmers and ranchers, by ditch, siphon, and tunnel to big reservoirs outside the city. The famed Los Angeles Aqueduct was finished in 1913, literally in the face of the embattled farmers of the Owens Valley, who tried to hold off the construction crews in a latter-day battle of Lexington. The farmers of Owens Valley lost, but to this day the survivors and their descendants carry a grudge against the City of Angels. Under the doctrine of "highest use," Los Angeles secured the waters and made ready for growth of a permanent nature. Never again would the city's ambitions be curtailed by water shortage.

But little more than a decade passed before even this laboriously acquired supply was not providing for Los Angeles' water needs. After an immense and almost bloody controversy with neighboring states, Los Angeles and nearby cities tied into the

Colorado River project at Parker Dam on the California-Arizona border about 242 miles from Lake Mathews, the terminal reservoir. Some $220,000,000 was authorized for an elaborate system of ditches, tunnels, and siphons, and the first water from the Colorado River was delivered to the Los Angeles area in 1941. Again the future of the city was avowed secure. By 1950, however, the tremendous war growth of Los Angeles, which seemed to be permanent, and the truly phenomenal upsurge of industry, which showed no signs of slackening, once more started the city fathers worrying about water. The population of the Los Angeles area grew from 2,916,403 to 4,367,911 between 1940 and 1950, an increase of 49.8 per cent. These newcomers put an added strain on the available water supply, and Californians looked longingly toward the great Colorado River for even more water.

The mere suggestion by California that she should have more water from the Colorado River generated a bitter controversy with water-short Arizona. Arizona citizens rose up in arms. They had never been happy with the original six-state compact which awarded 7,500,000 acre-feet of Colorado River water to the upper-basin states of Utah, Colorado, New Mexico, and Wyoming, and a like amount to the lower-basin states of Arizona and California. In 1949 the argument between California and Arizona flared into a bitter feud, and it has continued since that time. To a considerable degree it points up the conflict between agricultural and industrial demands for water.

Arizona has supported the so-called central Arizona project, which would bring water 241 miles from the Colorado River at Parker Dam to the Phoenix area of central Arizona through the Granite Reef Aqueduct, a scheme estimated to cost about $738,000,000. It was said that Arizona needed an additional 1,200,000 acre-feet of water at once to "rescue" thousands of acres of farm land in the Phoenix area. Californians, on the other hand, have opposed the project. They want extra Colorado River water for their growing population, industries, and, to a lesser extent, for their agriculture. Representative Clair Engle of California called the central Arizona project a "fantastic scheme." It was an attempt, he said, to seize California's share of water from the Colorado River "at the expense of the taxpayers of the United States." Senator Ernest W. McFarland of Arizona, however, accused California of trying to "gobble up much more than the lion's share" of Colorado River water. And so the controversy raged at mid-century, and it still has not been decided how water from the Colorado will be divided between the growing demands of these two states. The demand for water in the lower basin of the Colorado is so immense that unless the river develops new volume from somewhere there will soon not be enough to go around. It must also be remembered that a treaty with Mexico calls for 1,500,000 acre-feet annually.

Add to this contretemps the demands of new water-users nearer the source of the great river. The San Juan Basin in New Mexico wants more water. If the Gunnison is ever diverted under the Rockies to the east, as has been urged in some quarters, this will subtract from the Colorado's supply. Landholders on various minor tributaries grow restive and dream of their own water-use projects. Great as the Colorado is, somewhere along the line there is a point of diminishing returns.

A similar situation is arising in the Central Valley of California. If all the water that is needed for manufacturing and population growth in the Bay Area is used up by more farmers, what will serve the newcomers? If more newcomers do not arrive, who will buy the farmers' surpluses?

But north of San Francisco, in a land of trees (the redwood preserve), of mining, and of little acreage suitable for a highly productive agriculture, there are a half-dozen rivers running away to the ocean, doing man little good. It's the West's oldest problem, good water too far from good land. Will the sheer demand of thirsty people and industries force the creation of gigantic river-relocation projects? It has been suggested that water from the Klamath River could be moved to arid Southern California. And there are those who have even proposed diverting water from the mighty Columbia to California. The cost of such projects would run into fantastic figures, perhaps $5,000,000,000. But the original Los Angeles project seemed, at the time it was proposed, to be outside the realm of reasonable contemplation. Who knows, if the population pressure is great enough, another redoing of the western map may take place.

The one thing that seems sure is that when land usage and human usage collide the farmer loses out.

The Power Ceiling

Another collision point between farm and city, which are more completely interdependent here than in any place else in the country, is the limitation of fuel. Developed coal is not plentiful in this area, although Utah and New Mexico have huge deposits. However, water power has provided cheap electricity for the rapidly growing West Coast industries. But the drain on hydroelectric power continues to run ahead of generating facilities.

In the north, the Bonneville power project is already at its peak production. Grand Coulee, with its tremendous power output, has not been able to keep up with industrial growth and the consequent power demand. The new McNary Dam can help, but it cannot solve the power-shortage problem. The conflict between farmers and power is illustrated by the situation at Shasta Dam.

To keep up with the power demand, Shasta must lower the lake level all winter. When the summer irrigation season comes on and precipitation is low, a double demand is put upon the stored supplies. If the farmer is to have water when he needs it, a high water level must be maintained during the winter, or a year's production is lost. But if the farmer gets his needs, then industry must be held back. In short, despite the original plans and arguments about there being enough for both, as we have heard before and will again, many a combined power-and-irrigation project of the West cannot supply both under modern demands.

The Pacific Northwest, like California and Arizona, has shown and is continuing to show trmendous growth. The Seattle area had 732,992 people in 1950 compared to only 504,980 a decade before. The population increase of the Portland area was over 40 per cent during the same period, nearly as great as that of Seattle. Industry has been growing by leaps and bounds. Aluminum at Spokane, atomic works at Hanford, aircraft at Seattle, and hundreds of other major and minor industries are increasing the demands for power. It is possible that the Northwest will grow industrially so great that even the mighty Columbia cannot serve both power user and farmer? At the moment the thought may seem fantastic, but it has happened elsewhere.

Though the West is the fastest-growing part of the nation, though some population students think it will eventually outdo the East in population and industry (because of the wealth of raw materials close at hand), and even though its agriculture can outyield that of any other region, certain grave limitations appear. It seems fantastic that a land that boasts such mighty streams as the Colorado, the San Joaquín, the Sacramento, the Columbia, and its very respectably sized tributary, the Snake, should ever want for water. But the hard truth is that urban man, industrial man, and the farmer are coming close to a fight for the precious fluid in the not too distant future.

The Western Farm

Against the background of water and the lack of it, what is the importance of agriculture on the Western Slope? Possibly the first idea could come from the list of leading agricultural counties as shown by the 1950 census. The ratings show that California had seventeen of the top twenty-five counties ranked on the basis of the value of farm products sold. All of the first four were in California, and no other state had more than one county among the first twenty-five. In order of value of farm products sold, the counties were:

	Sales		*Rank*	
County	1949	1944	1949	1944
Los Angeles, Calif.	$156,962,336	$129,449,240	1	1
Fresno, Calif.	144,006,192	102,906,480	2	2
Kern, Calif.	122,066,240	75,177,399	3	5
Tulare, Calif.	105,410,932	98,851,260	4	3
Maricopa, Ariz.	92,190,697	47,117,174	5	14
San Joaquín, Calif.	86,852,427	83,463,043	6	4
Weld, Colo.	78,049,617	42,258,728	7	19
Imperial, Calif.	75,197,726	50,444,660	8	10

Lancaster, Pa.	69,681,490	46,974,186	9	15
Stanislaus, Calif.	65,641,451	58,046,649	10	8
Monterey, Calif.	57,833,000	38,152,271	11	22
Orange, Calif.	56,539,256	63,385,541	12	7
Sussex, Del.	56,469,005	47,600,584	13	13
Yakima, Wash.	55,886,315	65,004,514	14	6
Merced, Calif.	54,779,522	41,186,233	15	20
Aroostook, Maine	54,509,885	48,162,988	16	12
Hidalgo, Tex.	53,300,422	28,313,863	17	30
Santa Barbara, Calif.	52,942,969	23,976,918	18	39
Sonoma, Calif.	52,247,052	49,196,275	19	11
Riverside, Calif.	51,599,291	44,964,818	20	17
Polk, Fla.	51,178,252	43,214,340	21	18
San Bernardino, Calif.	50,110,892	55,174,508	22	9
Santa Clara, Calif.	49,986,738	46,909,873	23	16
Ventura, Calif.	49,542,289	38,516,762	24	21
Kings, Calif.	43,765,553	23,192,714	25	41

Of the 100 leading agricultural counties in the United States in 1949, 30 per cent of them were in the five states of Arizona, Idaho, Washington, Oregon, and California.

To many easterners and midwesterners, the agricultural wealth of the West is easily overlooked. Much of the area appears lonely, desolate, unproductive. Much of it is breathtakingly beautiful, with forest-blanketed mountains and rapidly flowing streams. But where, they may ask, are those great farm riches shown in the statistics? It is true that the acres of cropland harvested are relatively few, but, as mentioned before, they are highly productive. The seven Far Western States under consideration had only 21,644,416 acres of harvested cropland in 1949, which was just a little less than Iowa's 22,547,337 acres. Of the harvested cropland on the Western Slope, 10,454,538 acres, or nearly half, were irrigated.

Those who are unaware of the intensive cropping in the irrigated regions of the West are surprised when they learn that Los Angeles County is the first-ranking agricultural county in the United States. This county sold farm products valued at $156,962,336 in 1949. In fact, Los Angeles *County* produced a greater value of agricultural commodities than any of the *states* of New Hamp-

TABLE 83.—*Number and acreage of irrigated farms in the Far Western States, 1939–50.*

	Number of irrigated farms		*Acres of irrigated land in farms*	
	1950	1940	1949	1939
Idaho	29,413	29,898	2,137,237	1,895,048
Ariz.	7,822	10,339	963,560	575,464
Utah	21,126	22,612	1,137,995	911,135
Nev.	2,819	3,264	727,498	755,636
Wash.	16,928	17,426	589,035	493,982
Ore.	17,663	16,159	1,306,810	1,030,228
Calif.	90,755	84,310	6,438,324	4,276,554

Source: *United States Census of Agriculture, 1950,* II, 62–63.

shire, Vermont, Rhode Island, Connecticut, Delaware, West Virginia, Wyoming, Utah, or Nevada.

As in other areas of the United States, agriculture in the Far Western States is characterized by tremendous diversity, perhaps even more so than in any other region. Soils, topography, and climate all help account for these variations. For example, look momentarily at Oregon. The coastal section has a normal rainfall of about 75 inches, but it may reach as much as 130. The heavy rainfall helps provide lush pastures, and dairying has become the major farm enterprise, especially in Tillamook and Coos counties. Farms are relatively small, averaging around 125 acres. Moving eastward into the Willamette Valley, one finds a mild climate fairly free from extremes, as much as 50 inches of precipitation a year in the northern part, and a highly diversified agriculture. Most crops, including fruits and nuts, are raised without irrigation, although some supplemental irrigation is used in the summer months to boost output. When one gets east of the Cascades, the rainfall declines sharply. Most of eastern Oregon gets only from 9 to 14 inches of rain annually. Here the land is given over principally to extensive operations, with big grain and livestock ranches predominating. Almost any other Far Western State could have been used to illustrate the agricultural extremes which prevail in this region.

TABLE 84.—*Number of farms in the Far Western States, 1870–1950.*

	1950	1940	1930	1920	1910	1900	1880	1870
Idaho	40,284	43,663	41,674	42,106	30,807	17,471	1,885	414
Ariz.	10,412	18,468	14,173	9,975	9,227	5,809	767	172
Utah	24,176	25,411	27,159	25,662	21,676	19,387	9,452	4,908
Nev.	3,110	3,573	3,442	3,163	2,689	2,184	1,404	1,036
Wash.	69,820	81,686	70,904	66,288	56,192	33,202	6,529	3,127
Ore.	59,827	61,829	55,153	50,206	45,502	35,837	16,217	7,587
Calif.	137,168	132,658	135,676	117,670	88,197	72,542	35,934	23,724

Source: *United States Census of Agriculture, 1950,* II, 55–57.

A brief summary of the western crop picture (livestock will be considered later) looks something like this. In Utah wheat is the principal grain crop, followed by barley. The state ranks seventh in sugar-beet production, with 457,520 tons in 1949. The feed requirements of the state's extensive livestock industry have made alfalfa a major hay crop, and alfalfa seed produces important cash income. Vegetables, including potatoes, bring farmers additional money. With the exception of wheat, practically all of the crops are grown under irrigation.

Moving northward into Idaho, the lowly potato holds the spot-

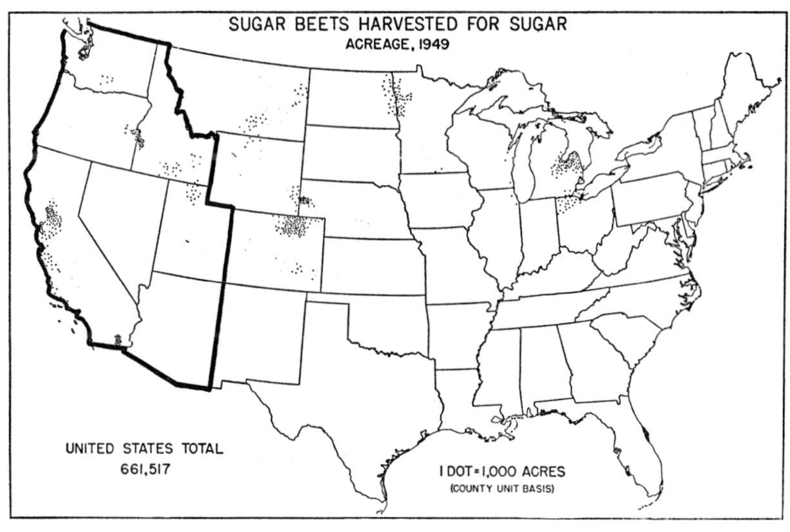

light. Idaho usually ranks second in potato production being exceeded only by Maine. The state produced 49,000,000 bushels in 1950, although the usual output is around 37,000,000. In 1949 potatoes brought Idaho farmers a little over $36,000,000, and they represented 18.5 per cent of the value of all crops sold. Twin Falls and Canyon (Caldwell) counties along the Snake River are the richest farm areas in the state, ranking thirty-first and thirty-seventh, respectively, among the counties of the United States on the basis of agricultural products sold. Idaho is exceeded only by California and Colorado in sugar-beet production. In 1949 the state grew 1,080,387 tons, which had a value of over $11,000,000. Fruits play an important role on some Idaho farms, but they are not a very significant part of the state-wide farm pattern. As is true over much of the West, alfalfa is a leading crop.

The major income-producer in Idaho is wheat. It represented about 40 per cent of the cropland harvested in 1949, when 1,469,598 acres were devoted to this crop and over 34,000,000 bushels were raised. Most of the wheatland is fallowed in the summer, and the crop is grown mainly in the southern part of the state and in the counties of Nez Percé, Latah, and Lewis, which make up a part of the famous Palouse region. The value of all crops sold in the state in 1949 was $153,836,501.

Going westward into Washington, the picture of agriculture is again one of great contrasts and variations. In the eastern section of the state, especially the southeastern, where rainfall is skimpy but where it generally comes at the proper time, winter wheat is the chief crop. Much of the land is hilly to mountainous, and midwesterners are likely to marvel at the ability of farmers to cultivate the steep slopes and hillsides. Caterpillar tractors are the most common type of farm power. The average-size farm there in 1949 was 1,172 acres. The average value of land and buildings per farm totaled a little over $84,000, and the average value of farm products sold, mostly wheat, was $18,013. The United States Department of Agriculture reported that the pea and winter wheat farms of southeastern Washington–northwestern Idaho were the most prosperous in the country, netting their operators an average of $13,538 in 1953.

TABLE 85.—*Average number of acres per farm in the Far Western States, 1870–1950.*

	1950	1940	1930	1920	1910	1900	1880	1870
Idaho	328.3	235.8	224.3	198.9	171.5	183.4	173.9	186.3
Ariz.	3,833.7	1,388.9	742.7	581.7	135.1	333.2	176.8	126.8
Utah	449.4	287.4	206.7	196.8	156.7	212.4	69.4	30.2
Nev.	2,271.2	1,059.4	1,185.6	745.2	1,009.6	1,174.7	378.1	201.3
Wash.	248.8	185.9	190.9	199.8	208.4	256.0	215.9	207.6
Ore.	339.8	290.9	300.1	269.7	256.8	281.0	259.9	314.9
Calif.	266.9	230.1	224.4	249.6	316.7	397.4	461.8	481.7

Source: *United States Census of Agriculture, 1950,* II, 799.

However, expenses of operation and investment in machinery and equipment are exceptionally high on these farms. By looking at an actual situation one may get a clearer picture than by studying official reports and averages. A distant relative of one of the authors operates a farm of 2,100 acres in the Palouse area. Since acreages have been cut, he raises about 600 acres of wheat, 900 acres of spring crops (peas, lentils, barley, oats, etc.), and 700 acres of summer fallow. His machinery in 1953 included 3 caterpillar tractors, 3 combines, 5 plows, 6 drills, 5 trucks, and a great many other machines. His investment in machinery and equipment to handle the 2,100 acres was $53,000. Even on the smaller wheat farms, those in the 400- to 600-acre class, investments in machinery usually run $25,000 or more.

Washington's Whitman, Lincoln, and Adams counties, in that order, are the nation's leading wheat producers, with a normal annual output of about 12,000,000, 10,000,000 and 8,000,000 bushels, respectively. It is not uncommon for this area to produce forty or fifty bushels of wheat per acre, and a crop failure is rare. Many farmers (locally they are called ranchers) alternate wheat with green peas, which are processed at Walla Walla, Dayton, and other towns. Dry field and seed peas and green peas for processing brought Washington farmers over $15,000,000 in 1949. Walla Walla and Columbia counties ranked second and third among the nation's green-pea producers. Hops and sugar beets are also important in the state's farm economy. In 1953 field and seed crops made up 40 per cent of the value of farm production, with wheat, of course, comprising the major part of this percentage. Hay is the second most important field crop.

Washington and apples are associated in the public mind like Mississippi and cotton and Iowa and corn. And well they might be. Washington is by far the leading apple state. Yakima, Chelan (Wenatchee), and Okanogan counties, just east of the Cascades, are the heart of the apple country. These three counties harvested most of the state's 29,681,000 bushels in 1949. Income from apples far exceeded that from all other fruit crops, and it usually ranks second to the income from wheat. In 1953 apples brought Washington growers a whopping $103,275,000. Only wheat provided farmers with more money. Pears, strawberries, prunes, and cherries are the other most important fruits. Yakima County not only ranks first in apple production, but also in pear production. Most of the fruit farms are highly specialized operations. Washington fruit farms averaged about fifty-two acres in 1949 and had an average value per acre of $442. It is not uncommon, however, for good orchard land to go as high as $2,000 an acre.

The total value of Washington farm production in 1953 was $672,383,000. Of this amount, 40 per cent came from field and seed crops, 22.4 per cent from fruits and berries, 3.7 per cent from vegetables, and 3 per cent from specialties. The remaining 30.9 per cent was derived from livestock and livestock products.

Across the Columbia River to the south is Oregon. Like Idaho and Washington, Oregon's chief grain crop is wheat, which occupied about 32 per cent of the cropland harvested in 1949. Most of the wheat is grown in the Columbia Basin, which extends roughly from Hood River eastward to Elgin. About 25 per cent of the state's crop is grown in Umatilla County. In Gilliam County wheat provides about 70 per cent of the total farm income. Most wheat is grown under dry-land farming conditions, and a two-year summer-fallow rotation is followed. A wheat-pea production pattern is also common. Umatilla County ranks first in the nation in acreage and production of English green peas.

Grain and hay crops made up 20.6 per cent of Oregon's cash farm income in 1950. Fruits and nuts ranked second with 8.8 per cent. Oregon is the country's leading pear state, with Hood River on the Columbia River and Jackson County in southern Oregon producing the bulk of the crop. In the Willamette Valley, lying between the Cascades and the Coast Range, an extremely varied crop pattern exists. Fruit and berries are raised in large quantities. Potatoes and truck crops of about all kinds are grown, along with nuts such as walnuts and filberts. Oregon ranks high in the production of hops, about 75 per cent of which are raised in this region. A major part of the state's $8,000,000 nursery enterprises are also located here.

TABLE 86.—*Average value of farm land and buildings per acre in the Far Western States, 1870–1950.*

	1950	1940	1930	1920	1910	1900	1880	1870
Idaho	$ 69.82	$ 32.94	$ 44.64	$ 69.43	$46.38	$13.20	$ 8.64	$ 5.11
Ariz.	15.13	5.99	17.50	29.70	37.93	7.07	8.32	5.92
Utah	43.37	21.14	39.41	48.26	34.60	12.33	21.38	12.39
Nev.	19.24	12.57	15.71	28.11	14.59	6.09	10.19	7.12
Wash.	84.64	39.08	57.17	69.49	48.84	13.60	9.82	6.13
Ore.	59.82	26.51	38.12	49.86	38.99	13.14	13.50	9.36
Calif.	154.32	70.97	112.33	104.67	51.93	24.56	15.79	12.36

Source: *United States Census of Agriculture, 1950,* II, 55–57.

One of Oregon's most significant agricultural developments during the last decade has been the expansion of the forage- and cover-crop seed industry. Red and alsike clover seed, rye grass seed, and vetch seed are among the chief income producers. Forage seeds produced 7.3 per cent of the total farm income in 1950, amounting to over $28,000,000. From an income point of view, Oregon agriculture is well balanced between crops and livestock. From 1926 to 1930 the income from the two sources was about even. In the late nineteen thirties animal income grew to a point where it was 53.2 per cent of the total. In both 1945 and 1950, however, that trend was reversed and cash crops furnished a little over 55 per cent of the farm income.

When discussing western crops, one need not be detained in Nevada. The value of all crops sold there in 1949 amounted to only $4,449,198. This was just about equal to the cherry crop in Oregon!

In Arizona, however, the desert has been made to bloom like a rose, and agricultural wealth and income have increased rapidly. In 1950 the cash receipts from farm marketings amounted to $278,-865,000. Despite lower prices, this reached $370,000,000 by 1953. Most of the state's farm income is produced in the three counties of Yuma, Maricopa, and Pinal. In 1949 Arizona land in farms totaled 39,916,440 acres, but there were only 883,717 acres of cropland harvested, mostly irrigated, or 2.2 per cent of the land in farms. By 1953, however, irrigation had expanded until 1,300,-000 acres, including pasture, were under the ditch or sprinkler.

Cotton has become the main cash crop. In 1950 Arizona produced 474,000 bales on 275,000 acres; by 1953 the state's output was estimated at 1,023,000 bales and the acreage had jumped to about 682,000. This acreage, however, was to be reduced substantially in 1955 under the federal crop-control program. The cotton crop is irrigated and production is highly mechanized, including the use of mechanical pickers. There were 2,000 mechanical cotton pickers in Arizona in 1953, and for the first time more than half the crop was picked by machine. A good picture of cotton growing in this area can be seen in the fact that Pinal and Maricopa counties ranked sixteenth and forty-second, respectively, in acreage in 1949, but rated fifth and eighth in production. Arizona's average yield of upland cotton in 1953 was 740 pounds an acre. For the state as a whole, cotton occupied 42.2 per cent of the cropland harvested in 1949. Of the $99,504,662 farm income from field crops, $75,000,000 was derived from the white lint. The $200,-000,000 cotton crop in 1953 was more than the cash receipts from all other farm products combined.

Although cotton brings more money than any other crop, Arizona is best known for its vegetables. Vegetable acreage jumped from 1,865 in 1909 to 74,256 in 1949, and to 95,000 in 1953. Maricopa County alone had 46,733 acres of vegetables with a gross product valued at $16,868,411 in 1949. The county ranked eighth in acreage and fourth in production. Yuma County, the other leading vegetable area, ranked eighteenth in acreage, but sixth in output. Winter and spring lettuce, carrots, and cantaloupes are the main vegetable and fruit crops. The state ranked second in both lettuce and cantaloupe acreage in 1949. Altogether, vegetables brought Arizona farmers some $30,000,000. The state also has a rapidly growing seed industry. The value of seeds sold in 1949 was $2,400,000.

Some of the most highly capitalized and largest gross-product farms in the country are found in Arizona. For example, the average-size cotton farm in 1949 was 660 acres, with an average value of land and buildings per farm of $84,121. Products sold from these farms averaged $57,428, about 91 per cent of which came from cotton. The 243 enterprises classified as vegetable farms are even further from the traditional concept of American agriculture. These farms averaged 837 acres, land and buildings had an average value of $97,157, and the average gross product was $122,788. As mentioned earlier, there are an estimated 3,000,000 to 5,000,000 acres of land which could be brought into cultivation if enough water were available. The great threat to Arizona agriculture is the lack of water. Although irrigated acreage about doubled between 1946 and 1953, actual reductions occurred in some local areas because of the scarcity or high cost of water. By 1953 approximately 70 per cent of Arizona's irrigation water came from pumped wells, and in most sections the water level was dropping at a dangerous rate. The average decline in Maricopa County has

TABLE 87.—*Acres of cropland harvested, and acres of irrigated cropland harvested in the Far Western States, 1939–49.*

	Total acres of cropland harvested		*Acres of irrigated cropland harvested*		*Per cent of cropland harvested which was irrigated*	
	1949	1939	1949	1939	1949	1939
Idaho	3,647,885	2,935,350	1,703,601	1,578,741	46.7	53.8
Ariz.	883,717	525,974	839,037	471,372	94.9	89.6
Utah	1,279,469	966,088	847,271	761,093	66.2	78.8
Nev.	421,202	435,855	412,929	430,743	98.0	98.8
Wash.	4,236,705	3,569,803	448,743	409,161	10.6	11.5
Ore.	3,218,767	2,824,316	893,304	730,682	27.8	25.9
Calif.	7,956,671	6,534,562	5,309,653	3,732,215	66.7	57.1

Source: Compiled from the *United States Census of Agriculture, 1950,* II; and *United States Census of Agriculture, 1950, Irrigation of Agricultural Lands,* III, 38.

been 6 or 7 feet a year. In Pinal County the average pumping lift has reached about 300 feet.

In our brief consideration of western crops, a discussion of California agriculture has been purposely left until last. The state is so fabulously rich, so remarkably varied, and can boast of so many agricultural virtues that the present authors approach any discussion of it with trepidation. There is nothing about California farming which is conducive to brief treatment, and this makes our task even more difficult.

To start with, it might be stated that cash receipts from farm marketings in California have exceeded the $2,000,000,000 mark every year since 1946. In 1951 and again in 1952 gross farm income was slightly above the $2,700,000,000 mark. This was higher than either Texas or Iowa, the other leaders. Another way of looking at the California farm picture is to consider that the state has more farm income than the other ten Western States combined, if Colorado is omitted. California farmers operated only about 2.5 per cent of the nation's farms in 1952, but they received 8.3 per cent of the total receipts from farm marketings.

According to the 1950 census, California had 137,169 farms. They included 36,613,291 acres of which only 7,956,671, or 21 per cent, represented cropland harvested. About 66 per cent of the harvested cropland was irrigated. The irrigated land, of course, was by far the most valuable. One study showed that annual income from irrigated land averaged $280 an acre while that from nonirrigated land averaged only $30. The average-size farm in 1949 was 267 acres, with 58 acres of harvested cropland. However, there are many very large enterprises, especially in the Central Valley. Outside of livestock farms, cash-grain, cotton, and vegetable farms are usually the largest. In 1949 California had 6,001 farms of over 1,000 acres each. The total land per farm on these large spreads was 4,249 acres, and the gross product sold averaged $83,921. The average value of land and buildings per farm reached an almost unbelievable $236,797.

Some of California's farms are several-million-dollar enterprises, but even the relatively small farms are highly capitalized. For example, in San Benito County 100 acres, or a little less, is considered adequate for an owner-operator to make a good living, mainly from potatoes and sugar beets. In 1954, with land at $800 an acre, desirable machinery and equipment costing about $21,000, plus $8,700 for an irrigation well, motor and pump, and pipe, an original investment came to well over $100,000.

The richest area of California agriculture is in the immense Central Valley, which extends roughly from Redding in the north to Kern Lake in the south. It is enclosed on the west by the Coast Range and on the east by the Sierra Nevada. The valley is about 450 miles long and averages 40 miles in width. In the southern end precipitation is usually less than ten inches a year. Irrigation waters are impounded during the winter rains and from the mountain snows, or are pumped from the underground water reservoirs. About 75 per cent of California's crops are grown in this great interior valley.

On the basis of value, cotton outranks all other crops in California, a lead established in 1947. Only Texas and Mississippi grow more cotton. Kern County (Bakersfield) is the nation's top cotton-producing county. While it only ranked ninth in acreage in 1949, it was first in output. In 1953 this single county grew 319,000 acres and produced 512,710 bales, which was more than the entire

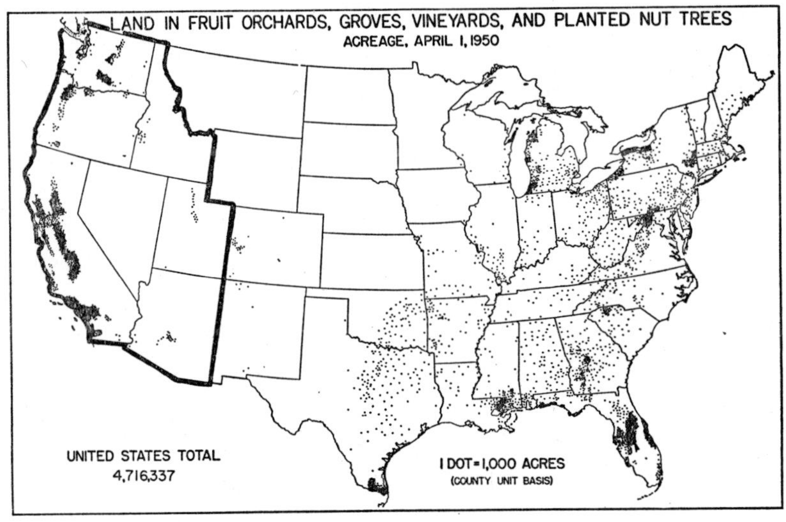

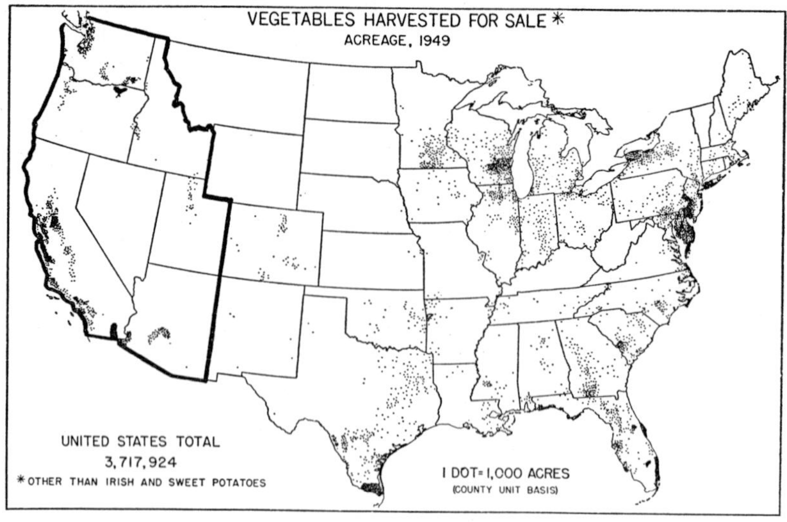

state of Oklahoma produced. Production reached the fabulous average of 770 pounds (over a bale and a half) to the acre. The state average was 632 pounds per acre compared to a national average of only about 270 pounds. Other leading cotton counties are Fresno, Tulare, and Kings. The total state cotton acreage in 1953 was 1,375,000, and the value of cotton and cotton seed amounted to $318,354,000, or about 42 per cent of the value of all field crops.

Nowhere in the world is cotton production so highly mechanized, Mechanical picking especially has reached its most advanced stage here. There were only a handful of mechanical pickers operating in the south and west of the San Joaquín Valley in 1945, but by 1950 the number had increased to 1,450, and by 1951 there were 3,700 in the state. While only about 16 per cent of the cotton was picked by machines in 1949, about 54 per cent was harvested in that fashion in 1951.

Hay and barley occupy more acreage than cotton, but they rate a poor second and third, respectively, from the standpoint of farm income. Cotton, hay, barley, rice, potatoes, and beans, in that order, were the ranking field crops in 1953. California ranks first in barley production, is usually third in rice output, and is exceeded only by Michigan in acres of dry field and seed beans. The state grew about

48,000,000 bushels of potatoes in 1953 and 3,306,000 tons of sugar beets. Alfalfa is a major crop and production per acre reaches between four and five tons. The total value of field crops alone in 1953, including the leading field seeds, was $766,106,000.

Besides this vast farm production, California is famous for its vegetables and fruits. Vegetable acreage increased from 57,194 in 1909 to 537,681 acres in 1949. Vegetables occupied 14.9 per cent of the acreage of all crops harvested. California has more lettuce acreage than all the rest of the states combined; it is also first in cantaloupe production. In fact, the state produces almost every vegetable imaginable, and does it on a larger scale than most anywhere else. Monterey, Imperial, and San Joaquín counties were the nation's three leading vegetable counties on the basis of dollar value in 1949. In 1952 and 1953 the commercial vegetable crop brought California farmers $375,651,000 and $365,197,000, respectively.

California's fruit and nut crop is even more fabulous. The value

TABLE 88.—*Value of farm products sold, and per cent of value of farm products sold represented by crops and by livestock products in the Far Western States, 1939–49.**

	Value of farm products sold		*Per cent of value of farm products sold*			
			Crops		*Livestock and livestock prod.*	
	1949	1939	1949	1939	1949	1939
Idaho	$ 281,025,323	$ 83,890,896	54.7	51.3	45.0	48.3
Ariz.	203,936,809	39,430,477	65.9	48.6	33.7	51.2
Utah	130,287,725	39,877,227	28.7	35.1	71.3	64.9
Nev.	34,007,030	11,250,999	13.1	14.3	86.9	85.7
Wash.	365,209,027	117,488,446	61.4	56.8	37.6	42.8
Ore.	298,079,076	98,549,850	50.9	42.7	47.0	54.3
Calif.	1,741,961,237	451,836,458	61.1	62.2	38.8	37.7

Source: *United States Census of Agriculture, 1950,* II, 752–54.

* The value of farm products sold does not represent total gross farm income. It does not include the sale of some products, the value of farm products used by the farmer, etc. The value of farm products sold as shown in the census and the cash receipts from farm marketings published by the Bureau of Agricultural Economics are not the same.

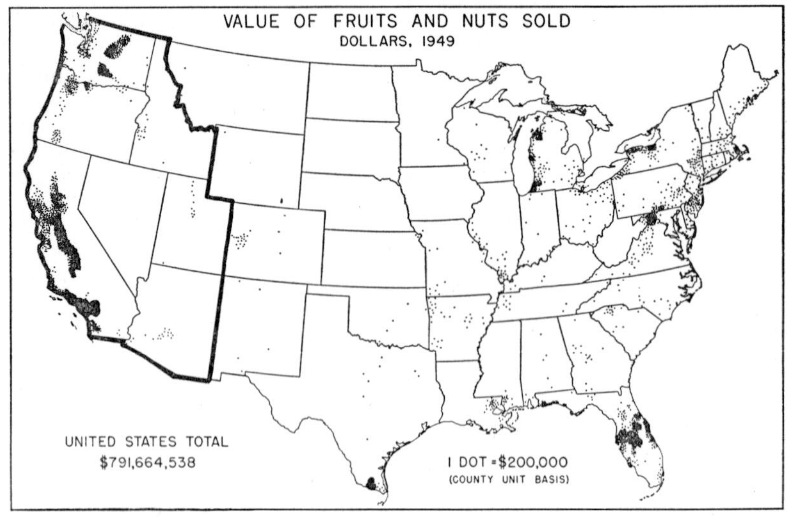

of these crops alone in 1951 was just about the same as the entire farm income in Virginia, or $503,543,000. Almonds, walnuts, pecans, and filberts are produced by the thousands of tons. All of the fresh and dried figs, the olives, and the lemons were produced in California. The state also grew 87 per cent of the plums, 89 per cent of the apricots, 81 per cent of the avocados, and 94 per cent of the grapes in 1952. Pears, peaches, grapefruit, and, of course, oranges are grown in large quantities. And Los Angeles County is the nation's leader in the production of nursery and greenhouse products, flowers, and vegetable seeds. This list of firsts could be expanded to great lengths, but it would serve no purpose. Suffice it to say that the Western Slope, particularly Washington, Oregon, and California, is rich agriculturally and probably will maintain its national standing for some time to come.

Livestock will play a major part in helping the seven Far Western States to maintain their agricultural position. While livestock is not as important here as it is, say, in the Corn Belt, income from this source is highly significant. In Nevada, for example, livestock and its products made up 86.9 per cent of the value of farm products sold in 1949. Livestock is also the main source of farm income in Utah. But in Idaho, Washington, Oregon, Arizona, and California, crops usually exceed livestock in their contribution to farm welfare.

Cattle, dairy, and poultry products are the chief sources of income from livestock. Sheep and hogs are of relatively little importance in the total picture. Extensive cattle and sheep ranching exists in most of Utah and Nevada and in southern Idaho and eastern and southern Oregon. About 66 per cent of Nevada's farm income is derived from cattle and sheep, mostly cattle. In Utah the value of cattle and sheep sold in 1949 totaled over $43,000,000, which was about 33 per cent of the value of all farm products sold. Although there is a good deal of ranching in eastern Washington and Oregon, the western part of those states stresses dairying. The Puget Sound area competes with Wisconsin but does not surpass it in processed milk and is the home of Carnation. Farming in Tillamook and Coos counties along the Oregon coast is primarily devoted to dairying. About 90 per cent of the agriculture in Tillamook County centers around the dairy industry, and the region has become widely known for its cheddar cheese. Millions of gallons of fluid milk are produced in the Pacific Northwest to supply the rapidly growing populations of Portland and Seattle, as well as lesser cities. Over most of the region west of the Cascades, beef-

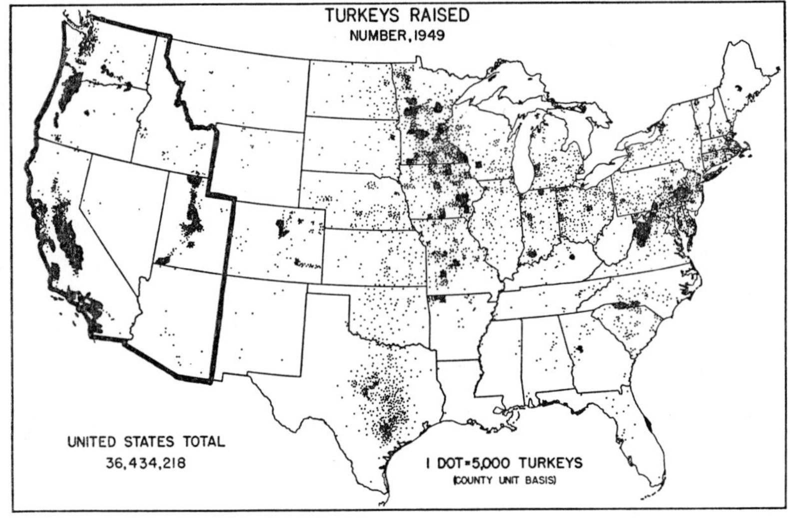

cattle numbers are growing, and one sees many small herds of white faces, Angus, and Shorthorns.

California had 2,756,737 cattle in 1950, ranking seventh among the states. By 1953 this had increased to 3,283,000 head. Of these, about 900,000 were milk cows. During the period of high cattle prices in 1950, 1951, and part of 1952, cash receipts from the sale of cattle and calves were generally more than those received from dairy products. But in 1953 dairy products again made up the principal item in the income from livestock. Dairy products grossed California farmers $323,000,000 in 1953. Practically all of this came from the sale of whole milk. There was a terrific increase in the demand for fluid milk in California in the nineteen forties, and the pounds of whole milk sold jumped from 3,156,165,204 in 1939 to 5,237,763,273 in 1949. Dairymen in Los Angeles County alone sold 1,104,803,000 pounds of whole milk in 1949, which was over twice as much as was sold by any other county in the country. Stanislaus, Merced, Tulare, and Fresno counties also have large numbers of cattle and milk cows. Maricopa County, Arizona, ranked twelfth in the number of cattle on farms in 1950. The largest dry-lot feeding operation is not in Iowa but in Phoenix.

Poultry and poultry products add tremendously to farm income, especially in Utah, Washington, Oregon, and California. In fact, income from poultry is greater than that from dairy products in Utah, $24,567,540 to $15,809,151 in 1949. California, Utah, and Oregon are the big turkey states in the West. California raised over 7,000,000 in 1949. The egg capital of the world is Petaluma in Sonoma County, not far north of San Francisco. In 1949 that county sold over 37,000,000 dozen eggs. Their value was $18,-244,209. Petaluma can and does sell eggs competitively on the eastern metropolitan markets, and broiler production has been expanding all along the West Coast.

Truly, the emigrant from any other part of the country has the widest possible choice of what kind of farming he will engage in and how large his farm will be. There is no average or usual-size farm here: he can choose a 100,000-acre domain, a 10-acre, intensively cropped acreage, or anything in between.

Surrounding San Diego, Los Angeles, the Bay Area, Portland,

TABLE 89.—*Economic classification of farms in the Far Western States, 1950.**

	Per cent of all farms† considered commercial	*Per cent of commercial farms in each economic class*					
		I	*II*	*III*	*IV*	*V*	*VI*
Idaho	80.3	5.2	17.1	28.3	26.8	16.6	5.9
Ariz.	64.9	21.6	18.3	16.0	15.1	19.2	9.9
Utah	70.8	5.5	12.5	23.1	27.2	22.7	9.0
Nev.	74.4	12.1	18.8	18.5	21.9	19.5	9.1
Wash.	56.4	7.9	17.1	20.4	21.1	22.6	10.8
Ore.	57.6	6.3	16.0	20.5	23.0	23.4	10.7
Calif.	72.4	14.2	19.0	22.1	20.8	17.5	6.5

Source: *United States Census of Agriculture, 1950,* II, 1133.

* For the definition of the economic classes of farms, see Table 5.

† The largest number of noncommercial (part-time and residential) farms in the Far Western States is in Washington and Oregon, where 43.6 and 42.4 per cent, respectively, are part-time and residential. Idaho had the lowest per cent of such farmers among the states on the Western Slope in 1950, with only 19.7 per cent.

and Seattle are heavy concentrations of part-time farmers. Both Washington and Oregon had over 40 per cent part-time and residential farmers in 1949. Although their total contributions to state and county income figures are not large, their stabilizing effect on an otherwise boom-and-bust economy is. They also have something to do with the wide and healthful diet that is characteristic of the whole area. The highest wages in the country are paid in this area, and fruits, vegetables, and dairy products probably bring the lowest prices. The result is a balanced diet of great sufficiency.

In general, wherever there is a valley with water in this region, there is agriculture, and it usually is prolific. Yet in times gone by it was not necessarily prosperous from a cash standpoint, although generally adequate from a subsistence standpoint. In the great wheat region of southeastern Washington and eastern Oregon this has not been true. Rather the boom-and-bust cycle has been similar to that of the Great Plains Wheat Belt.

Also, in the past, there have been many migrations of get-rich-quick farmers, lured on by the florid advertising campaigns of land promoters who should have been in jail—where not a few finally arrived. Many of the "suckers" were professional people, teachers, and nonfarm white-collar workers who became absentee landlords in orange, apple, cotton, and other promotions. After these owners had gone broke, the little "One-Acre-and-Independence" tracts were usually gathered together in adequate-size units by second or third owners. Today the bulk of the land is soundly held, and it is not likely that many more such schemes will crop up.

It must be noted and underlined that there is no more good farm land that is cheap in this region from the Mexican to the Canadian border. Probably there is no more land outside of irrigation projects that should be farmed at all—with the exception of tree farms, of which many are needed. In irrigation projects, there is very little land not yet under cultivation which should be plowed. The best bet for anyone wanting to settle on the Western Slope is to buy a going project where audited books are available.

Transportation, Migration, & the Future

From almost the time of the coming of the first railroad to the Western Slope, the greatest cross the settlers had to bear was the high cost of transportation to and from the East. The phrase, "Add ten cents west of the Rockies," angered the westerners, who charged that they were being treated like second-class citizens. Even as recently as 1940, when J. Russell Smith updated his monumental *North America,* there was deep concern about this factor and its effect on the future of the region.

If this resentment has not changed, at least its effect, once all-important, is being somewhat minimized, and the probability of a change in the freight rates themselves is also nearer to reality now than at any time in the past. The reason for this, of course, is the greatest migration of people in recent times. The census of 1950 reported that 3,272,000 people migrated to the West Coast States between 1940 and 1950.

To a land where agricultural surpluses were the rule rather than the exception, the coming of the emigrants was an almost unmixed blessing. The newcomers became consumers, for most of them went to the cities. Their presence lured manufacturers because of the labor supply and the new market they offered. When the war-boomed industries made their inevitable contraction, new peace-time industries burgeoned in their wake. Instead of a recession, a boom in building and industry took place.

A news story which appeared on January 23, 1948, declared:

> "Last year alone [1947] industrial growth in Los Angeles exceeded factory investments for the entire five-year pre-war period 1936–40. According to the Los Angeles Chamber of Commerce, industrial development totaled $118,570,000 during that time. For 1947, just through the first eleven months, the total reached $119,821,500."

The San Francisco area reported a $63,000,000 industrial investment. In the first eight months of 1947, Seattle industries spent $48,000,000. Portland kept in step. Examples of growing industry in the West could be multiplied at will. But the important point is this: These new industrialists are complaining that they are being penalized by unfair freight rates. As most of them are onetime easterners and know the ropes, there is a good chance that their weight thrown behind the long-time, native freight-rate fighters may force a more amiable view from the railroads.

In any case, the moving of such a vast body of consumers into a near-at-hand market has had and will continue to have a permanently positive effect on western agriculture. Already the demand for livestock is greater than the local supply. Certainly many fruits and vegetables once thrown away because of minor blemishes or falling below grade will find consumers. Yet in the great export crops of citrus, nuts, dried fruits, and canning vegetables, the output is so huge that not even the millions of new "at home" customers can make more than a dent.

The only three apparent sources of relief are the relaxation of transportation rates, new forms of products (which being lighter will ship cheaper), and lower costs of production through mechanization and better seed strains. What will happen in the first category is, of course, problematic. The new industrialists can point out the rising volume of export freight. They can argue that possibly the high rates were justified when the rails had to traverse hundreds of miles of no-earnings country to carry a small volume. But now, when the volume both ways is up and mounting, the cost and net-profit ratios have shifted. Once it was common for cars to go one way empty. Now, except for refrigerator cars, it is possible to get two-way paying loads. Even should relief come from these and other arguments, it is still dubious if the West could compete in transportation with Florida and the Río Grande.

This negative circumstance need not be fatal, however. Oranges probably never would have come into prominence if they had been sold as fresh fruit alone. Orange juice made the difference. Tomatoes would not have become the large contributors to farm income they are if ketchup, chili sauce, tomato paste, and, most important, tomato juice had not been developed and sold to the public. Likewise, raisins as an ingredient flavor in Christmas cookery, walnuts as a once-a-year luxury, turkeys as a Thanksgiving tradition, and many other occasional-use foodstuffs would not have become important money-makers without the change in traditional consumption patterns and tastes brought about by national advertising campaigns.

The possibility of marketing a food product in several forms has many westerners hard at work. Fruit wastes and surpluses are being put up in pureed, quick-frozen forms that have a new taste, ship cheaper than the fresh product, and are preserved indefinitely. An orange processor is expanding his plants as fast as he can to produce a homogenized fresh orange juice that rivals the juice-right-off-the tree. It will be marketed in automatic dispensers in factories and public places as a rival to the soft drinks now so enormously quaffed by the public. A few years ago only a small fraction of the Willamette Valley strawberry crop went into canned or processed forms, but now the biggest part is quick-frozen.

These only indicate a few ways that freight rates can be overcome. One is to reduce weight. Another is to pay the rate on a higher-priced processed product rather than on the fresh. Still another is to get the product in a prepackaged form which makes the rate unimportant percentage-wise.

Lastly, there is the possibility of cutting field and processing costs through mechanization, chemical treatment, or better industrialization. When the Japanese, the last wave of the West Coast's stoop labor, were removed post-Pearl Harbor, the effect was supposed to be disastrous. But the Western Slope has always been a particularly fertile field for new farm technology. The Japanese had hardly been interned, however wrongly, when the sugar-beet harvester appeared in the fields. Perhaps it would have come anyway, for work had been in progress for years, but come at this time it did and not a minute too soon. The final release and quick acceptance of this machine were dependent on segmented seed, a development of Roy Bainer of the University of California.

Previously, the sugar-beet seed had grown in rosettes, a cluster of seeds around a central element. Bainer found a way to separate the seeds. When they were planted in clusters, they grew in the same manner. The necessary thinning was a heavy, onerous job. As the farmer had to hire labor to do this, there did not seem to be much use in spending large sums of money for mechanical harvesting. With segmented seed, the spring and summer labor demand was cut to a fraction. Then the almost human harvester was in high demand. Today the high cost of labor in the sugar-beet fields has almost disappeared.

This was the starting gun for a veritable flood of machines. One-man hay balers went into the Imperial Valley and soon were coupled to bale elevators of local make. The elevators were coupled to portable trays so that whole loads of hay could be transported and set on the ground under open barracks, untouched by human hands.

Hop harvesters followed. The tree shaker appeared, a homemade device costing about a hundred dollars that simplified and cut the costs of nut and some fruit harvesting. A glorified vacuum sweeper cut the costs of almond harvesting. The airplane moved into the rice fields, seeding, fertilizing, and fumigating. A combine harvester eliminated more costs. Today rice is no longer a human-labor crop but is entirely mechanized.

So machine-minded have the western folk become that any list of innovations out today is obsolete tomorrow. And most of them tend to cut costs of producing farm products. The newest and fastest growing technique, pioneered in this area, is weeding, disinfecting soil, and controlling insect, botanic, and fungus pests by chemical and oil sprays and dusts. The carrot crop is now almost entirely handled by chemical means throughout its growth life.

No Utopia of farming is envisaged for the Western Slope. But the very difficulties apparent and the history of the people of this region in combating difficulties suggest that all agriculture may benefit from the victories that will come from western fields. Possibly even the defeats may be of value. Already a partial dehydration-freezing combination has been born in California, indicating that no longer will the West pay for water when it ships its produce to market. This might have strong ameliorating effects on the old freight-rate bugaboo.

No look to the future from this area can be adequate without mention of potential markets. Oceania has a meager diet from the standpoint of nutrition and variety. It is possible that western foodstuffs might find a market there? Alaska, never self-sufficient, is a very definite possibility if its long-awaited growth takes place. This in turn may depend on how great our dearth of pulp becomes, how badly we want to discover and develop minerals we are now running short of, or what the defense picture may be in another few years. In any case, the possibility of more markets here is fair. War-torn Asia remains an enigma. Yet, some day, political differences may be composed. If so, and if these countries are reorganized so as to come into the modern economic world, the potentialities of a market for foodstuffs among people who cannot easily become self-sufficient in foods, fats, fibres, and oil are limitless. True, they must have buying power. But it is not impossible that, once peace is established, strong co-operation on the part of the friendly nations could raise that buying power tremendously.

These are only hints, but they should be included because the West is one part of the nation's farm that seems to have great potential in new overseas markets, even though that potential does not seem very close today. If the potential ever becomes a reality, more than likely it will be in large measure because agricultural products have been put into new forms to cut transportation costs. As this is the one part of the country where the problem of transportation rates is paramount, it may be that in solving a domestic issue the Western Slope will find the way to open a foreign market.

In the meantime, this area faces probable surpluses along with the rest of the country, surpluses in everything but water and power. It hardly needs argument, just the mere asking of the question should be enough to any agricultural student (although it doesn't seem so important to other "students"). Still—where will the production from new irrigated acres be sold? Do we really need any more reclamation at this particular time?

One answer may be suggested: Although it does not now seem likely, it may be that one day, unless the balance of the nation gets soil-conservation religion, the Western Slope with all the irrigation it can get will be needed to keep us from being a have-not nation.

Conclusion—Tomorrow's Heritage

FOR GENERATIONS the American Farm had a relatively static quality. Its limitations were the amount of land a man and his family could work, the slow pace of the horse, the distance to market, the difficulties in the preservation of perishables, the lack of roads, and the techniques, largely brought from the Old World, which tended to resist change.

Then a clanking, fire-spitting monster appeared in the fields. It was costly, cumbersome, given to vagaries, sometimes more of a danger than a help—but it presaged the greatest revolution seen since the beginning of agricultural time. It was the steam tractor.

The steam tractor was only a partial success, but it implanted in many minds the idea that the farmer did not have to pace himself to the physical limitations of the horse. It suggested that sweat was not necessarily ennobling, that physical prowess was not a mandatory ingredient in making a crop. It came to mean that men could dream, contrive, invent, and start using their heads as well as their hands.

The steam tractor was succeeded by the internal-combustion engine. This small step ahead was not fraught with great success. Costs were high. Repairs frequent and expensive. Open bearings burned out. And many a would-be maker gave up in despair.

By the time the tricycle type of machine appeared in the early twenties, there were probably more people convinced that the tractor would never supplant the horse than to the contrary. Progress in mechanization limped along at best. The day of ultimate freedom from physical limitations seemed dim on a far horizon.

Then a dreamer and innovator put some airplane tires on a tractor in a Florida grove in the early thirties. Farming America did not know it then, but an age began dying as the Era of the Machine began living.

Despite depression, many men's resistance to change, drought, the Dust Bowl, and war clouds in the sky, the machines moved inexorably ahead, displacing work animals, releasing millions of acres that pastured and fed the beasts, and, much more important, freeing the minds of men from the bonds of three-miles-per-hour farming.

Scarcely had it become apparent that the Machine was king when it became even more apparent that it would not rule alone. The Chemical dynasty moved in to share the power.

Progress then speeded up and dynamism became as prevalent as the *status quo* had once been. For the first time man did something about weather rather than just talking about it. Bugs, benign and malign, no longer responded freely to their own laws but came under man's manipulation. Hybridization opened more avenues of progress. Crops were designed to fit the new conditions. A vast ferment swept from coast to coast as laboratories, greenhouses, crop breeders, industrial chemists, machine designers, petroleum engineers, and even atomic researchers trained their minds on farm problems.

So in the span of life of most current farm operators, agriculture has heaved, turned, and burgeoned as never before in all history. Its great revolution continues apace.

Today we see farms growing larger, farmers becoming fewer, the work week contracting, and the self-sufficient husbandman of yesterday changing into an integral part of the modern complex of machine-and-chemical living, as dependent now on factory and oil well as any other vocation in this modern world.

With these changes has come a new awareness of the absolute necessity to conserve. The new man on the land does not question the law of conserve or die. Land depletion he knows is as unnecessary as diphtheria, yet his father accepted both as inevitable. Forests are not a thing to be chewed up with more waste left behind than board feet brought out. Now trees are a crop. For every one cut another is planted. They are harvested—not lumbered off to bare ground. Waterways are grassed down. Gullies are dammed up. And there is a growing swell of anger at that minority, the "suitcase farmers," who still base their plans on greed rather than husbanding the soil.

The millennium is not with us, but new philosophies herald better days. And those philosophies suggest that more change is in store for us. For instance—and only a few of the many possible examples will be cited—crop shifts will critically affect whole areas of the land.

Until recently, we thought the range was immutable, permanently dedicated to the prime source of meat. Now questions are raised. Planted, irrigated pastures turn off more and better meat at costs that are rapidly becoming less than range costs. At the same time, the rangemen are taking a good hard look at their traditional practices and starting to meet the new competition by chemical and physical clearing of their natural pastures of noxious growths, by seeding to more desirable strains, by developing new sources of water, and, of course, by constantly improving the quality of herds.

Only a few years back soybeans were a novelty. Now they are one of our great industrial and feed crops. Lespedeza, originally a solely southern crop, is creeping northward as scientists adapt it to greater extremes of climate than it was ever thought it could bear. Seeds used to be one of our more important imports. Now they are a permanent part of our domestic production.

The South is departing from cotton and becoming a huge pasture. Anhydrous ammonia and new hybrids are making a new Corn Belt along with the pastures. The geographical center of the cotton crop is Texas, not the Delta. And more milk is being produced in every portion of the land than ever before in history.

More shifts and changes would seem to be imperative from economics and government regulation. With export markets declining, something other than wheat must come to the Great Plains. Falling water tables denote mandatory changes in the Southwest. And everywhere the growth of shrubs, industrial expansion and dispersion, and the constantly growing network of highways contract the land available.

Still other changes are in the making as our diet evolves. We are no longer a meat-and-potatoes people. We are not a roast-on-Sunday-and-leftovers-the-rest-of-the-week or a turkey-on-Thanksgiving-and-none-the-rest-of-the-year people any more. Instead, our diet, already the most diversified in the world, is rapidly multiplying the number, kinds, and methods of preparation. Now the fresh markets get constantly increasing competition from processed foods. The trend toward less and less kitchen preparation and more and more reliance on the processor is apparently permanent. Millions of working housewives demand it. Millions more want more time for bridge, golf, social, and religious activities—and concomitantly less time in the kitchen.

Satisfying these new wants starts a reaction that runs back to the farm. It suggests that processors rather than housewives will sway the planting and harvesting plans. Some strains of plants lend themselves to mass processing better than others, and plant breeders are turning their attention to the demands of tomorrow. Plans, techniques, and field practices are changing.

How far and how fast these and many other changes now discernible will develop, no man can prophesy. But the present writers know that, without updating, this book will be obsolete before many years have passed. Change is the order of the day. You can't stop it. Too many people in eager competition are urging it along. All the observer can do is to pause at a given time and tell himself that this is what has happened and where we are now, and make some educated guesses as to where we are going.

However, one would be completely out of step with the times if he did not find this surge and ebb, this revolution, to be the exhilarating thing it is. In truth, Dynamism is the word for our mid-century agriculture, and while it greatly complicates national agricultural problems, understanding it is a prerequisite for developing a successful and workable farm program.

Notes on Sources and Additional Reading

THE conventional bibliography common to books of this kind is not offered here for several reasons. First, this book purports to be a work of original observation and experience in various parts of agricultural America, rather than a distillation of the thoughts of others. Second, the literature bearing directly on this subject is sparse and, in this amazingly changing scene, very often obsolete. Third, it is obvious from the sources cited on tabular material that the documentation is largely from the *United States Census of Agriculture, 1950,* II (General Report). In the latter regard, our job has been to pick out those statistics that were germane and put them in juxtaposition with observable fact. Finally, we look upon this book as more interpretation than exposition.

Since much of the statistical material has been obtained from the census of agriculture, a word is in order about this source. The authors are fully aware of the inadequacies of the agricultural censuses. Figures from census to census are not strictly comparable for many categories of data, and therefore the student must use utmost care in drawing conclusions. For example, changes in the number of farms from decade to decade have sometimes been because of the failure to apply strictly the definition of a farm as given by the Census Bureau. Furthermore, enumerators have not been consistent in their use of standard instructions in census taking, thereby giving faulty results. Different census dates also affect some results. If the census is taken on January 1 there will be less livestock reported than if the enumeration is made on April 1 or June 1, when spring calves, pigs, and other livestock would be counted. Authorities who have carefully studied census data over many years believe that chief crop- and livestock-production figures are understated around 5 to 10 per cent. Students dealing with recent agricultural production should compare the census figures with those given annually by the United States Department of Agriculture in *Agricultural Statistics*. Despite the many problems involved in using census data for agriculture, we have made no effort to adjust or revise the sometimes distorted census figures. Overall they are probably the best data available. For attempts to make adjustments in the census data for a particular area, see John D. Black, *The Rural Economy of New England* (Cambridge, Harvard University Press, 1950).

The student who may want to pursue some individual topic further will find helpful material in the following studies. It will be noted that none of these books, articles, or documents precisely fits into the category that we have essayed to enter, but each has a bearing on some facet or other. The job we have tried to do is based primarily on the 40,000 miles traveled by one of the authors in all forty-eight states each year, studying agriculture, working with farmers, and in publishing the findings in many media, plus the experience in actually farming or managing farms in a dozen different areas engaged in by both authors, against the professional studies which both perform in their respective fields.

United States Department of Agriculture Publications

Agricultural Statistics, 1940, 1945, 1950, and 1953.

Bachman, K. L., and Ronald W. Jones. *Sizes of Farms in the United States* (Technical Bulletin No. 1019 [July, 1950]).

Generalized Types of Farming in the United States (Agriculture Information Bulletin No. 3 [February, 1950]).

Hecht, Reuben W., and Glen T. Barton. *Gains in Productivity of Farm Labor* (Technical Bulletin No. 1020 [December, 1950]).

Irrigation Agriculture in the West (Miscellaneous Publication No. 670 [November, 1948]).

Johnson, Sherman E. *Changes in American Farming* (Miscellaneous Publication No. 707 [December, 1949]).

Land Utilization, A Graphic Summary (A Co-operative Report with the United States Department of Commerce [December, 1952]).

Wooten, H. H. *Major Uses of Land in the United States* (Technical Bulletin No. 1082 [October, 1953]).

Yearbook of Agriculture. See especially *Soils and Men* (1938); *Farmers in a Changing World* (1940); *Climate and Man* (1941); and *Crops in Peace and War* (1950–51).

Articles and Books

Baker, Oliver E. "Agricultural Regions of North America," *Economic Geography,* Vols. II–VIII (October, 1926–October, 1932). For a background on agricultural regions, the beginning student will want to consult this series of articles by Mr. Baker. The titles, dates, and pages of these are: "The Basis of Classification," Vol. II (October, 1926), 460–93; "The South," Vol. III (January, 1927), 50–86; "The Middle Country Where South and North Meet," Vol. III (July, 1927), 309–39; "The Corn Belt," Vol. III (October, 1927), 445–65; "The Hay and Dairying Region," Vol. IV (January, 1928), 44–73; "The Spring Wheat Region," Vol. IV (October, 1928), 399–433; "The Middle Atlantic Trucking Region," Vol. V (January, 1929), 36–69; "The Pacific Subtropical Crops Region," Vol. VI (April and July, 1930), 166–91; 278–309; "The North Pacific Hay and Pasture Region," Vol. VII (April, 1931), 109–53; "The Grazing and Irrigated Crops Region," Vol. VII–VIII (October, 1931; October, 1932), 326–64; 326–77.

Black, John D. *The Rural Economy of New England*. Cambridge, Harvard University Press, 1950.

Bright, Arthur A., Jr. (ed.) *The Economic State of New England*. New Haven, Yale University Press, 1954. (For the section on agriculture, see pp. 99–136.)

Bullock, Benjamin F. *Practical Farming for the South*. Chapel Hill, University of North Carolina Press, 1946.

Erickson, F. C. "The Broken Cotton Belt," "*Economic Geography,* Vol. XXIV (October, 1948), 263–68.

Fulmer, John L. *Agricultural Progress in the Cotton Belt since 1920.* Chapel Hill, University of North Carolina Press, 1950.

Graham, Edward H. *Natural Principles of Land Use.* London, Oxford University Press, 1944.

Langsford, E. L. "Over-all Adjustment in Southern Agriculture," *Journal of Farm Economics,* Vol. XXXII (November, 1950), 773–86.

Malin, James C. *The Grassland of North America.* Lawrence, Kansas, 1947.

Saunderson, Mont H. *Western Land and Water Use.* Norman, University of Oklahoma Press, 1950.

Selby, H. E. "The Importance of Irrigation in the Economy of the West," *Journal of Farm Economics,* Vol. XXXI (November, 1949), 955–64.

Smith, J. Russell. *North America.* New York, Harcourt, Brace and Co., 1942.

Towner, J. Allen. "Alabama's Shifting Cotton Belt," *The Alabama Review,* Vol. I (January, 1948), 27–38.

Van Dersal, William R. *The American Land.* London, Oxford University Press, 1943.

Weaver, John C. "Changing Patterns of Cropland Use in the Middle West," *Economic Geography,* Vol. XXX (January, 1954), 1–47.

———. "Crop-Combination Regions in the Middle West," *The Geographical Review,* Vol. XLIV (April, 1954), 175–200.

Miscellaneous

Proceedings of the Sixth Annual Cotton Mechanization Conference, 1952. Memphis, the National Cotton Council, 1952.

Proceedings of the Seventh Annual Cotton Mechanization Conference, 1953. Memphis, the National Cotton Council, 1953.

Study of the Agricultural and Economic Problems of the Cotton Belt. 80 Cong., 1 sess., *Hearings before the Special Subcommittee on Cotton Committee of Agriculture, House of Representatives, July 7 and 8, 1947.*

The state agricultural experiment stations, either alone or in co-operation with the United States Department of Agriculture, have made studies on types of farming in various states. These publications contain a great deal of valuable information on soils, weather, crops, and related data. However, in many respects, most of these studies are outdated and need to be revised in light of recent agricultural changes. A list of these publications can be found on pages 34 and 35 of *Generalized Types of Farming in the United States* (USDA Agriculture Information Bulletin No. 3 [February, 1950]).

The various state departments of agriculture generally publish an annual or biennial report, reviewing agriculture in the individual states. Much helpful data for this study were gleaned from these publications. In addition, unpublished information was obtained from county agricultural agents and actual farm operators. As mentioned earlier, much of the material for this book has been derived from personal observation.

Index

The Agricultural Regions
of the United States

has been set in Linotype Old Style No. 7, and printed directly from type. Characterized by notable evenness of color on the page, this type has enjoyed long popularity in book and periodical printing, and because of its lack of eccentricities seems peculiarly appropriate to this book.

University of Oklahoma Press : Norman